HIPAAHelp from *Three Wishes I*

Post Office Box 222, Armbrust Pennsylvania 15616-0222
E-mail: mail@hipaahelp.info
(724) 838-9509 for a human, messages, and fax.

Colleagues,

Please accept my gratitude for purchasing this book. I have put a great deal of effort into it and fully expect it to meet your needs for complying with the HIPAA legislation and regulations.

For those eager to jump in, on the back of this page is a Quick Start list.

I am trying hard to meet the needs of psychotherapists struggling with these regulations. Please let me help us all by sending me corrections and other materials you find or develop and want to share. Email, fax, write, or, if you must, phone. If you want or need more, please do contact me and give me a chance to find or develop what is missing. Write, fax, or email me.

Modifying the forms and handouts in the book

The forms can be found at this website: <http://www.HipaaHelp.info/forms/>

The HIPAA regulations specifically ask you to modify the materials for clients and offer not sample forms. I have composed those in the book but please to tailor them to your practice.

They are available online in .rtf which almost any word processor can open and modify and in ASCII or plain text if you must use that version which loses all the formatting.

Please do note that these are copyrighted so see the LIMITED PHOTOCOPY LICENSE three pages ahead. I specifically and vigorously recommend against using the forms without reading and understanding the issues discussed and explained in this book.

Updated information on HIPAA

Check our Web Site <www.hipaahelp.info/updates> regularly for the latest developments about HIPAA as it relates to psychotherapists and small practices. If you would prefer to have the UpDates sent to you by email and you did not order this book from our website (www.HIPAAHelp.info.) please send an email asking to be put on the HIPAA UpDates mailing list to <mail@hipaahelp.info. You won't get lots of new spam.

Updates about HIPAA will be posted <u>only</u> at: <http://hipaahelp.info/updates/>
Do not type the < or the >.

Thanks and best wishes,

Ed Zuckerman, PhD

Quick Start for HIPAA Compliance

1.   If you have any doubts that you need to comply with HIPAA see section 120 for a decision tree.

2.   I believe that you can implement HIPAA in your practice at three levels of effort: Basic, Legal, and Complete (my terms). You should decide with which you are most comfortable before going too far and doing too little or too much. See section 180 for guidance.

3.   For these approaches, section 222 lists the forms needed by each level of effort. You can go to each form, photocopy it onto your letterhead, and put it into practice. All the forms are also on the UpDates site listed on the previous page. You can download them and modify them to suit your practice.

4.   Section 221 contains a list of *all* the steps to take to implement HIPAA.

5.   HIPAA requires you to train your employees at the time you become HIPAA-compliant. Sections 260-263 cover what the training should address and ways to document it.

6.   HIPAA requires that you amend or rewrite contracts with your Business Associates. Read section 270 covers this.

If you need more, look around the book but if something you really need is missing send me an e-mail and let me know so I can get started on it ASAP.

Ed
<mail@hipaahelp.info>

Continuing Education Credits are available for reading this book

Four Continuing Education credits are available for Counselors, Social Workers, and Psychologists for reading this book. Contact J&K Seminars at their website or at 800-801-5415 or at 1861 Wickersham Lane, Lancaster PA 17603-2327

HIPAA Help

A Compliance Toolkit for Psychotherapists

for

Maintaining Records' Privacy and Security,
Managing Risks, and Operating Ethically
and Legally Under HIPAA

Edward Zuckerman, PhD

Revised Edition

Three Wishes Press

Copyright Information

Published by   *Three Wishes Press*
                Post Office Box 222
                Armbrust, Pennsylvania 15616-0222
                www.threewishespress.com

Last digit is printing number   9 8 7 6 5 4 3 2 1 of 11/05

ISBN 0-9727168-1-5

Dedication

To my dear friend Paul Loera, PhD,
without whose enthusiasm and encouragement
this book would never have seen the light of day.

The artwork on the cover is by Lilly Zuckerman

About the Author

Edward Zuckerman earned his PhD in Clinical Psychology from the University of Pittsburgh. He has worked in many settings including community mental health, inpatient psychiatric and general hospitals, state institutions for the adult retarded, teaching college classes, and for many years, independent general practice of clinical psychology. He lives now in rural western Pennsylvania with his family and lots of farm animals.

If you find you need basic but detailed information on psychiatric medications please have a look at *PsychMeds@YourFingertips* from www.PsychMeds.info .
While you are there download the latest version of the fre*e List of 100 Psychiatric Medications.* And if you find you need the ICD-9-CM mental health diagnoses, please have a look at the *Reference List of ICD-9-CM Diagnoses.*

Ed is the author of the best-selling *Clinician's Thesaurus: A Guidebook for Wording Clinical Reports* (available now in a sixth edition) and *The Paper Office: Forms, Guidelines, and Resources to make your psychotherapy practice work ethically, legally, and profitably* (now in a third edition) and the co-author of *Rewarding Specialties for Mental Health Clinicians* and a author of *The Authoritative Guide to Self Help Resources in Mental Health: Books, Movies, Internet Sites, etc.*

These books are available from

72 Spring Street
New York, NY 10012

1-800-365-7006
www.guilford.com

More information about these and other publications
is available at the Guilford website.

Table of Contents

Conventions used in this book

When a word has **an initial capital letter** it usually means the form or document and when uncapitalized it means the process. For example, consent and authorization are the what the client can do while Consent and Authorization are the paper forms on which he or she agrees to those actions.

The addresses (URL-Universal Resource Locator) of websites are indicated inside < > marks so that all the characters can be read. Do not type in the < or > marks. If you find errors or changes, please do send me an e-mail so that I can post it for others.

The **HIPAA regulations** and Guidances are indicated in quotation marks and cited in square brackets [ ] unless the heading makes the reference clear. In all other cases I may have interpreted the regulations and omitted wording and sections which, in my opinion, do not apply to clinicians and therapists in solo or small practice groups.

Appropriate audience

The proper audience for this book are solo and small practices of mental health professionals of all disciplines. It does not address the requirements HIPAA imposes on larger clinical entities such as inpatient programs in psychiatric or other hospitals, any kind of residential programs, rehabilitation centers, partial hospital or intensive outpatient clinics, etc. or any kind of non-mental health services.

Just FYI: The OCR has issued a caution about misleading marketing on HIPAA training. *What You Should Know About OCR HIPAA Privacy Rule Guidance Materials: Be aware of misleading marketing claims* is available at
<http://www.hhs.gov/ocr/hipaa/misleadingmarket ing.html>

Disclaimer
(This is necessary because we live in The Great Age of Litigation)

The information in this publication is offered with the understanding that the author is not engaged in rendering legal, financial, ethical or other professional advice and expressly disclaims any and all warranties in connection with this material. This information is not intended as, and does not constitute, legal or other professional advice. If you require legal or other professional advice, you should consult an attorney or other appropriate professional.

Inclusion of any product or service offered through its mention in this book or by means of a linked website does not constitute endorsement by the author of any policy or position or product.

We all live in a probabilistic universe in which we must tolerate uncertainties, accept known, unknown, and unknowable risks, and yet be fully responsible for the consequences of our actions. Like has to be live forward but can only be understood backward (Soren Kirkegaard)

Production of this book

This book was written on a Macintosh G4 computer using the Mariner Write word processor and the final layout was done in Microsoft's Word. The text is set in Palatino and the heads in Arial typefaces. It was printed at Victor Graphics (thank you, Stephen) in Baltimore.

100   Preparing for HIPAA

110   What is HIPAA?

Its title, *The Health Insurance Portability and Accountability Act (HIPAA) of 1996,* gives some clues to its nature but does not do justice to its sweep and intentions.

Why and from whence it came - Politics in action

The original goal was to prevent arbitrary exclusion from insurance coverage with the "Pre-existing Conditions Not Covered" gambit. Some may recall the horror stories presented in testimony to Congress by those who could not leave a exploitative job because of their or their family member's health needs. If they were to change jobs or lose their job they would not be able to get coverage for these pre-existing[1] conditions. As a result Congress passed the Kassebaum and Kennedy Bill prohibiting this discrimination. Health insurance thus became generally portable. (See section 940 for more on portability). At the same time, the evidence was accumulating of criminal practices.

Reduction of fraud and abuse

The title incorporates accountability by which it means to reduce fraud and other kinds of financial waste. The US General Accounting Office has estimated that 11 cents of every healthcare dollar is spent fraudulently. In 1998 this would be about 100 billion dollars! HIPAA incorporates a Fraud and Abuse Control System, provides both financial and criminal penalties, uses the Office of Civil Rights and other agencies for enforcement, and stipulates protections for whistleblowers. To find the criminal practices better data was needed and so more computerization became necessary. The Administration of health care needed to be simplified.

Reduction of costs through Administrative Simplification

The practices of the insurance industry were also wasteful. The U.S. General Accounting Office estimated that more than 20 cents of every healthcare dollar is spent on administrative overhead in our healthcare system (at that time. It may be 30 cents now). For comparison, Medicare spends about 5 cents and Social Security about 2 cents. HIPAA was designed to reduce the costs of health care by implementing standardized, universal, computerized transactions between payers and providers using Electronic Data Interchange (EDI). Such methods will reduce clerks, mistakes, processing time, and

---

[1] These are, of course, "existing" conditions, not "pre-existing ones. This kind of new vocabulary serves its creators' purposes. Consider "medical necessity," "provider," "member," etc.

overhead. In 1993, WEDI (the Workgroup for EDI) estimated that providers would save $9 billion annually, and the healthcare industry at large would save $26 billion annually, through using EDI. I believe these to be vast underestimates.

Q: Will the use of standardized forms, terms, and computerized data save you any money?

A: Lazarus (2001) surveyed 20 group physician practices and using an admittedly Quick and Dirty HIPAA Benefit Calculation Estimator for Physician Practice he obtained an estimated an average annual potential benefit of $7,200 per provider, exclusive of implementation and annual operating costs. The potential business operation savings were identified in the following areas: Business Office - 51%, Managed Care - 12%, Bad Debt, Postage, etc. - 37%. These benefits are obtainable by implementing the Transaction Standards. Granted that these were for larger practices than most mental health therapists operate and that the costs of implementation were excluded (but may be quite small for therapists) the savings can be substantial. However, this computerization also implies more sharing of personal health information and so raises privacy concerns.

Protection of privacy through Administrative Simplification[2]

Computerizing health information allows better control of it and so can *increase* privacy if strong techniques are used to safeguard it. Financial data can be segregated from medical data and routine demographic information from more sensitive clinical and historical data. Access can be limited to only those who need to know each part of one's information. Those who do access it can be authenticated and their access documented.

Putting it all together

In its wisdom, Congress acknowledged both the need for privacy legislation and its own likely failure to provide it. So according to HIPAA, if Congress failed to pass privacy legislation (I. e. The Patients Bill of Rights) by August 21, 1999, the responsibility for privacy protection would fall to the Department of Health and Human Services (DHHS). Congress didn't and so DHHS has.

HIPAA's regulations include enormous detail about EDI transactions, client privacy education and protection, computer security, staff training, ways to evaluate the risks of loss of security, identification numbers for providers and businesses, and much more. Its effects will continue to evolve as it is implemented, expands to other areas, and interacts with state laws and the codes of ethics of the professions.

As you can see HIPAA will require a lot of expensive and complicated work by the health care system. Fortunately, therapists won't have to do as much as most others because they are small operations (HIPAA is scalable) and they have already done much to assure the privacy of their clients' information. See section 140.

---

[2] This term has been the butt of jokes but it should be understood in light of the thousands of local codes used by different insurers, types of providers, government payers, medical specialties, etc. Much fun has also been directed at the size of HIPAA. It is not "1500 pages" or "a doorstop." The text of the actual regulation covers only 32 pages in the Federal Register. The preamble that precedes the regulation covers 337 pages in the Federal Register. Over half of the preamble is devoted to summarizing and responding to the more than 52,000 comments received by HHS.

120   Do I have to comply with HIPAA?
A decision tree

Q: I have heard that HIPAA (the Health Insurance Portability and Accountability Act) is big, complicated, and a real burden so I would love to be able to escape it. I am a therapist in solo practice. Does HIPAA apply to me?
A: Probably but the answer hinges on several sub-questions:
- Is your work health care or not?
- Are you a health care provider who is considered a Covered Entity?
- Do you or will you engage in certain electronic transactions (information sharing) about a client's health insurance?
- Do you make or keep records in any electronic form?

Let us look at these questions in more detail and in the concepts HIPAA uses.

1. **Perhaps you will not fit the definitions in the act.** Consider these criteria:
    a.   You will not be a health care provider after April 14, 2003[3] OR
    b.   Your practice will have 10 or fewer professionals AND
    c.   You will not be submitting claims to Medicare.[4]

If these are true you need not become HIPAA Compliant. Don't do anything different just for HIPAA. There are no papers to be submitted. However, there may be compelling reasons for becoming compliant anyway. See section 130.

2. **Is your practice area or client base excluded because it is not health care? First, what is health care?**

> Care, services, or supplies related to the health of an individual. It includes, but is not limited to, the following:
> (1) Preventive, diagnostic, rehabilitative, maintenance, or palliative care, and counseling, service, assessment, or procedure with respect to the physical or mental condition, or functional status, of an individual or that affects the structure or function of the body; and
> (2) Sale or dispensing of a drug, device, equipment, or other item in accordance with a prescription. See 45 C.F.R.160.103.

If you are not doing health care by this definition, you are excluded from HIPAA.

3. **If you do health care, by the definitions above, perhaps the populations you serve are excluded?**
    a.   Forensics is not considered health care. Do you do only child custody or competence to stand trial evaluations? Do you treat only under court order? Do you evaluate or treat only inmates?
    b.   School psychology is not considered health care and your records are covered by the *Family Educational Rights and Privacy Act* (FERPA) of 1974. These records are specifically excluded in HIPAA. If you provide evaluation and/or psychological treatment to students you must become informed about FERPA and its subtleties because some of your records may contain PHI which you or others created and so is HIPAA-covered.

---

[3] This is the date for the implementation of the Privacy Rule. There are also Security and Transaction Rules with later implementation dates but they don't apply if you don't need to comply.

[4] Technically all Medicare claims must be submitted electronically after October 16, 2002. The dates don't match because different parts of HIPAA have different deadlines. Also, the implementation of these dates is highly dependent on enormous efforts, costs, and skill. Expect delays.

    c. Worker's Compensation evaluations and treatment are health care but doing this work does not make you a CE. The data are allowable disclosures because HIPAA says that you should obey WC rules on disclosure (§ 164.512(l).

    d. Psychotherapeutically treating those injured in motor vehicle accidents is healthcare but does not make you a CE.

If your clientele is entirely made up of these populations you are excluded from HIPAA compliance. There may be other excluded populations of which I am not presently aware.

4. You might be doing health care for some of your work. Do you do these?

    a. Employee Assistance Programs (EAPs). If you do exit counseling or similar non-therapy, non-clinical, interventions they are likely not covered by HIPAA. If you do drug and alcohol counseling, stress management, provide diagnoses, or offer other kinds of treatment, these activities are likely subject to HIPAA.

    b. Perform evaluations and treatment paid for by the Office of Vocational Rehabilitation. I don't know. It seems like it would be because it creates PHI and is for treatment but get consultation. Call OVR and speak to their Privacy Officer.[5]

5. How do you handle insurance claims?

You *must* comply if a or b is true as of April 14, 2003 and afterwards about how you handle insurance claims.

    a. You submit *electronic* claims for your treatment for covered services to insurance companies.

Actually, HIPAA applies to several kinds of **electronic data transactions,** not just billing and doing any of these will require you to comply with HIPAA. Here is the official list:

      Health care claims or equivalent encounter information
      Health care payment and remittance advice
      Coordination of benefits
      Health care claim status
      Enrollment and disenrollment in a health plan
      Eligibility for a health plan
      Health plan premium payments
      Referral certification and authorization
      First report of injury
      Health claims attachments
      Other transactions that the Secretary may prescribe by regulation

If you are not sure and want more detail, a transaction is a **covered transaction** if it meets the act's definition for the type of transaction. The regulatory definition for each type of covered transaction can be found in the following sections of the regulations:

    45 C.F.R.162.1101: Health care claims or equivalent encounter information transaction is either of the following:

    45 C.F.R.162.1201: The eligibility for a health plan transaction is the transmission of either of the following:

    45 C.F.R.162.1301: The referral certification and authorization transaction is any of the following transmissions:

    45 C.F.R.162.1401: A health care claim status transaction is the transmission of either of the following:

    45 C.F.R.162.1501: The enrollment and disenrollement in a health plan transaction is the transmission of subscriber enrollment information to a health plan to establish or

---

[5] This is a benefit of HIPAA: all healthcare organizations now have an identifiable person to whom you can address questions.

terminate insurance coverage.

45 C.F.R.162.1601: The health care payment and remittance advice transaction is the transmission of either of the following for health care:

45 C.F.R.162.1701: The health plan premium payment transaction is the transmission of any of the following from the entity that is arranging for the provision of health care or is providing health care coverage payments for an individual to a health plan:

45 C.F.R.162.1801: The coordination of benefits transaction is the transmission from any entity to a health plan for the purpose of determining the relative payment responsibilities of the health plan,

  b. You do not create and submit the bills yourself but rely on a clearinghouse or someone else who submits them on your behalf (e.g. a hospital where you provide services, a billing agent).

If you do not do a or b, stop. You are not covered by HIPAA.

If you don't presently submit claims as above but your patients submit their paper bills to insurance companies for reimbursement, you do NOT have to comply. However you will be pressured to submit electronically over the next year or so. It may be advantageous to comply with HIPAA voluntarily now for simplicity and some advantages.

This pretty well covers everybody who does not have a cash-only practice.

6. Consider the information in your records. Is it PHI (Protected Healthcare Information[6])? Here is a formal decision tree, adapted from the one online at <http://www.cms.hhs.gov/hipaa/hipaa2/support/tools/decisionsupport/default.asp

  a. Does the information identify an individual, or is there a reasonable basis to believe that the information can be used to identify the individual?

If no, information is not protected. If yes, proceed to b.

  b. Does the information relate to the past, present, or future physical or mental health or condition of an individual or the provision of health care to that individual or the past, present or future payment for the provision of health care to an individual?

If no, the information is not protected. If yes, proceed to c.

  c. Was the information created or received by a health care provider, health plan, public health authority, employer, life insurer, school or university, or health care

If not, the information is not protected. If yes, the information is individually identifiable health information (IIHI). To determine whether it is protected health information, proceed to d.

  d. Is the information education records that are covered by the Family Educational Right and Privacy Act (FERPA) or post-secondary student medical records, as described in 20 USC 232g(a)(4)(B)(iv)?

If not, the information is not protected. If yes, the information is protected health information subject to the privacy standards of HIPAA.

---

[6] Since the Security Rule became final in April 2005 HIPAA has addressed how EPHI – Electronic PHI must be handled. For all citations to PHI consider that EPHI is included.

7. You keep only paper records, nothing electronic, so HIPAA doesn't apply to you, Right?

Originally the HIPAA rules were to apply only to electronic records and not paper ones but this is no longer true. Background information in the final rule, indicates that the rule will apply to all individually identifiable health information transmitted or maintained by a covered entity regardless of form (65 Fed. Reg. 82496.).

8. You keep records of your thoughts and the process of therapy, which you would prefer to not share with the client or anyone else. Does HIPAA address these notes?

Yes. Under HIPAA you may keep such Psychotherapy Notes quite private. So, it may be advantageous to you and your clients to become compliant with HIPAA for the assurances of the privacy of your notes.

9. You have fewer than 10 full time employees, so you don't have to comply with HIPAA. Right?

Sorry. If you submit any of the transactions listed above in electronic form, or a third party does so on your behalf - you must still comply with the HIPAA standards regardless of the size of your practice.

10. You might think "I don't take Medicare patients so I don't have to comply with HIPAA." True?

Yes. However, while the law technically only pertains to Medicare claims, the same transaction codes and procedures will be implemented by all insurers for all claims to simplify their business transactions. Therefore you will have to go along with the privacy and security rules of HIPAA because you will be going along with the transaction rules and HIPAA does not permits partial compliance.

In conclusion

Based on these considerations, let me offer my congratulations. You struggled to become a therapist or a psychologist or clinical social worker or clinical counselor or psychiatrist. Then, through the grace of Managed Care you became a provider. Now by command of HIPAA, you are **a Covered Entity, a CE.** (Remember this acronym.) New titles for everyone, but not more pay. Ah, progress.

130   Why you should become HIPAA-compliant (even if you don't have to)

Becoming HIPAA-compliant involves some effort, time, and a little money. Why bother if you don't have to? Let me count the whys.

1. Many of the requirements are also **consistent with the best practice**s of protecting privacy and privacy is crucial for psychotherapy.

2. Although you may not presently need to be compliant, at some future time, when some action triggers your having to comply, there will be **no grace period to adapt.** Your whole practice, including privacy forms and notices, staff training, client records and contracts with your business associates, will all have to be compliant as of that date.

3. Not complying by **not using electronic transactions will slow down payment of your claims** and **may raise your costs** because insurers are likely to impose fees for paper claims. While you are prohibited from passing these costs along to Medicare clients you could possibly do so to your private pay clients.

4. **HIPAA does not permit partial compliance**. The Privacy, Security, and Transaction rules will apply to all clients and all parts of your practice as soon as you are a CE.

5   While complying does not prevent a suit, not complying does not in any way lessen your liability over mistaken disclosures and may increase it. Courts are likely to view the Privacy Rule as setting the standard for protecting PHI and so, in a lawsuit or state licensing board complaint, **you may be judged by HIPAA's rules as the standard.**

6.   There are significant **penalties**[7] for violation of the privacy regulations. Also, compliance with the them is likely to greatly reduce potential disclosures and any resultant vulnerability to fines and other penalties

7. When you are HIPAA-compliant **you can use the Psychotherapy Notes** exemption to prevent an insurance company or your client from accessing these special notes. You can also limit the amount of information you send to an insurance company to that in (what I call) the Routine Progress Note and can use the Minimum Necessary PHI rules.

Despite all this, there might be advantages to you and your clients of not becoming HIPAA-compliant. See the Association of American Physicians and Surgeons, Inc. at <http://www.aapsonline.org/> consult legal counsel to evaluate your risk exposure.

---

[7] Under "General Penalty for Failure to Comply with Requirements and Standards" of Public Law 104-191, the Health Insurance Portability and Accountability Act of 1996, Section 1176 says that **the Secretary can impose fines for noncompliance as high as $100 per offense, with a maximum of $25,000 per year on any person who violates a provision of this part.**
Under "Wrongful Disclosure of Individually Identifiable Health Information," Section 1177 states that a person who knowingly:
• uses or causes to be used a unique health identifier;
• obtains individually identifiable health information relating to an individual; or
• discloses individually identifiable health information to another person,
• shall be **fined not more than $50,000, imprisoned not more than 1 year, or both:**
• *if the offense is committed under false pretenses*, be **fined not more than $100,000, imprisoned not more than 5 years, or both;** and
• *if the offense is committed with intent to sell, transfer, or use individually identifiable health information for commercial advantage, personal gain, or malicious harm*, be **fined not more than $250,000, imprisoned not more than 10 years, or both.**

140 Why you shouldn't worry too much about HIPAA

I don't have a Top Ten List but consider these:

1. As a mental health professional, **you are probably already 90% in compliance** with HIPAA because you protect privacy by assuring informed consent, using properly legal request/release forms, sharing only the minimum necessary information, being discrete in discussions and note-taking, etc.

2. HIPAA is **scalable** meaning that large organizations have to do much more to implement security and privacy controls than you do. I believe you will need little more than a few pieces of paper, some staff training, a policies and procedures manual, and some clear thinking about how you handle information in your practice.

3. Requirements are flexible. In several difficult situations your **professional judgment** can be used concerning consent, what should be revealed to clients and their families, allowing the amending of your records, etc. In other places the word reasonable is used. Of course, reasonable design or scalable scope can not be used to allow you to violate any regulation.

4. There are **no "HIPAA Police"** to come to your office and routinely or even randomly check on your compliance. There are no forms to fill out and file, no yearly reports to send to Washington, etc.

5. The Department of Health and Human Services has said that, except in situations of deliberate and profit-seeking violations of privacy their approach to enforcement of the HIPAA rules will be **educational and not punitive.** Though a rule on enforcement is not required by HIPAA, HHS published on April 17, 2003 the interim final Enforcement Rule, "Civil Money Penalties: Procedures for Investigations, Imposition of Penalties, and Hearings."

6. HIPAA **does not create a separate legal right of action.** It does not create any way for a client to sue you for violating his or her rights because of breaking the HIPAA rules - an "unauthorized release of Protected Healthcare Information". Of course, he or she could still sue you in state or local courts but would have to show damages due to your negligence, just as in any malpractice action.

7. You can transfer most of the burden of assuring the **security** of your computerized records to the developers of your computer systems. You will still be responsible but they will do the heavy lifting.

8. Similarly, you can quite easily safeguard the privacy of your computerized records with just common utility programs for backup, password access, and encryption.

150   HIPAA is an opportunity to upgrade your practice

We therapists are supposed to be experts on making lemonade when given only lemons to work with. (I don't know about you but I get a lot of lemons referred.) Well, HIPAA qualifies as a lemon – a complex, unfunded mandate, with deadlines and teeth – and which does not seem to provide any new benefits to us or our clients.

This book will show you how to cope with HIPAA but I urge you to consider how it might actually be an opportunity to improve your practice (I won't claim that it is a blessing in disguise.).

1. It can push you to move to an **electronic medical record (EMR).** Prices have dropped and functionality has increased. Programs now available include functions beyond efficiently generating and accessing progress notes and submitting your insurance claims. They can help you to assess clients, evaluate outcomes, write reports of all kinds, schedule clients, provide client education and some treatments, increase record security and many other functions.

Unfortunately deciding if and when you should make the move, finding which programs are available, comparing programs and features, etc. are beyond the scope of this book. I know of no one comprehensive resource in this area and I am not an expert.

2. It can push you to move from paper to what HIPAA calls **electronic transactions**. When fully implemented you will be able to verify coverage instantly online, obtain authorizations rapidly, send basic demographic information, submit bills, receive faster payments, etc. You will be able to track non-payments and other follow-up chores with the speed of electrons not postal atoms. Your costs very likely will be lower.

3. In a small office you may not need a **Policy and Procedure Manual** but it is always a good idea for reference when you are not present, when you train staff, to deal with personnel problems which will arise, and other legal and practical reasons. HIPAA will require you to develop at least part of such a manual and you can easily expand it to meet other legal and functional needs. See more on this manual in section 800.

4. HIPAA requires you to **train your staff** in confidentiality. Doing so will require you to articulate some issues, respond to questions, learn what your staff currently understands of privacy, plug some holes, and significantly reduce your risk of a very common source of ethics and legal complaints.

5. There are likely to be **simplifications** and economies to come from reorganizing your office in some ways you may not know of or have been putting off. HIPAA requires you to examine the flow of information in your office and so you will discover some opportunities for improvements. For more on this kind of Gap Analysis, see section 250.

6. Since **you will have to discus privacy** with all current clients (when you give them your NPP (Notice of Privacy Practices. See section 400) you can do some teaching about your and your profession's responses to these issues, the problems HIPAA was designed to resolve, and the risks they face.

160 What will change under HIPAA?

This Privacy Rule really just creates a floor of basic privacy protection for all clients across the country and across settings. Most of the HIPAA requirements are already being met or exceeded by mental health clinicians. We already get informed consent before releasing information, evaluate what we send out to eliminate irrelevant or sensitive information, and we keep records of what we release. HIPAA does not add burdens in these areas; actually its floor or protection is lower than what most of us do currently.

HIPAA will require some adaptations to how we run our offices, what we tell clients about the information they entrust to us, and how we share that information. Below is a quick overview of the impacts on us. It is intended as both an orientation to the issues this book will address and a reassurance that the changes are not radical and can be handled without great disruption of our usual ways of working.

Big changes

- In many jurisdictions clients could see their records but with many obstacles. All clients now have the legal right to **examine** and receive **copies** of all of their records.

- All clients now have a legal right to request **amendments** to their records to account for errors and omissions and to have those requests and reasons included in their records.

- When clients discover that their privacy has been violated **they can now complain** to more than just the provider, and his or her licensing board, or ethics committee, or to a bureaucratic health plan. They can complain to the Secretary of DHHS and have the federal Office of Civil Rights investigate.

Small changes

- If requested, clinicians must **tell clients of some of the less routine disclosures** of their PHI the professional has made over the last six years (from 4/14/03 on). Providers must, of course, keep such a record of disclosures.

- Providers and health plans generally **can refuse to treat** a client who does not *consent* to the sharing of their PHI for *routine* treatment, payment and health care operations (TPO). This applies except in emergencies or where providers can presume consent.

- Insurers will be able to get a lot of information but **not Psychotherapy Notes** and usually not the whole chart.

Losses of privacy

- Consent as we understand it has been removed. It is no longer required and is now only an acknowledgment of being notified of the provider's procedures and of one's rights. This consent is blanket, required for receiving treatment, not time limited, and is not in any sense informed. It allows disclosure much more freely than at present. This is a very low floor of privacy but fortunately will apply only where local laws are silent on a topic.

- **Redisclosure** - disclosing another provider's records in your possession - is now almost required and does not require informed consent or the permission of the professional who created the record. Again, more protective local laws will prevail.

Good ideas and practices now made requirements

- Providers must give clients a **written notice** of how they can use, keep, and share the clients' PHI. This is called the Notice of Privacy Practices or NPP.

- Providers and health plans generally *can't* deny treatment or payment if the client does not *authorize* the sharing of their PHI for *non-routine* disclosures (*not* for TPO - treatment, payment and health care operations). This is actually a mixed blessing.

- Practices have to have **written privacy procedures**, including administrative, physical, and technical safeguards, for who have access to protected information, about how protected information will be used within the organization, and under what conditions the information will be disclosed to others.

- There must be a designated **Privacy Officer** in each practice to ensure compliance with HIPAA by evaluating privacy practices, training employees, being aware of developments in the law and regulations, and responding to complaints. Clients will know to whom to go with a problem.

- Practices have to **train and monitor all their employees** around privacy and the ways of safeguarding it. Practices will need to have clear sanctions and ways to mitigate the harmful consequences of an unauthorized disclosure of PHI[8] and ways to ensure against retaliation against "whistleblowers."

- Practices must establish procedures for clients to learn about their privacy rights, inquire about their records, and lodge complaints.

- Practices now have to require that their business associates (such as billers, accountants, telephone answering services) treat any PHI they receive with the same care as the provider does.

- Violations of privacy rights *can* result in very large penalties.

Little or no change for most therapists

- Providers must obtain a specific authorization for disclosures other than for TPO. We already seek authorizations from clients for these releases as well as for TPO disclosures, under state laws, and will continue to do so.

- Clients can ask to be contacted and communicated with through more private methods or locations. We have generally honored these kinds of requests.

- Clients can ask for some limitations on how much of their PHI can be disclosed and to whom. We usually respect these wishes.

- Out psychotherapy notes now have much greater protection from access by third parties. We have been vigorous in protecting our notes.

---

[8] Since the Security Rule became final in April 2005 HIPAA has addressed how EPHI – Electronic PHI must be handled. For all mentions of PHI consider that EPHI is included.

170   Privacy issues and views

I am not an expert on privacy and its contemporary political, social, and economic dynamics so below I present some perspectives which are not as widely heard as those issuing from the Secretary of the Department of Health and Human Services (DHHS). Each has some truth and deserves the attention of all of us since we all participate in health care in different ways.

- "You have zero privacy anyway. Get over it." Scott McNealy, CEO of Sun Microsystems (January 22, 1999)

- "BUSH ADMINISTRATION ELIMINATES RIGHT OF CONSENT FOR PERSONAL MEDICAL INFORMATION August 13, 2002

    Tomorrow, the Bush Administration will publish in the Federal Register amendments to the current Health Information Privacy Rule that will eliminate the right of privacy for health information for all Americans.

    1. The final rule eliminates the right that each citizen has under the pre-amendment rule (which is also the Bush rule) to not have identifiable health care information used or disclosed without consent. This change effectively **eliminates the right of medical privacy for all citizens for treatment, payment and health care operations, which is most uses.**

    2. The loss of medical privacy inevitably leads to a **loss of access to quality health care** because clients will not seek health care or make medically necessary disclosures if they do not believe the information will remain private.

    3. The amendments go beyond simply eliminating the right of consent in that **they substitute "federal permission"** for the use and disclosure of identifiable health information. Thus, the federal government will provide consent on behalf of each citizen for all covered entities to obtain their identifiable health information, regardless of the individual's wishes.

    4. The Administration **misleads the public** in its press release by stating that the amendments provide the public with more control over their health information when, in fact, they eliminate the only meaningful control the public has under the current Privacy Rule.

    5. It is important to remember that **the Administration is reversing its position** on this vital privacy issue despite the fact that it put these regulations into effect on April 14, 2001 after an additional comment period announcing them as a great victory for consumers. The right of consent under federal law vested in every citizen effective April 14, 2001. **That right will be extinguished on August 14, 2003.** That will clearly be a dark day for quality health care and the civil rights of all citizens." (Boldface added) Deborah Peel, MD, Past President, NCMHPC. From the American Psychoanalytic Association at <http://www.apsa-co.org/ctf/pubinfo/hhselim.html> Accessed Nov. 30, 2002.

- (Sue) Blevins (President of the Institute for Health Freedom) and other patient advocates are not exaggerating, according to James Pyles, a Washington, D.C., health care attorney who worked for six years in the Office of the General Counsel for the U.S. Department of Health, Education, and Welfare. "This is a serious blow," says Pyles. **"Privacy will be meaningless. There is no accounting for [routine] disclosures in this rule, so there will be no paper or electronic trail to follow if your information gets into the wrong hands."** (Boldface added) From Lankarge, Vicki (2002). *Giraffe's medical records are confidential but yours will soon be up for grabs.* Insure.com. <http://www.insure.com/health/privacy402.html> Accessed Feb. 6, 2005.

Who has access to my medical records?[9]

1. **Government agencies** may request your medical records to verify claims made to Medicare, MediCal, Social Security Disability and Workers Compensation.

2. **Insurance companies** require you to release your records before they will issue a policy or make payment under an existing policy. Medical information gathered by one insurance company may be shared with others through the Medical Information Bureau (see below).

3. The **Medical Information Bureau** (MIB) is a central database of medical information. Approximately "20% of consumers" are on file in the MIB's computers. Over 750 insurance firms use the services of the MIB, primarily to obtain information about applicants for life insurance and individual health insurance. A decision on whether to insure you is not supposed to be based solely on the MIB report. The MIB does not have a file on everyone but if your medical information is on file, you will want to be sure it is correct. You can obtain a copy at no cost by call**ing 866-692-6901.** <www.mib.com>

4. **Employers** usually obtain medical information about their employees by asking employees to authorize disclosure of medical records. This can occur in several ways.
- When medical insurance is paid by employers, they may require insurance companies to provide them with copies of employees' medical records.
- Self-insured businesses establish a fund to cover the insurance claims of employees. Since no third party is involved, the medical records that would normally be open for inspection by an insurance company are accessible to the employer. Most large corporations are self-insured.

Unfortunately, the laws in only a few states require employers to establish procedures to keep employee medical records confidential. (For example, California Civil Code §56.)

5. Your medical records may be **subpoenaed** for court cases. If you are involved in litigation, an administrative hearing or worker's compensation hearing and your medical condition is an issue, the **relevant** parts of your medical record may be copied and introduced in court. See number 5, below.

---

[9] Most of the following is adapted from Fact Sheet #8 from the Privacy Rights Clearing House. 3100 - 5th Ave., Suite B, San Diego, CA 92103. Voice: (619) 298-3396; Fax: (619) 298-5681; E-mail: prc@privacyrights.org. <http://www.privacyrights.org>

What kinds of state laws exist now?[10]

While many states have laws that address specific areas such as HIV/AIDS or genetic testing **only a handful of states have anything approaching comprehensive privacy protections for medical records.** These states are **California, Hawaii, Maine, Maryland, Minnesota** and **Wisconsin**. The lack of comprehensive privacy protections means that more often than not, people are vulnerable to unwanted and unexpected exposure.

- Only 18 states have statutes restricting how insurance companies can use and disclose health information.
- Only 20 states require doctors to allow people to see and copy their own medical record. Of these states, only 9 allow people to appeal the decision if a doctor refuses to provide access.
- Only four states Hawaii, California, Connecticut and Maryland have laws that restrict how employers can use medical information.

The Health Privacy Project has published a report that summarizes the medical records confidentiality and access laws of each of the 50 states. It is available on its web site, <www.healthprivacy.org/info-url_nocat2304/info-url_nocat.htm>

What can I do to protect the privacy of my medical records?[11]

1. When you are asked to sign a waiver for the release of your medical records, try to **limit the amount of information** released. Instead of signing the "blanket waiver," cross out some parts and write in more specific terms.
    Example of blanket waiver: "I authorize any physician, hospital or other medical provider to release to [insurer] any information regarding my medical history, symptoms, treatment, exam results or diagnosis."
    Edited waiver: "I authorize my records to be released from [X hospital, clinic or doctor] for the [dates of treatment] as relates to [the condition treated]."

2. If you want a specific condition to be held in confidence by your personal physician, bring a **written request** to the appointment that revokes your consent to release medical information to the insurance company and/or to your employer for that visit. You must also pay for the visit yourself rather than obtain reimbursement from the insurance company. To be especially certain of confidentiality, you may need to see a different physician altogether and **pay the bill yourself**, forgoing reimbursement from the insurance company.

3. Use caution when filling out **medical questionnaires**. Find out if you **must** complete it, what its purpose is, and who will have access to the information that is compiled. Also, before participating in informal **health screenings**, find out what uses will be made of the medical information that is collected. Use the same discretion when visiting **Web sites** and when participating in online discussion groups.

4. Ask your health care provider to use caution when **photocopying** portions of your medical records for others. Sometimes more of your medical record is copied than is necessary.

5. If your records are **subpoenaed** for a legal proceeding, they become a public record. Ask the court to allow only a specific portion of your medical record to be seen or not to be

---

[10] Adapted from *New Federal Health Privacy Regulation*, April 2002. From the Health Privacy Project, Institute for Health Care Research and Policy, Georgetown University, 2233 Wisconsin Avenue, NW Suite 525 Washington, DC 20007. Phone 202.687.0880; Fax 202.784.1265. www.healthprivacy.org

[11] These six ideas are modified from Fact Sheet #8 from the Privacy Rights Clearing House, Ibid.

open at all. A judge will decide what parts, if any, of your medical record should be considered available. After the case is decided, you can also ask the judge to "seal" the court records containing your medical information.

6. Find out if your health care provider has a policy on the use of **cordless and cellular phones** and **fax machines** when discussing and transmitting medical information. Cordless and wireless/cellular telephones are not as private as standard "wired" telephones. Because they transmit by radio wave, phone conversations can be overheard on various electronic devices. Fax machines offer far less privacy than the mail because frequently many people in an office have access to fax transmissions.

Additional ideas[12]

"**Talk about confidentiality concerns with your doctor.** Your health care provider should be able to help you understand the uses of your health information, and may be able to offer certain assurances of confidentiality. For example, some providers keep treatment notes separate from the general medical chart to help ensure that the most sensitive information remains confidential. Your provider may also be able to help you understand the current limits of confidentiality, such as what kinds of information he or she is required to provide for insurance purposes.

"**Register your objection to disclosures that you consider inappropriate.** Registering objections may not result in immediate change, but sharing your concerns will help to educate your providers, plans, and others seeking health information. These entities should be aware that **lack of privacy impacts how you seek and receive your health care.**"

For more information

The American Health Information Management Association, <www.ahima.org> AHIMA, 919 N. Michigan Ave. Chicago IL 60611-1683. Phone: (800) 335-5535. They offer a website for creating you Persona Health Record <http://www.myphr.com/> Accessed Sept 25, 2005.

For help with the Americans with Disabilities Act, call the nearest Technical Assistance Center, (800) 949-4232. <www.pacdbtac.org> or <www.adata.org> Accessed Sept 25, 2005.

Contact the Privacy Advocate of the U.S. Dept. of Health and Human Services regarding privacy-related programs of the DHHS: 200 Independence Ave., SW, Washington, D.C. 20201. Phone: (202) 690-5896. The general number for the DHHS is (877) 696-6775. Its Office for Civil Rights can be reached at (866) 627-7748. <www.dhhs.gov> Accessed Sept 25, 2005.

The Health Privacy Project of Georgetown University, at The Institute for Health Care Research and Policy, Georgetown University, 2233 Wisconsin Avenue, NW Suite 525 Washington, DC 20007. Phone 202.687.0880; Fax 202.784.1265. <www.healthprivacy.org> Accessed Sept 25, 2005.

The web site of the California Medical Association, <www.cmanet.org> offers booklets on how to get your medical records and how to file a complaint at <http://www.cmanet.org/publicdoc.cfm/21/725> Accessed Sept 25, 2005.

---

[12] These ideas are from the Institute for Health Care Research and Policy, Ibid

180   How to use this book

Because the regulations allow flexibility and risk assessment before you go on to implement HIPAA in your practice you should ask yourself this question: What are my resources of time, money, and energy and what are the risks I am willing to accept in complying?

Functions this book serves

- An orientation and introduction to the law and its regulations at they apply to small and solo psychotherapy practices.
- A step-by-step path to HIPAA compliance by providing forms, guidelines, materials for training staff and making decisions, etc.
- A source for the forms and client education materials you need. Almost all can be simply photocopied while others serve as templates for tailoring your own. See www.hipaahelp.info/forms.
- Solid evidence of your HIPAA compliance efforts, if you are ever investigated.
- A reference to answer questions about HIPAA's complexities. All of the regulations bearing on small therapy practices have been reproduced so you can refer to them if needed.
- A permanent place to keep further HIPAA documents, advisories, and new materials.

Efforts vs. benefits in becoming HIPAA compliant

In my opinion, you can choose how to implement HIPAA. Here are three possibilities as I see them.

1. These are the **basic** and absolute minimum efforts you must do to comply (and not be easily seen as non-compliant). You might do these now and leave the next levels for future implementation.
    a. Identify a privacy officer.
    b. Develop a long and shorter NPP and give one to all your present and new clients.
    c. Reprint the Consent form and get it signed after the NPP was read.
    d. Slightly modify your Authorization to request/release records.
    e. Conduct and document staff training in confidentiality.
    f. Renegotiate or amend contracts with your business associates.

2. These are additional efforts you should make to be in **legal** compliance. If you are investigated after a complaint these would show you have made a sincere effort to comply.
    a. Implement procedures to assure that the minimum necessary information is released, complaints are addressed, and clients can amend their records.
    b. Develop or add to your practice brochure that addresses and explains all the issues.
    c. Create a HIPAA Policies and Procedures Manual (see section 800).
    d. Do a preemption examination for all items in your practice brochure and authorizations and make any needed changes to your forms, policies, and procedures.

3. These are the additional efforts you could make to be in complete compliance in all aspects of your practice and safe from any kind of complaint or investigation.
    a. Develop a complete Policies and Procedures Manual for a MH practice
    b. Do a full preemption study for all areas of your practice specializations
    c. Computerize your records

This book contains all you need for the first and second options and some guidance for the third. The steps to compliance (section 221) are structured levels of effort..

200 Core ideas

210   Terminology and components of HIPAA

The Health Insurance Portability and Accountability Act of 1996 (August 21), or Public Law 104-191, was designed to improve the efficiency of health care services by standardizing electronic data, and to protect privacy of this data by imposing procedures and standards across the country. The full text of the Act can be found at <http://www.hhs.gov/ocr/hipaa>

The rest of this section – the 200's – is a quick overview of the essential ideas, terms, and topics which we will expand upon throughout this book.

The main parts of HIPAA

The parts of HIPAA which apply most to therapists, though large and detailed, can be divided into three sections, each with a number of rules and standards.

1 . The Electronic Health **Transactions** Standards concern health insurance programs - eligibility for benefits, processing claims, coordination of benefits, and so forth. These require the adoption of "Standard Code Sets" for each kind of transaction to describe disorders and interventions. Your billing service, clearinghouse, billing program's developers, and the insurers you deal with will develop and provide most if not all of these for you (perhaps at some cost).

2. The **Security** and Electronic Signature Standards concern methods for verification of the identity of data users and the accuracy of electronically transferred data. Again, your

billing service or billing program's developers will handle some parts of this for you.
3. The **Privacy** Standards concern the maintenance of confidentiality and the access to an individual's health information. You are responsible for becoming compliant to these complex standards by April 14, 2003.

This whole book and the largest part of HIPAA is about personal information and maintaining its privacy. Let us first look at what information we are talking about and then at what privacy means.

Confidentiality, Privacy and Privilege

We often use the words interchangeably but they differ in important ways.

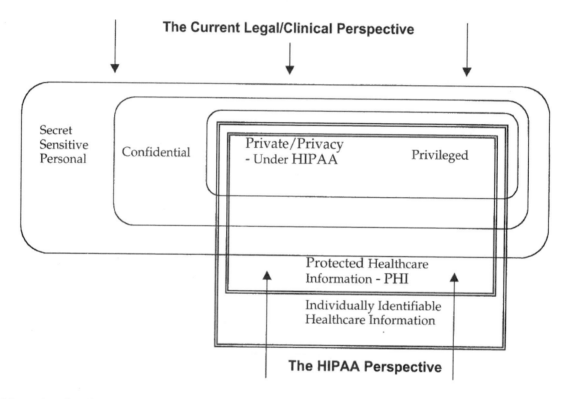

Many kinds of information exist which a person might consider personal and sensitive and want to keep from others. Each person has his or her own reasons and concerns. What is **confidential** is information given to another person with the belief and trust that he or she will not disclose it to any unauthorized person because, in some way, the one who gave it would suffer. It is believed that such information must be sensitive for some reason, and that therefore it needs to be protected against revelation or improper use and must be given only to those who should have it. **Privacy** is the legally established right of individuals to keep information about themselves from being disclosed to anyone. **Privilege** is the special protection given to information shared in some professional relationships (with a lawyer, physician, priest, and by extension, us) and is created by laws. It is the responsibility of the health care provider to control the access to that information. HIPAA is a serious attempt to codify the rules for the use and release of health care information about individuals. Terms like personal, sensitive or confidential have no legal standing in health care and so should be avoided.

Health information

Whenever you go for health care from anyone for anything, health care information is created and it is tied to your identity (by name, number, address, etc. See section 950 on de-identifying) and so it is individually **identifiable health care information** (IIHI) The regs say such information relates to the past, present, or future physical or mental health or condition of an individual or the provision of health care to that individual or the past, present or future payment for the provision of health care to an individual or that the information (was) created or received by a health care provider, health plan, public health authority, employer, life insurer, school or university, or health care clearinghouse. (§ 164.501).

If this information is not covered by the Family Educational Right and Privacy Act (FERPA) or post-secondary student medical records, as described in 20 USC 1232g(a)(4)(B)(iv) it is considered **protected health information (PHI)** (Another memorable acronym) and is subject to the privacy standards of HIPAA.

The HIPAA regulations concern how this information is to be kept private when it is collected, created, stored in your office, shared with other treaters, used in training or research, and sent to insurers. It is the *information* in the record that is protected by this law, and so not only electronic records (word processor, fax, data entry), but paper records, and even oral communications such as conversations, telephone calls, and messages, as well as most consultations and teaching, are covered.

The uses of health information

A client's PHI is mainly used in **treatment, payment, or health care operations** or **TPO.** (One more necessary acronym, but almost the last.) Exact and extended definitions can be found in § 164.501, but here are the gists.

Treatment is when a provider offers or manages health care or related services, consults with other providers, or makes a referral.

Payment includes what a health care plan does to obtain premiums, determine eligibility or coverage, and provide reimbursement. These can include activities such as coordination of benefits with other insurance, assessment of the client's health status and needs, determining the medical necessity of care, and reviewing utilization.

Health care operations means the variety of activities conducted by the CE or the CE's organization which are not for treatment or payment. These can include quality assessment and improvement activities; review of the performance, competence, or qualifications of health care or non-health professionals, training; accrediting, licensing, or credentialing of professionals; medical review; auditing functions such as fraud and abuse detection and compliance programs; and a variety of actions to support business administration, planning, customer service, grievance resolution, due diligence, and so forth

As you can see, almost every kind of a clinician's activity is covered, and thus a client's consent to participate (by signing the Consent form. More on this in section 430) allows a great deal of freedom to share information about the individual.

Use ≠ disclosure

HIPAA recognizes two functions associated with PHI: use and disclosure. **Use** is the "sharing, employment, application, utilization, examination, or analysis of PHI within an entity that maintains such information" and **disclosure** is the "release, transfer, provision of access to, or divulging in any other manner PHI outside the entity holding the information.

HIPAA and privacy

HIPAA creates a kind of national **floor** of very basic privacy rights. In reality, most of the methods you currently use for consent and release will still be needed (over and above some new HIPAA procedures), because your state's laws take precedence (preempt HIPAA) if they more stringently protect the client's privacy.

Consents ≠ Authorizations

Once notified of his or her rights through reading your **Notice of Privacy Procedures (NPP)** (One more essential acronym) the client signs a "**consent**," and treatment may begin. The consent allows **you to use and disclose** his or her PHI for TPO among all CEs[13] such treaters, treating agencies, those in training, health insurers, managed care organizations, and others (see § 164.506). If the PHI ever needs to be used for other than TPO or disclosed to anyone outside the organization who is not a CE, a written release (**Authorization**) is required.

Routine progress notes and psychotherapy notes

The HIPAA Privacy Rule considers clinical records to be of two main kinds - the familiar **progress notes** which are not given a name in HIPAA but I am going to call **Routine Notes** and the **Psychotherapy Notes**. Psychotherapy notes are given much more extensive protection but routine notes are the main way PHI is supplied for TPO.

Crosswalking and the preemption of state laws by HIPAA

HIPAA does not come onto a stage empty of rules about the privacy of medical records. Each state and the federal system has laws, regulations, procedures, court decisions, practices, and rules. Acknowledging this patchwork of laws, HIPAA has a fine general rule: the law which is more protective of client privacy wins out (prevails, applies, takes precedence over the less protective law, even where the less protective one is HIPAA. Therefore, the laws of each state must be examined and compared with HIPAA (this is called **crosswalking**) because the more stringent will **preempt** the less. There is one other protective design in the HIPAA law and it has important consequences: where the state laws are silent on a privacy issue that HIPAA addresses, HIPAA prevails. This introduces some new privacy rights such as a right to amend one's records.

There are, as you would expect in any law addressing such complex issues, many more subtleties, ramifications, qualifications, and exceptions. That is what the rest of this book is about.

---

[13] Aren't you pleased with yourself? You read the last as "his or her Protected Healthcare Information for Treatment, Payment of Healthcare Operations among all Covered Entities" didn't you?

220   Implementing HIPAA in your practice

Fully implementing HIPAA in a large organization will require many people-years of work. However because of the scalability and cost-benefit analysis built into HIPAA compliance, small practices will have to do much, much less.

1. The HIPAA act itself offers a detailed schedule for implementing it and suggests that you analyze the differences between your current privacy practices and what HIPAA requires (a Gap Analysis) and assess the vulnerabilities of your current records and procedures (a Risk Analyses). More on these can be found in sections 250 and 180.

2. Implementing HIPAA requires integrating (crosswalking) HIPAA's rules with your state and local laws to discover which are more stringent (protective of privacy) and operating under those. This preemption analysis is extraordinarily difficult and complex and those who have done it typically charge their clients hundreds and thousands of dollars. Since this is beyond our resources I have made **two simplifying assumptions**. I will assume that you already have:

    a. A Practice Brochure[14] for client education which addresses such topics as fees and payments, confidentiality and its limitations, how long you will keep client's records and how you will release them, reaching you in an emergency, your background and approach to treatment, etc.

    b. A form to Release and/or Request Records and that meets both your state's laws and your profession's codes of ethics.

These will have addressed many of the privacy issues and will be based on your state's rules so you only have to compare them with what this book describes about HIPAA's rules to do your preemption analysis.

3. HIPAA is scalable to the size and resources of your operation. In light of this, before you go further, you should review the options I offered in section 180 on efforts vs. benefits and decide what level of compliance you will now implement. The tasks below have been marked to indicate whether they are at the **Basic (B), Legal (L), or Complete (C) levels.**

Below is my suggested list of what a small practice should do and in what order. The items are in a time sequence, not importance, or complexity and most will require less effort than they appear to. You might photocopy this to guide your efforts

---

[14] Although you might have titled it "Information For My Clients," "What You Should Know About Therapy," or Welcome to My Practice," I will use the more generic title in this book. If you have not yet developed these materials or want to upgrade them, may I modestly suggest that you have a look at the very best quality, most comprehensive, and most authoritative resource on operating a practice legally and ethically – *The Paper Office* (3rd edition, 2003) from Guilford Press. More information about the book is available at <www.thepaperoffice.com>

221   A To Do List

To Do List for HIPAA Compliance

Dates
Initiated   Finished

❏   Designate **a Privacy Officer** to be the staff member to become more aware of HIPAA and of threats to the *privacy and security* of your office's PHI, to evaluate uncommon requests for records, train staff, and respond to questions and complaints. See section 230 for more. B, L, C.

❏   Have the privacy officer do a **gap analysis** examining all current ways your office handles client information (PHI) seeking out potential problems and failures of privacy or security with using or disclosing PHI and then looking for gaps between your practices and what HIPAA requires in these practices. See section 250 for more. L, C

❏   Develop **a plan** for implementing HIPAA in your practice which includes both sides of the equation. On one are the privacy standards, client rights, and system and administrative practices. On the other are the effort/benefit analyses and scalability factors. See section 180. L, C

❏   Develop a **Notice of Privacy Practices** which includes the mandated contents and educates clients about their new rights. While a separate document, it should mesh with your Practice Brochure to generate informed consent while meeting federal, state, local and ethical standards. See section 410 for more. B

❏   Develop a **Consent form**. See section 430 for more. B, L, C

❏   Compare your current procedures, your state's current requirements, and HIPAA to decide where HIPAA does and doesn't **preempt** your current practices. See section 260. L, C

❏   Consult with peers and published resources to evaluate the adequacy of your current practices in terms of what are today's legal and ethical best practices. Develop any changes needed to upgrade your office's procedures. (*The Paper Office* by Ed Zuckerman covers all these issues.) L, C

❏   Revise your **Practice Brochure** to include the HIPAA-guaranteed client access and amendment rights, and others you may not have included such as offering alternative ways to communicate with clients and instruction on how to complain about possible privacy violations. See section 600 for more. B, L, C

❏   Develop the versions of an **Authorization form** which are required for disclosures for other than TPO. Integrate this with your current Request for/Release of Records forms. See section 440 . B, L, C

❏ Modify your office procedures as necessary to have the above forms read, understood, and signed as soon as treatment begins. B, L, C

❏ Devise **policies and procedures** to implement the Minimum Necessary Information to be released when you send out your records and the many other administrative requirements for security and privacy. See section 530 for more. L, C

❏ Develop policies and procedures to handle clients' requests for **examining, copying, and amending their records.** See sections 550 and 630 and 640 for more. L, C

❏ Develop a **complaint process** which includes whom to contact, a plan for corrections, prohibition of retaliation, and needed documentation. See section 660 for more. L, C

❏ Identify all businesses who performs service for you and which use your PHI. Amend or revise your contract with these Business Associates. Assure yourself that the **Business Associate** intends and is able to adhere to the relevant rules. See section 270 for more. C

❏ Based on a careful assessment of current procedures, staff functions, and how you will implement HIPAA develop, implement, and document all needed **training** programs for all staff. See section 260 and 871 for more. L, C

❏ Create methods for those who discover privacy violations to report them without fear of **retaliation**, for you to **mitigate** any damage, to prevent future violations, and to carry out **sanctions** as necessary against staff, peers, business associates, and, of course, create needed documentation. For all of these see section 860. C

❏ If you have or intend to computerize your records, work with the system's **vendor** to develop and use safeguards that meet the demands of the Security and Privacy Rules to prevent intentional or accidental disclosures. See section 330 for more. C

❏ Keep appropriate **records of your HIPAA efforts** and compliance. These include contents and times of staff training, an accounting of disclosures, and copies of requests for records. See sections 261, 652, and 650. L, C

❏ **Monitor adherence** to policy and procedures, make necessary changes, and document both. Devise changes as HIPAA policy and procedures are elaborated, modified, or interact with other policies. C

❏ **Consult** with legal, financial, and professionals to answer questions and review efforts for compliance, legality, appropriateness, etc. C

222   List of forms for a HIPAA-compliant practice

The last section was a "To-do list" of activities toward compliance. Below is a list of the actual materials which need to be generated (by a clinician). They are clustered into three categories **for basic, legal, and complete compliance** but do read the next level because, due to the nature of your practice, you may find some materials you are more likely to need. Please be aware that these levels are my own opinion and would very likely not be the recommendation of a lawyer seeking to protect you. I am not a lawyer and this is not legal advice.

Forms and other materials – Basic Compliance

1. Notice of Privacy Practices. See section 410 for more.

2. A "Form to Acknowledge Receipt of the Notice of Privacy Practices and Consent to Use and Disclose PHI." I call this the **Consent** and the regulations refer to it as consent but the larger title better explains its role. See section 430 for more.

3. Authorization to send to request PHI from other CEs. See section 460 for more.

4. A client's Request Form to examine his or her PHI or obtain a copy. See section 631

Forms and other materials – Legal Compliance

5. Form to Complain about a violation of a client's privacy. See section 661.Although rarely needed it is essential to have on hand.

6. Staff training materials. See sections 260, 261, 262, and 263.

7. Business associate contract provisions. See section 270.

8. Request form to amend one's PHI. See section 641.

Forms and other materials – Complete Compliance

Although unlikely to be needed they are explained and included in this book so you will have them if necessary. They are not listed by importance.

9. Authorizations to use or disclose PHI internally to the practice. See section 450.

10. Authorizations to use or disclose PHI for research participants. See section 470.

11. Authorizations to use or disclose psychotherapy notes. See section 480.

12. Form to revoke an authorization. See section 490.

13. Request form to limit disclosures to family, friends, or others. See section 611.

14. Request form for an alternate method of contact. See section 621.

15. Request for an accounting of disclosures of an individual's PHI. See section 653.

16. A HIPAA Compliance Policy and Procedures Manual. See section 800 .

User-friendly forms

I have tried to design the needed forms and materials to practices ranging in size from a solo part-timer to a group practice with a dozen or so full time equivalent professionals and with resources ranging from a copy machine down the street to networked computers and many software options. Therefore, materials in the book are available in different formats.

A. Forms which can be used as is. They appear on separate pages, with the book's information (title, page number) at the top of the page where it can easily be covered by your letterhead and then photocopied.

B. Forms which need some modifications. You might retype these or scan them into your word processor. I did not believe that there is so much material that a CD-ROM was worth creating and imposing its extra cost upon you. I have placed copies on the website <www.HIPAAHelp.info/forms/> which is also listed at the bottom of the first page. You can download them and modify them easily on your word processor.

C. Content which needs to be added to your current forms. As you work through the book some issues or concerns will suggest content that you can develop and add to your forms. Generally these are sentences or a paragraph or two and so are best typed in.

Disclaimer: I really cannot know your particular needs so please adapt the materials to your practice. I do not believe a small practice needs to have more than the above-listed ones to implement the Privacy Rule unless a very complex situation arises and then the proper response is consultation with a health care lawyer. Other documentation is needed for compliance with the Security Rule – see section 700.

223 Schedule for Implementing HIPAA

Although many of these dates have passed, the schedule for implementation of the different parts of HIPAA is summarized here to show you its scale and sweep

Title of the Standard	Date Published	Compliance Date
Standards for Electronic **Transactions** 65 08 FR 50311	8/17/2000	10/16/2002 or 10/16/2003
Standard for **Electronic Signatures**	Removed 12/02	May be in later regulations
Standards for **Privacy** 65 FR 82461 **Privacy Guidance** 67 FR 14775	08/14/02	04/14/2003

      (THIS WAS THE BIGGIE DATE FOR MENTAL HEALTH CLINICIANS)

Unique **Identifier for Individuals**
   Work on this identifier was halted due to privacy concerns.

Standard Unique **Identifier for Employers** CMS-0047-F	05/31/02	07/30/04 Uses employer's Tax ID# or EIN (Employer Identification Number)
Standard Unique Health Care **Provider Identifier** CMS-0045-F	3/03	05/23/05 to 5/23/07 See section 331
Standard Unique **Health Plan Identifier** CMS-4145-P	Estimated 11/05	Unknown
Security Standards CMS-0049-F	2/20/03	4/20/05
Standard for **Claims Attachments** CMS-0050-P	Estimated 10/05	Unknown

Enforcement Procedures   4/18/05
CMS of DHHS will enforce the Transactions and Security Rules while the Office of Civil Rights will enforce the Privacy Rule.

An unofficial but very thorough Compliance Calendar is available at
<http://www.hipaadvisory.com/regs/compliancecal.htm>

230   The privacy officer

The HIPAA regulations require that you select someone to be your organization's privacy official and this should be your first order of business in complying with HIPAA.

The officer should be yourself in solo practice (and not your office manager or secretary as they can change and you, the professional will be held responsible for HIPAA compliance anyway). In a group, select the best qualified person not the one with the most free time.

The officer's duties involve designing, implementing, and monitoring privacy policies to comply with the HIPAA rules. The security side is also important in that this person will deal with the technical issues of hardware and software, training of all staff, etc. so it may make sense to have a single privacy and security officer.

Q: I am a solo practitioner, but I share an office with several other professional mental health practices. Can we share a privacy official?
A: Yes. Several practices can share a privacy official, as long as each practice fulfills the requirements of the regulation. But if you have little communication with them or any question about how well they will fulfill the regulation's requirement it might be better to have your own privacy official.

Q: Is each department of a multi-treatment center with many programs required to have its own privacy official?
A: Probably not. The whole organization can, if sufficiently integrated in its procedures and records, be considered a single CE and so need only one privacy official.

Sample job descriptions

For those needing them for more complex organizations or for guidance several have been posted on the Internet and a search will, no doubt, find others.

The American Health Information Management Association
<http://www.ahima.org/infocenter/models/PrivacyOfficer2001.asp> Accessed September 23, 2005.

North Carolina Healthcare Information and Communications Alliance, Inc. (NCHICA).
<http://www.nchica.org/HIPAAResources/Samples/JobDescriptions/hospital.html#PrivacyOfficer> Accessed Sept. 24, 2005.

231   Duties of the privacy officer

In a large organization there might be an office with several staff members but for a small practice here are some guidelines for what the Privacy Officer should expect to do.

Responsibilities

Responsible for the CE's privacy (and likely the security) program and associated policies.

Role functions

1. Provide leadership in creating and implementing a privacy program.

2. Maintain compliance with federal and state laws related to privacy, security, confidentiality, and protection of information resources.

3. Develop privacy policies and procedures that include but are not limited to: NPP and Consent; use and disclosure of PHI; responding to individual requests for restriction of use and disclosure of PHI; access, inspection and copying of PHI; amendment of PHI; accounting of disclosures; Policy and Procedure Manual, and other administrative procedures as needed. Maintain copies of all versions of these.

4. Receive and record complaints and/or questions about the privacy program

5. Investigate all allegations of non-compliance with privacy policies.

6. Develop and implement a privacy training program. Do the initial training of all employees relating to the privacy and security program. Train all new employees, volunteers, trainees, and other persons who are not business associates but are likely to have contact with PHI. Do retraining for all employees on a periodic basis.

7. Develop sanctions for failure to comply with the privacy policies and procedures by all members of the workforce and the business associates.

8. Ensure that no intimidating, discriminatory, or other retaliatory actions take place against anyone who files, testifies, assists or participates in any investigation, compliance review, proceeding or hearing related to a privacy violation or opposed any unlawful act or practice.

9. Develop a corrective action plan to mitigate any deleterious effects of a use or disclosure of PHI by business partners.

10. Periodically revise the organization's privacy program in light of changes in laws, regulations, or company policy.

11. Develop procedures for documenting and reporting self-disclosures of any evidence of privacy violations to legal counsel, and if appropriate to the appropriate government regulatory body according to corporate policy.

This list is adapted from the job description at North Carolina Healthcare Information and Communications Alliance, Inc. (NCHICA).
<http://www.nchica.org/HIPAAResources/Samples/JobDescriptions/JobDescriptions.htm> Accessed Sept. 24, 2005.

240   Preemption of state laws by HIPAA

Nothing in this legislation was better intended and yet more productive of confusion and complexity than what is called preemption. Congress clearly intended to create a set of privacy guarantees which was consistent across the states and across the entire health care system; inclusive of all providers and insurers, medical and mental health, and all diagnostic groups and service populations. It was intended to sweep away the hash of partial, non-overlapping, inconsistent laws and court decisions in different states and levels of courts and replace them with clear and enforceable rules. The health care industry also wanted this total federal "preemption" of the mass of state laws to simplify their own procedures. Unfortunately Congress failed to pass a Bill of Patient's Rights and the bureaucrats had then to write the regulations had to deal with this lack of foundation and principles and also with the fact that many states had already passed quite strong privacy legislation.[15] As a result we have § 160.201 to .205 which try to clarify how the newer rules in HIPAA are to interact with the older rules in each state. This is loosely referred to as the preemption problem or, by the more optimistic, "challenge."

The problems with current state legislation

Current state legislation is a patchwork and varies greatly from state to state. Some states have general guidelines and others very specific statutes on the privacy of health information. Some are organized by disease and some by classes of information (e.g. clinical data, lab tests, or the vital statistics of demographics, admission and discharge). For example, only about half of the states have a general law that prohibits disclosure of health information without client consent and some of these address only hospital records. State law commonly exempts from informed consent to disclose information for payments or for emergency care or to law enforcement officials, etc. In other cases where an authorization is required it may be weakened by an absence of time limits or its applicability to multiple disclosures.

As a result of such weak controls, clients seeking to protect their privacy and avoid embarrassment or discrimination do not share critical information with their providers or lie or avoid health care altogether and so suffer. This situation also unnecessarily raises costs for all of us and privacy protection is irregular and undependable.

HIPAA was intended to provide a national policy on privacy but has become simply a federal floor of privacy controls and even so the regulation must interact with current state laws. This working out of these thousands of potential interactions, called **crosswalking,** will be done in the conference rooms, committees, legislatures, and courtrooms of this country over the next few years.

The General Rule

Acknowledging this patchwork of laws, HIPAA has a general rule: the law which is more protective of client privacy has precedence over the less protective law, even where the less protective one is HIPAA. Therefore, the laws of each state must be examined and compared with HIPAA because the **more stringent** will apply and override (**preempt**) the weaker. Further, where the state laws are silent on a privacy issue that HIPAA addresses, HIPAA will prevail. This will be important.

---

[15] Some states have adopted very comprehensive privacy laws and others have their laws fragmented under dozens of pieces of legislation. If you are interested in a model state privacy law, have a look at *Privacy and Security of Public Health Information* by Lawrence O. Gostin and James G. Hodge, Jr. It is available on the net at http://www.critpath.org/msphpa/privacy.htm Accessed Sept. 22, 2005.

More specifics

1. Covered entities must comply with both federal and state privacy laws and regulations when they can do this. When they cannot, the preemption issue arises and frames the conflict.

2. HIPAA's rules preempt (override, apply instead of) state laws[16] that are **contrary** to the HIPAA regulations. There are four exceptions to this rule for:
    a. State laws which are necessary to prevent fraud and abuse and similar legal and administrative functions for reporting or investigation. For example, the reporting of child abuse.

    b. State laws which require health plans to provide information for management audits, monitoring, or licensure.

    c. State laws which concern controlled substances.

    d. State laws about the privacy of PHI which are **contrary to** or **more stringent** than the federal requirements. Few states have laws about Electronic PHI and so HIPAA's Security rule will apply widely

As you can immediately see, the last exception contains the sticking point.

3. What does it mean for a state law to be **contrary** to a federal law? It means, when courts make this decision, that
    a. it is not possible to comply with both OR

    b. the state law is an obstacle to achieving the purposes and intent of the federal law (i.e. HIPAA). (I don't know more about this.)

4. What does it mean for a state law to be **more stringent** than the federal law? It means that the state law meets one or more of these six (quite sensible) criteria:
    a. The state law prohibits or restricts a use or disclosure in circumstances where HIPAA would allow such use or disclosure. This applies except if the disclosure is to the client (the person the PHI is about) or if the Secretary of DHHS has decided the disclosure is required for HIPAA. (These two are the only mandated disclosures.)

    b. The state law gives the client greater rights of access to or amendment of his or her records. This exception does not apply to state laws that allows or prohibits disclosures to a parent, guardian, or person acting *in loco parentis* about a minor.

    c. The state law requires giving the client more information about the use, disclosure, rights or remedies regarding his or her PHI.

    d. The states' law concerning consent or authorization (releases) is more limiting of the scope or duration, increase the privacy protections afforded (such as by expanding the criteria for), or reduce the coercive effect of the circumstances ...   [160.202(4)] and so increases the privacy protection. The logic is that the more criteria or thresholds, the less information will be released and the greater the privacy.

    e. The state law requires more detailed record keeping or accounting of disclosures or reporting of more information or **retaining the records of this for longer time period.**

---

[16] *State law* as used here means any statute, regulation, rule, common law, or other state action having the force and effect of law.

f. Where the state law provides greater privacy protection in any other way. For example, laws about confidentiality for those with AIDS/HIV, mental health, alcohol and drug abuse, other sexually transmitted and communicable diseases, and genetic information add stringency to the more general laws on privacy.

See below for a procedure to follow in evaluating possible preemption.

5. And who decides when the laws are contrary or more stringent? The Secretary of DHHS. And how does the Secretary decide? (You are going to love this.) Your state government has to submit a request (for a determination that the state law is excepted from preemption) in writing, with all the laws, reasons, etc. and await an actual and final *determination* (not an *advisory opinion*, which are not available from DHHS on HIPAA questions). Of course there are likely to be hundreds if not thousands of such requests. What do you do in the meantime? You obey the state law.

Case example

In Pennsylvania, if I consult another professional on a case and do not identify the client or give information which would allow the consultant to identify the client, I do not need an Authorization. However, if I will be identifying the client, I do need an signed Authorization (my familiar Authorization to Release Information). This is different from HIPAA under which these are both disclosures for the purpose of treatment and so need only the Consent and not an Authorization. How do I decide which law to obey? Answer: Follow the one which offers the greater protection of the client's privacy. In this case, Pennsylvania law.

What about my professions ethical rules?

First, **HIPAA is discipline blind.** It applies equally to all healthcare professionals who create PHI or EPHI.

Second, we need to draw some distinctions. Each profession's code of ethics applies only to those members of the association unless it has been written into the state's licensing law in which case it applies to all licensed professionals and whatever professional work they do. This makes ethical violations legal ones as well.

My advice: Obey your state laws. If they conflict with your ethics, try to negotiate and *always* consult with your peers (and document the consultation) and with your profession's state association. In the words of a famous legal expert, Never worry alone.

Finding your state laws

There are a number of web resources which may be helpful but remember your state's laws and regulations may be under any number of not obviously related headings. All URLs below were accessible on Sept. 22, 2005

1. The Health Privacy Project at Georgetown University has developed a number of papers on this subject.
- Their comprehensive and critical report on state statutes entitled *The State of Health Privacy: An Uneven Terrain (A Comprehensive Survey of State Health Privacy Statutes)* has been updated for 2002 and is online at <http://www.healthprivacy.org/info-url_nocat2304/info-url_nocat.htm>
- There are also summaries for each state available at <http://www.healthprivacy.org/info-url_nocat2304/info-url_nocat_search.htm>

- Their document Health Privacy 101, an excellent introduction to the topic is at: <http://www.healthprivacy.org/info-url_nocat2302/info-url_nocat.htm>

2. The Legal Information Institute at Cornell Law School has links to the state statues on the Internet organized by topic at: <http://www.law.cornell.edu:80/topics/state_statutes.html#health> You will have to search by topic and then by state, but it is quite complete.

3. The BehaveNet® Directory of Behavioral Health Laws is at: <http://www.behavenet.com/law/> Go to a state and then you will need to search under the topic the state has used to organize its laws.

4. If you want to see how complicated this interaction of state laws and HIPAA will be, an organization in North Carolina has examined their laws and done the cross-walking. It is entitled *Analysis of the HIPAA Privacy Rule and Selected North Carolina Statutes 12/11/01* and consists of more than 250 pages. It is available at: <http://www.nchica.org/HIPAA/Samples/Portal.asp>

241 Preemption decision work sheet

How can you deal with the needed crosswalking of HIPAA with local laws? There are only two ways I can see. First, the Practice Organization of the American Psychological Association and APA's insurance sales arm, APAIT, sell an online continuing education program (HIPAA Privacy Rule Online Compliance Course) which allows you to print out state-specific HIPAA forms. See <http://www.apapractice.org/>. This is the result of an extensive crosswalking effort and was created by lawyers and psychologists but still contains a strong disclaimer. Pricing begins at $175 for those members of APA who pay the clinician's special assessment and rise from there to $575 for others. Second, consider my approach in which I have made two simplifying assumptions which seem justified:

1. You already know a great deal about your local laws since you were trained there, have attended ethics and legal issues continuing education programs, and had lively discussions with your colleagues.

2. You are already in compliance with your local rules. Your procedures and client education materials follow your rules.

Therefore, you can read the HIPAA rules and compare them with your current practices and make preemption decisions.

This form is not meant to be the definitive method for evaluating the circumstances of a conflict between state laws and HIPAA nor a way to assure an absolutely correct conclusion. It is meant to help you collect the necessary information and then think through the issues. As you proceed take all the time and writing space you need. If the issues are more complex than your understanding please consult appropriate resources like lawyers with experience in this area.

Preemption decision work sheet for therapists

1. Background

    a. What is the issue in conflict? Summarize and clarify.

    b. What has been the procedure in the past in this office or agency (if relevant)?

    c. What do HIPAA's privacy and security rules say about the issue? (Include citation(s) to section(s) of HIPAA.) Note: HIPAA applies only to CEs (Covered Entities) and state law may apply to all kinds of clinicians, non-CEs (such as all psychologists) or non-CE parts of a hybrid entity.

    d. What does the state law or regulation say? (Include citation(s) as necessary) You may need to look at each part, section, or even sentence. Some examples are laws and regulations on medical records, genetic testing, HIV, mental health/substance abuse, pharmacy, and workers compensation. Also look at your state's licensing law for your profession.

    e. What does your profession's Code of Ethics say about this issue? (where relevant). The American Psychological Association's code has been revised for June 2003 and is online at < http://www.apa.org/ethics/> The code of the National Association of Social Workers is at <http://www.socialworkers.org/pubs/code/default.asp> and the code of the American Counseling Association at <http://www.counseling.org/resources/ethics.htm>

2. Exceptions to preemption

Generally, HIPAA is seen as preempting state law but there are exceptions (restated here for therapists). Does this issue fit any of these four?

   a. The issue relates to some kind of **public health activities** such as reporting, surveillance, investigation, intervention or compliance/enforcement of health plans or other CEs.

   ❑ No, the issue doesn't and so HIPAA does not apply, local laws do.

   Note: The exception below is very like the one above but is subtly legally different.

   b. The Secretary of Health and Human Services has **granted an exception** and so you should follow the state law. These exceptions include when it's necessary to prevent fraud and abuse; ensure state regulation of insurance; permit state reporting of health care delivery or costs; serve compelling public health, safety or welfare needs; address a compelling reason that outweighs the privacy intrusion; or regulate controlled substances.

   ❑ No exception has been made and so HIPAA does not apply, local laws do.

   c. The state laws and HIPAA are **contrary** in that:
   ❑ It is not possible to comply with both OR
   ❑ the state law is an "obstacle" to achieving the purposes and intent of HIPAA.
   ❑ They are not contrary and so HIPAA applies.

   d. State law or regulation is **more stringent** (more protective) than the Privacy Rule. Does the state law do any of these six things?

   1. Prohibits or restricts the use or disclosure of PHI in circumstances where HIPAA would allow such use or disclosure?

   ❑ Yes   ❑ No

   Note that this rule does not apply when disclosure is to the client or where the Secretary of DHHS has decided the disclosure is necessary for HIPAA.

   2. Gives greater rights of access or amendment to the client?

   ❑ Yes   ❑ No

   Note that this does not apply to state laws that require you to release information about a minor to parents. For example, if your local laws require you to notify a parent before providing treatment to a minor, HIPAA does not take precedence.

3. Provides more information to the client about the use or disclosure of PHI or the client's rights and remedies concerning such use or disclosure?

   ❑ Yes   ❑ No

4. When it concerns the release of information through consent or authorizing the disclosure, the local law does one or more of these:
- ❑ specifies a narrower scope or duration of the release.
- ❑ reduces the coercion involved in obtaining the consent or authorization.
- ❑ erects a barrier or obstacles to others' attempts to obtain PHI.
- ❑ increases privacy protection for individuals in this area.

❑ Yes ❑ No

5. Requires more detailed information to be included in the records **or that you maintain them for a longer period?**

❑ Yes ❑ No

6. Provide greater privacy protection to the individual in some other ways?

❑ Yes ❑ No

If any of these six are true - you answered yes - HIPAA does not apply.

3. **Decision or Disposition**

❑ This issue does fit one or more of the exceptions so state law applies.

❑ This issue does not meet one of the exceptions so HIPAA applies.

❑ I cannot meet both HIPAA and state law and I cannot decide what to do so I am referring the issue to:
- ❑ My legal counsel
- ❑ My professional organization
- ❑ My state agency: _____
- ❑ Other: _____

_____

_____   _____
Privacy officer - Name   Date

Follow up:

_____   _____   _____
Date   Procedure or Decision   Signature

_____   _____   _____
Date   Procedure or Decision   Signature

_____   _____   _____
Date   Procedure or Decision   Signature

250 Understanding the way your office handles PHI – Doing a gap analysis

The practical benefits of doing this work

Understanding how PHI and Electronic PHI comes into, is created by, moves around in, and leaves your office is not only a mental challenge but is essential for true HIPAA compliance. If you know this you can do at least the following:

1. Protect client's PHI from unauthorized disclosures and yourself from complaints and other problems.

2. Use the proper Consents and Authorizations to prevent problems.

3. Train your staff appropriately to protect you and your clients.

4. Assure compliance with the Security Rule and with the minimum necessary rules about PHI disclosures.

5. Understand your true needs when buying office equipment, especially computerized records and billing programs.

6. Protect other information besides PHI such as financial and employment records from those who should not have access.

7. Comply with the disaster recovery aspects of the Security and Privacy Rules which are all just good business rules and safer computer practices.

HIPAA expects you to do this analysis and compare your current practices with those specified by HIPAA. Finding these differences is called a **Gap Analysis**. The information gained is then to be used for a **Risk Analysis** (below) and as part of Security Rule compliance (see section 700.)

A. The core questions approach

This involves discovering the flow of clinical information through a series of questions and answers.

1. Who collects or generates information? E. g. therapists, clerks, intake workers, etc.

2. How is it recorded? E. g. clients filling out forms and checklists or taking tests, data entry into computerized forms, narratives on legal pads, typed into a laptop or desktop computer or a networked computer, etc. (This information will be useful for both security efforts and selecting the best privacy protection methods for each kind of data.)

3. What is contained in the records staff generate? E. g. Psychotherapy or routine progress notes, demographics, financial information, histories, etc.

4. What information is received from outside the office? E. g. teacher reports, report cards, school evaluations and IEPs for special education, pediatricians' medical records, reports from agencies like mental health centers, hospital records, OVR evaluations, etc. And many kinds of clinical notes.

5. Which of 3 and 4 is PHI or EPHI? And so what kinds of controls on access and distribution will this need?

6. How is the PHI moved around in the office? Who reads what and for what purposes? What persons or roles/functions get which information? (The future question will be, Do they need to access or receive all this PHI to do their jobs?)

7. What happens to PHI when each has used it? How is it stored? (The future questions concern access, safe storage, retrieval and disposal.)

8. How is PHI/EPHI sent out of the office? What media are used and to whom is it disclosed? Is it used for TPO or other purposes? (This bears on transmission security)

B. Drawing a picture of your office's information flow

An alternative approach is more visual than verbal. Take a few blank pages and start to draw people or locations and connect them with arrows where information flows. On each line indicate what kind of information in what form comes from one and goes to the other. This is a flow sheet or chart. It can be fun. Try it while recognizing that No one can do something new well or without discomfort (Ed's Third Law). It *will* take a few tries. Here is a first approximation.

Information from outside the office

Phone calls from	*Mail, etc.*	*Faxes*	*Other*
Clients	Bills to be paid	re insurance	Hand
Professionals	Checks to be deposited	re professionals	delivered
Schools	Client records and reports	Client records and	
Parents of clients	Non-routine mail	reports	
Other branches of	Non-clinical mail		
the practice			
Agencies, facilities			
Non-routine calls			

Information we create in the office

At intake	*During treatment*	*For insurance*
Demographic	Treatment plans	Initial authorizations
Clinical/Evaluations	Progress notes	Ongoing Treatment Reviews
Financial information	Further evaluations	Claims/Reimbursements
	Reports to referrers	

Information we store

Client paper files
with the following kinds of information:

Computerized information
with the following kinds of information:

Information we send out or give out by phone, etc.

Copies of client's files	*Reports to*	*Insurance forms*	*Reports*
	Schools		
	Referrers		
	Other Professionals		

Now, for a second go round, focus on PHI and EPHI. What form does it take and who receives it? Who gets what PHI, creates what PHI, and sends what PHI on to whom? Try this as a grid - who by what PHI - and enter checks or a note in each intersection:

List of types of PHI/EPHI[17]   **List of Persons**[18] (by title, function, or name)

	Me	Other MH professionals in the practice	Office manager	Billing clerk	Sec'y Recept.	Clients
Demographic						
Clinical						
Routine Progress Notes						
Psychotherapy Notes						
Evaluations						
Financial						
Re a Client						
Re your practice						
Whole chart						
Other						

- For more complex offices it may be helpful to indicate on the above chart the purposes for which each person needs the information.

- Another clarifying question is to ask, and indicate, what they do with the information: View it, it, Write it, Create it, Send it.

The gap analysis

The Privacy Rule requires you to examine the ways your office handles PHI – who, how, and where it is created, received, stored and distributed and disclosed. As part of this you are to look "gaps" where PHI might accidentally or deliberately have an "unauthorized use or disclosure." The risk assessment or analysis (the next step) identifies the potential size of the loss and problems you are likely to encounter. The results of this risk analysis will become the basis for the next step in the security process – risk management. It appears that gap analysis has been subsumed into the Risk Analysis (see section 700) required by the Security Rule which prescribes more formal structure and procedures. You still need the information but will go directly to the risk analysis.

---

[17] You might find it easier to enter the names of the forms you presently use and then consider what kind of PHI each includes.

[18] Additional persons or roles might include trainees, temporary staff, and answering service, accountant, etc. You may need business agreements with the last two. See section 290.

Understanding what HIPAA means by "risk"

Before we get into the swamp of the legal jargon, let me point out that risk analysis parallels **a very familiar metaphor** to clinicians. We understand that people have (1) diatheses (habits, genetics, history) which when exposed to a (2) stressor (from the environment or other people) sometimes exhibit a (3) dysfunction/disorder/symptom which requires (4) treatment with a (5) modality that includes (6) more specific interventions. HIPAA says that a (1) "vulnerability" or flaw when exposed to a (2) "threat" produces a (3) "risk' which, requires (4) "risk management" through generalized procedures called (5) "standards" and (6) more specific "implementation specifications."

Here is how this is formulated for HIPAA.

A **vulnerability** is "[a] flaw or weakness in system security procedures, design, implementation, or internal controls that could be exercised (accidentally triggered or intentionally exploited) and result in a security breach or a violation of the system's security policy" [meaning a an inappropriate use or disclosure of PHI/EPHI]. *NIST SP 800-30.*

A **threat** is "[t]he potential for a person or thing to exercise (accidentally trigger or intentionally exploit) a specific vulnerability." From *NIST SP 800-30.* Common threats include:

> "• Natural threats include floods, earthquakes, tornadoes, and landslides.
> • Human threats include intentional (e.g., network and computer based attacks, malicious software upload, and unauthorized access to EPHI) or unintentional (e.g., inadvertent data entry or deletion and inaccurate data entry) actions.
> • Environmental threats such as power failures, pollution, chemicals, and liquid leakage."

Considering these, **risk** is:

> "The net mission impact considering (1) the probability that a particular [threat] will exercise (accidentally trigger or intentionally exploit) a particular [vulnerability] and (2) the resulting impact if this should occur. …[R]isks arise from legal liability or mission loss due to—
> 1. Unauthorized (malicious or accidental) disclosure, modification, or destruction of information
> 2. Unintentional errors and omissions
> 3. (Information Technology) IT disruptions due to natural or man-made disasters
> 4. Failure to exercise due care and diligence in the implementation and operation of the IT system." *NIST SP 800-30*

Briefly: A Vulnerability triggered or exploited by a Threat equals a Risk.

This means that risk is not a single factor or event, but rather it is a combination of factors or events (threats and vulnerabilities) that, if they occur, may have an adverse impact on the organization (your practice and livelihood).

See section 700 on the Security Rule for more on this and the next step – Risk Management.

260   Training employees in privacy practices

Obviously, if your office is large enough to employ others you have to train them in your procedures and then monitor and supervise their work. HIPAA makes formal staff training in privacy policies and practices a requirement and this is certainly a good thing for you to incorporate to prevent problems[19]. This training must be in place by the implementation of the Privacy Rule (April 14, 2003) and must be documented (see section 261 for more.) At the end of such training, a formal Confidentiality Agreement with each staff member to maintain privacy is a good summary of the issues and reminder of the likely risks. See section 262 for more on these agreements.

Schedule for training

All current employees must receive training before April 14, 2003 (or the date you decide to make your office HIPAA-compliant) and all new employees within a reasonable period of time after being hired. While there is no requirement for regular retraining, HIPAA does require training when there has been a material change to your policies or procedures and so it would be a good idea to include regularly updated trainings in your plans.

Designing a training program

> The training requirement may be satisfied by a small physician practice's providing each new member of the workforce with a copy of its privacy policies and documenting that new members have reviewed the policies; whereas a large health plan may provide training through live instruction, video presentations, or interactive software programs. From *OCR Guidance Explaining Significant Aspects of the Privacy Rule - December 4, 2002.*

❑   All employees, permanent or temporary, part- or full-time, and anyone else with access to your PHI should be trained to protect you so make a list of persons or job titles and incorporate it into your documentation of training (see section 261)

❑   Staff *must* be trained in HIPAA and *should* be trained in your local laws and your professional ethics to protect your clients and yourself. In the next section is a checklist (adapted from Zuckerman, 2003) of the issues of greatest concern and likelihood but you should add items to fit your practice and revise the contents over time. It can be used to organize your training of employees and can also be used as an employee agreement to maintain confidentiality.

---

[19] Training in security procedures is not specifically mandated but is, of course, necessary.

The regulations

§ 164.530 Administrative requirements
(b)

(1) Standard: training. A covered entity must **train all members of its workforce** on the policies and procedures with respect to protected health information required by this subpart, as necessary and appropriate for the members of the workforce to carry out their function within the covered entity.

(2) Implementation specifications: training.

(i) A covered entity must provide training that meets the requirements of paragraph (b)(1) of this section, as follows:

(A) To each member of the covered entity's workforce by **no later than the compliance date for the covered entity;**

(B) Thereafter, to each new member of the workforce within a reasonable period of time after the person joins the covered entity's workforce; and

(C) To each member of the covered entity's workforce whose functions are affected by a **material change** in the policies or procedures required by this subpart, within a reasonable period of time after the material change becomes effective in accordance with paragraph (i) of this section.

(ii) A covered entity must **document that the training** as described in paragraph (b)(2)(i) of this section has been provided, as required by paragraph (j) of this section.

(e)

(1) Standard: **sanctions**. A covered entity must have and apply appropriate sanctions against members of its workforce who fail to comply with the privacy policies and procedures of the covered entity or the requirements of this subpart. This standard does not apply to a member of the covered entity's workforce with respect to actions that are covered by and that meet the conditions of § 164.502(j) or paragraph (g)(2) of this section.

(2) Implementation specification: documentation. As required by paragraph (j) of this section, a covered entity must document the sanctions that are applied, if any.

(g) Standard: **refraining from intimidating or retaliatory acts**. A covered entity may not intimidate, threaten, coerce, discriminate against, or take other retaliatory action against:

(1) Individuals. Any individual for the exercise by the individual of any right under, or for participation by the individual in any process established by this subpart, including the filing of a complaint under this section;

(2) Individuals and others. Any individual or other person for:

(i) Filing of a complaint with the Secretary under subpart C of part 160 of this subchapter;

(ii) Testifying, assisting, or participating in an investigation, compliance review, proceeding, or hearing under Part C of Title XI; or

(iii) Opposing any act or practice made unlawful by this subpart, provided the individual or person has a good faith belief that the practice opposed is unlawful, and the manner of the opposition is reasonable and does not involve a disclosure of protected health information in violation of this subpart.

261   **Content and documentation of training**

(on your letterhead)

Checklist for staff training in local laws and professional ethics

Dear Employee,

When people come to this practice for evaluation or treatment of their or their relatives' or children's mental health or developmental concerns they are likely to discuss very personal information which they want to remain confidential - to be known only to themselves and the therapist or clinician who is treating them. In the pages below we describe our office's rules designed to protect the confidentiality of all clients' healthcare information and any other confidential information in this office. You should assume that *everything* is confidential in this office and treat it accordingly.

As a condition of your employment we require that you read, understand, and agree to comply with these rules.

A checkmark below indicates that I discussed the topic with those present on this date: _____. I, _____ , conducted this training.

- ❑ The codes of ethics and guidelines of my profession.
- ❑ The main malpractice and ethics issues and risks - confidentiality, dual relationships, billing, and _____ .
- ❑ Procedures and limitations on releasing any kind of records.
- ❑ Procedures for photocopying records.
- ❑ How to respond to phone calls about clients.
- ❑ The organization, handling, and storing all paper material with client's names - charts, forms, photocopies, faxes, voice mail boxes, appointment books, phone messages and books, etc.
- ❑ Proper use of computer programs which contain client information in order to maintain its privacy.
- ❑ Not using clients names on the phone, in the waiting area or elsewhere where they could be overheard by unauthorized persons.
- ❑ Privately playing the answering machine or calling the answering service.
- ❑ Casual conversations and gossip about clients, in and out of the office.
- ❑ How the confidentiality of client's information extends after the death of the client or the professional, after my leaving this employment, and into the future indefinitely.
- ❑ That breaking confidentiality rules is grounds for immediate dismissal.
- ❑ How to handle questions of ethics, confidentiality, access, etc. raised by clients, other professionals, or by situations.

My signature below indicates that I have read and discussed:

- ❑ This office's Information for Clients brochure or the other routes to informed consent.
- ❑ Other client education materials of this practice (such as the Limits of Confidentiality handout and the Managed Care handout) as appropriate to my job functions.
- ❑ The NPP, Consent, and release forms, as appropriate to my job functions.

I have been informed about the above issues and guidelines, had the opportunity to raise any questions, and have had my questions answered. I believe I understand the issues and concerns about confidentiality and related issues and will ask the Privacy Officer, _____ or _____ when any questions or concerns arise for me.

I agree not to disclose any client information to third-parties, persons outside this practice/office/organization, other clients, or anyone else unless authorized to do so, in writing, by the client (or client's personal representative) and approved by my employing professional.

If a breach of this agreement or the confidentiality of any records should occur I agree to notify my employer immediately and within no more than 24 hours of its discovery.

I understand that any material breach of this agreement shall constitute good cause for my discharge from this employment. In addition, such breach may subject me to liability and legal damages.

Signature of employee	Printed name of employee	Date
Signature of employee	Printed name of employee	Date
Signature of employee	Printed name of employee	Date
Signature of employee	Printed name of employee	Date
Signature of employee	Printed name of employee	Date
Signature of employee	Printed name of employee	Date
Signature of employee	Printed name of employee	Date
Signature of employee	Printed name of employee	Date
Signature of employee	Printed name of employee	Date
Signature of employee	Printed name of employee	Date

262   Confidentiality agreements

Because an unauthorized disclosure of confidential information by employees could render you and your practice liable for damages, after training employees, you can ask them to sign a confidentiality agreement (in the next section) to reinforce the ideas and practices for assuring confidentiality. A small practice may not need a formal agreement like this but you still may find it useful for several purposes:

1. You can use it as an employee teaching tool to explain what protecting privacy really means in your practice because it contains varied examples of how privacy can be violated.

2. After review by your legal counsel and personnel consultants and with tailoring, it can become part of your employment contract when you hire, train, retrain, or need to dismiss staff.

3. It can serve as a basis for writing parts of your office's Policy and Procedures Manual or information usage agreements even without concern for HIPAA's rules.

This agreement is worded to apply to many staff and others and so you may have to modify some parts to fit the job functions of those who have access to PHI and other confidential information in your office. Besides employees, these might include students, volunteers, other mental health clinicians, and those covered under business associate contracts.

Optional additions

Depending on your professional activities you might want to add that confidential information can include:

* information about your and employees' personal lives.
* the practices and procedures you have developed for your office.
* salaries and other financial information about you and employees.
* trade secrets and scientific or technical information developed in your practice or by your employees. In this regard, you should consider using non-disclosure and non-compete agreements.

The form offered below is greatly modified from the materials listed as resources to be both more understandable to employees and to be most applicable to a small practice.

Resources

UCLA's version is online at
<http://www.healthcare.ucla.edu/shared/volunteering/ucla/student/Confidentiality%20Agreement.pdf>

Dougherty, M, and Scichilone, R. A. (2002). Establishing a telecommuting or home-based employee program. *Journal of AHIMA* 73, (7).
<http://library.ahima.org/xpedio/groups/public/documents/ahima/pub_bok1_013767.html?ReturnCode=2000> Accessed Oct. 1, 2005.
The version offered is quite conversationally written.

263   Confidentiality agreement for employees

(On your letterhead)

Agreement about confidentiality and privacy of healthcare information

Dear Employee,

When people come to this practice for evaluation or treatment of their or their relatives' or children's mental health they are likely to discuss very personal information which they want to remain confidential - to be known only to themselves and the therapist or clinician who is treating them. Some of this information may be recorded on paper and/or into computerized records and so these records must be treated with care. You, and every person who can access these records is being trusted by the client to preserve the confidentiality of their information - what the law calls their Protected Health Information or PHI. You should assume that *everything* is confidential in this office and treat it accordingly.

In the pages below we describe the rules this office has created to do our best to protect the confidentiality of all clients' PHI and any other confidential information in this office. As a condition of your employment we require that you read, understand, and agree to comply with these rules. However, there may be situations not covered by these rules and we expect that you will appreciate the need for privacy and take any extra steps or behave in a very cautious way in those cases. If you are unsure what to do, always ask for guidance from your supervisor or our privacy officer. When you are handling confidential information your careful efforts will be appreciated.

Please read, indicate your having read by checking the boxes, ask any questions you have, and agree to the following.

Confidential Information

You will have access to several kinds of information which must be treated confidentially. You may have access to information about:
- ❏ Clients, such as their clinical (medical) records, intake information, financial information, etc. All information about a client's care, treatment, history, or condition is confidential information. This extends to conversations you or others have with them.
- ❏ Employees, volunteers, or students such as their histories, salaries, employment records, disciplinary actions, problems, etc.
- ❏ This practice, such as its financial and statistical records, strategic plans, reports, memos, contracts, communications, proprietary computer programs or technology, etc.
- ❏ Other persons or organizations and their property.

We expect that you will treat all information in this office as confidential and share this confidential information only with those authorized to receive it.

Rules and Behavioral Examples

- ❑ I agree to respect the office policies and procedures about maintaining the privacy of health care information.

- ❑ I will do my best to prevent any unauthorized use or disclosure of any information received, stored or used in this office.

- ❑ I will not access, read, review, copy, alter, remove, lend, or destroy any file, report, or other form of PHI or other confidential information except as part of my work duties here and in accord with office policy and procedures.

- ❑ I will not knowingly let any false, inaccurate, or misleading information be included in any file or report.

- ❑ I will not use or let others use any PHI or other confidential information for any kind of personal benefit to me or them.

- ❑ I won't share or disclose any information about a client with any non-employee, my family, or my friends. I won't share any information which might allow a non-employee to identify a client or client's family.

- ❑ I won't discuss PHI or confidential information with another employee in any area where clients or non-employees could overhear. I will remind other employees of this rule when it is or could be broken or take other steps to maintain the privacy of this information.

- ❑ I will not install any software onto any computer in the office. I will respect the ownership rights of the software I use at work. I will not make copies of software for my own use or distribution to others. I will not use any non-licensed software

- ❑ I accept responsibility for all activities which use my access method such as a password, passphrase, access card, key or other device. I will not share any of these with anyone else or allow anyone to access or alter information using my access method. I will not try to access information using anyone else's access method.

- ❑ I understand that my computer files or e-mail can be searched, without advance notice, for business purposes, such as investigating theft, disclosure of confidential business or proprietary information, personal abuse of the system, or monitoring workflow or productivity.

- ❑ I understand my access privileges to PHI and other confidential information will be reviewed, renewed, or revised on a periodic basis.

- ❑ I will not use any office resources to engage in any kind of illegal activities or to harass anyone.

- ❑ I will report any violations of these rules to my supervisor or the Privacy Officer named below. Any report I make will be held in confidence as permitted by law and I will be free from any form of retaliation.

- ❑ I will act in accordance with these rules even after I am no longer employed in this office.

- ❑ I agree to maintain all protected health information in a manner consistent with local, state, and federal privacy regulations.

❑ If I have any questions about these rules and procedures or how and when they apply I will ask the privacy officer or my supervisor.

❑ If I violate the privacy of any client's PHI or other confidential information I understand I will receive disciplinary action up to and including loss of my job here.

❑ If I violate the privacy of any client's PHI or other confidential information I understand I may be subject to local, state, and federal penalties.

❑ By signing this agreement, I agree that I have read, have received a copy of, understand, and will comply with all the conditions outlined in this agreement.

_____   _____   _____
Printed name of employee   Signature of employee   Date

_____   _____
Printed name of practice's representative   Signature

_____   _____
Name of privacy officer   Telephone number

270   What about business associates?

Q: Why are there BA's?
A: To apply the privacy safeguards over PHI and EPHI[20] when it is shared with others who are not CEs and do work for you using your PHI. The HIPAA statute creates a class of organizations called Business Associates (BAs) who are not subject to the Privacy Rule (because they are not CEs) but still acquire PHI from CEs like you and do work with it on your behalf. You are required to get them to agree maintain the confidentiality of your PHI in their possession by adding privacy language to your contracts with them.

Q: Why do I have to be concerned with my BA's?
A: For two reasons:
1. Because they have access to your client's PHI and so could be disclosed and you might be held responsible by a court or licensing body for entrusting it to them.
2. Because, under HIPAA, you can be held responsible and punished for the conduct of your business associate when you have substantial and credible evidence of a privacy violation of the business associate agreement and don't do enough to fix the situation.

Who is a Business Associate?

Under HIPAA, a business associate is anyone who is not your employee but is an entity (person or organization) who, on your behalf, does anything that involves the use or disclosure of PHI received from you or from another BA. These activities include payment or health care operations activities (the P and O of TPO), such as claims processing or administration, data analysis, utilization review, quality assurance, billing, benefit management, practice management, etc

Who are my BA's?

Figuring out who are your BA's is not too difficult. Go through a list of those who provide services to you (perhaps by looking at your checkbook for the last few months or last year's Federal Income tax's Schedule C) and to whom you have paid business expenses and then, identify those who receive any kinds of PHI from you.

Some examples are organizations which:
• Answer your phones and take messages from clients.
• Transcribe your dictation (if they are not your employees but a separate service).
• Do your billing and claims processing, or print and mail your billing statements, etc.
• Attempt to collect your bad debts such as collection agencies and attorneys.
• Receive and destroy your records by shredding, recycling, or incinerating. If your janitorial service does this, they are your BA because they see PHI, even though in their regular maintenance functions they are not. To make matters muddier, if a entity performs more than routine handling of PHI they would be a BA but if they do it on your premises, under your direct control, the Privacy Rule allows you to treat them as part of your workforce and so you don't need a BA contract.
• Provide your temporary office help, because their employees see your PHI.
• Consult on implementing, upgrading, or otherwise provide tech support to your in-house billing or medical records program. An advantage of making such support people your BAs is that the responsibility for an unauthorized disclosure shifts to them.

---

[20] Since the Security Rule became final in April 2005 HIPAA has addressed how EPHI – Electronic PHI must be handled. For all citations to PHI consider that EPHI is included.

Persons who might be your BA's include:
- Your attorney if you discuss specific cases.
- Accountants who do your taxes if they see clients' checks or to whom you wrote refund checks. If they only see your aggregated income records without names they are not BAs. If they do only your employee checks or office taxes or accounts they are not BAs.

Who else might be my BAs?

The criteria are whether they receive PHI from you and are not employees. Depending on what they do for you your BAs might include some practice management consultants, accrediting organizations, and computer programmers or repairers who might work regularly on a computer which has your clients records on it.

If you use the Small Claims Court or a collection agency to recover unpaid fees owed to you, examine what information you send to them. If it is just name, dates of services, and fees, this may not be PHI but if you send more information or have any concerns, making them your BAs by amending your contract may be protective of both the client and yourself.

Test: Are those who are on the ancillary staff at a hospital and see clients and charts as teachers of students or staff CEs or BA's (of the hospital)? Decide and then see 1d, just below.

Who are *not* my BA's?

The regulations indicate three classes on non-BA's:

1. Generally, those who receive PHI in order to provide TPO are not BA's. For example,
   a. Health insurers.
   b. The hospital to which you admit clients.
   c. Fellow therapists and other professionals with whom you consult on clinical issues.
   d. Those who are on the ancillary staff at a hospital and see clients and charts as consultants. Those consulting on cases are providing treatment and so are CEs. Those teaching could be BA's because they are performing a service on behalf of the CE, the hospital. However, under HIPAA disclosures for teaching professional students are specifically labeled as treatment and so teachers are not BAs.
   e. Your peers in a joint practice.
   f. Pharmaceutical and other sales representatives with whom might discuss a clinical problem or case issue but who don't do anything on your behalf are not BAs.
   g. A computerized testing service is not a BA because you don't send it identifiable PHI (You use a case number instead of a name, right?).

2. Affiliated organizations who provide TPO to your client. These are called "organized health care arrangements" in HIPAA. Sharing PHI is covered under the client's initial Consent. Note, however, that these are covered by the Security Rule's provisions because they share electronic information and so need the safeguards. See section 700 on security.

3. Lastly, the law allows for accidental and incidental access (see section 540) which would not make some people your BAs. For example, those who clean your office might see client records you had left out inadvertently but, because such access is not part of their proper and contracted duties they are not BAs. Similarly, your copier repairer, Internet Service Provider (ISP), or phone company might have access but only infrequently, incidentally, and unintentionally.

However, if your computer support person must look at your office management program either in your office or by remote access, you should consider him or her a BA (See <http://www.stratfordsoftware.com/stratford/hipaacompliance.htm> for an example.) DHHS offers this:

> "For example, a software company that hosts the software containing patient information on its own server or accesses patient information when troubleshooting the software function, is a business associate of a covered entity. In these examples, a covered entity would be required to enter into a business associate agreement before allowing the software company access to protected health information." *OCR Guidance Explaining Significant Aspects of the Privacy Rule - December 4, 2002.*

Although mail delivery personnel (including UPS FedEx, couriers, etc.) may have some kind of access to PHI, they are not BAs simply because they act as conduits to simply transport the information and not use it no disclosure of PHI is intended.

How can I assess how well my BAs will protect the client's confidentiality?

Ask to speak to the person at the BA who is in change of insuring confidentiality. Then ask about how they train their employees in confidentiality and do they require them to sign a confidentiality statement. What methods do they have in place to protect confidentiality, recognize and deal with breaches, etc. Lastly, re-read your contract with them. When does it expire or have to be renewed?

Do I need to immediately redo my contracts with my BAs?

When your office becomes HIPAA-compliant add these provisions. Unfortunately, there are quite complex "transition period" contract rules to be addressed. An appropriate alternative is to include these provisions in a addendum to your current contract and wait for its expiration to rewrite the whole contract.

What do I have to do about my BAs?

- You have to have written agreements and confidence called "satisfactory assurances" that the PHI you share with a BA will be appropriately safeguarded. These create a contractual obligation but nothing more.

  > "Business associates, however, are not subject to the requirements of the Privacy Rule, and the Secretary cannot impose civil monetary penalties on a business associate for breach of its business associate contract with the covered entity, unless the business associate is itself a covered entity. For example, covered entities do not need to ask their business associates to agree to appoint a privacy officer, or develop policies and procedures for use and disclosure of protected health information." *OCR Guidance Explaining Significant Aspects of the Privacy Rule - December 4, 2002*

- Your contracts with them will have to include some HIPAA-required language (see below) to limit what they can do with PHI and EPHI, indicate what safeguards they use to prevent disclosures, and require them to apply the same restrictions to their agents or subcontractors.

- You do *not* have to monitor their compliance but you *do* have to act on any complaints you receive. You will have to investigate the problem and take actions to lessen the damage which may have occurred. If your efforts are not successful you must end the relationship or if that is not feasible, report the problem to DHHS.

What provisions do I have to add to a new contract?

A simple list would include statements for these:

❑ Citation of the HIPAA privacy and security rule regulations about business associates.

❑ Description of the permitted and required uses and disclosure of PHI and EPHI by BA's which may include their internal uses, keeping of records of their disclosures, obeying the laws, doing nothing contrary to the law and the contract, etc.

❑ A promise that any agent of the BA to whom the BA provides PHI or EPHI agrees to implement reasonable and appropriate safeguards to protect that PHI or EPHI.

❑ The BA's willingness to incorporate any amendments which a client has requested and which you, the CE, have agreed to.

❑ BA will use appropriate safeguards to prevent incorrect use/disclosure of PHI and EPHI including keeping records of disclosures, all spelled out in specifics, to define a minimum standard that is an "appropriate safeguard."

❑ The BA will provide information to the CE on its staff and the staff of other organizations to whom the BA allows access to your PHI or EPHI. Such information should include the job title/position, the type of PHI and EPHI to which the person has access, and how that access is limited for particular purposes or functions.

❑ BA will report unauthorized uses or disclosures of PHI and EPHI to you as soon as practicable when these are discovered.

❑ BA will ensure that any of their agents and subcontractors, agree to the same restrictions and safeguards.

❑ BA will make their policies, procedures, and records available to the Secretary of Health and Human Services for monitoring, when sought.

❑ BA will return or destroy all PHI and EPHI when the contract expires or is terminated.

❑ Allow the CE to terminate the contract for violating these provisions.

❑ Address the continuing development of the regulations based on laws, court decisions, or regulatory interpretations and the needs that may change as the business of the CE changes.

Obviously, I cannot give legal advice, and so the above is designed only to orient you to the issues to be addressed. Many consultants and lawyers will help you tailor a contract to your needs. Sample contracts are available on the Internet - see below.

Sample Business Associate Agreements

U.S. Department of Health & Human Services, Office for Civil Rights
<http://www.hhs.gov/ocr/hipaa/contractprov.html> Accessed Sept. 23, 2005
Here you will find the *Sample Business Associate Contract Provisions* as Published in FR 67 No.157 pg.53182, 53264 (8/14/02)

Look for the Business Associate Agreement (Contract)
<http://www.nchica.org/HIPAAResources/Samples/Portal.asp> Accessed Sept. 23, 2005

Sample Language for a Business Associate Contract
<http://www.conomikes.com/> Accessed Sept. 23, 2005

Business associate compliance plan
<http://www.nhvship.org/tools.htm>
Very well written legal language version. Accessed Sept. 23, 2005

HIPAA Collaborative of Wisconsin
<http://www.hipaacow.org/home/PrivacyDocs.aspx>
HIPAA Business Associate Addendum. About 4 pages to add to a current contract. Accessed Sept. 23, 2005

A Google search with "business associates" will find many others.

The regulations

§ 164.502 Uses and disclosures of protected health information: general rules.
(e) (1) Standard: disclosures to business associates.

(i) A covered entity may disclose protected health information to a business associate and may allow a business associate to create or receive protected health information on its behalf, if the covered entity obtains satisfactory assurance that the business associate will appropriately safeguard the information.

(ii) This standard does not apply:

(A) With respect to disclosures by a covered entity to a health care provider concerning the treatment of the individual;

(B) With respect to disclosures by a group health plan or a health insurance issuer or HMO with respect to a group health plan to the plan sponsor, to the extent that the requirements of § 164.504(f) apply and are met; or

(C) With respect to uses or disclosures by a health plan that is a government program providing public benefits, if eligibility for, or enrollment in, the health plan is determined by an agency other than the agency administering the health plan, or if the protected health information used to determine enrollment or eligibility in the health plan is collected by an agency other than the agency administering the health plan, and such activity is authorized by law, with respect to the collection and sharing of individually identifiable health information for the performance of such functions by the health plan and the agency other than the agency administering the health plan.

(iii) A covered entity that violates the satisfactory assurances it provided as a business associate of another covered entity will be in noncompliance with the standards, implementation specifications, and requirements of this paragraph and § 164.504(e).

(2) Implementation specification: documentation. A covered entity must document the satisfactory assurances required by paragraph (e)(1) of this section through a written contract or other written agreement or arrangement with the business associate that meets the applicable requirements of § 164.504(e).

§ 164.504 Uses and disclosures: organizational requirements.

(e)

(1) Standard: business associate contracts.

(i) The contract or other arrangement between the covered entity and the business associate required by § 164.502(e)(2) must meet the requirements of paragraph (e)(2) or (e)(3) of this section, as applicable.

(ii) A covered entity is not in compliance with the standards in § 164.502(e) and paragraph (e) of this section, if the covered entity knew of a pattern of activity or practice of the business associate that constituted a material breach or violation of the business associate's obligation under the contract or other arrangement, unless the covered entity took reasonable steps to cure the breach or end the violation, as applicable, and, if such steps were unsuccessful:

(A) Terminated the contract or arrangement, if feasible; or

(B) If termination is not feasible, reported the problem to the Secretary.

(2) Implementation specifications: business associate contracts. A contract between the covered entity and a business associate must:

(i) Establish the permitted and required uses and disclosures of such information by the business associate. The contract may not authorize the business associate to use or further disclose the information in a manner that would violate the requirements of this subpart, if done by the covered entity, except that:

(A) The contract may permit the business associate to use and disclose protected health information for the proper management and administration of the business associate, as provided in paragraph (e)(4) of this section; and

(B) The contract may permit the business associate to provide data aggregation services relating to the health care operations of the covered entity.

(ii) Provide that the business associate will:

(A) Not use or further disclose the information other than as permitted or required by the contract or as required by law;

(B) Use appropriate safeguards to prevent use or disclosure of the information other than as provided for by its contract;

(C) Report to the covered entity any use or disclosure of the information not provided for by its contract of which it becomes aware;

(D) Ensure that any agents, including a subcontractor, to whom it provides protected health information received from, or created or received by the business associate on behalf of, the covered entity agrees to the same restrictions and conditions that apply to the business associate with respect to such information;

(E) Make available protected health information in accordance with § 164.524;

(F) Make available protected health information for amendment and incorporate any amendments to protected health information in accordance with §164.526;

(G) Make available the information required to provide an accounting of disclosures in accordance with § 164.528;

(H) Make its internal practices, books, and records relating to the use and disclosure of protected health information received from, or created or received by the business associate on behalf of, the covered entity available to the Secretary for purposes of determining the covered entity's compliance with this subpart; and

(I) At termination of the contract, if feasible, return or destroy all protected health information received from, or created or received by the business associate on behalf of, the covered entity that the business associate still maintains in any form and retain no copies of such information or, if such return or destruction is not feasible, extend the protections of the contract to the information and limit further uses and disclosures to those purposes that make the return or destruction of the information infeasible.

(iii) Authorize termination of the contract by the covered entity, if the covered entity determines that the business associate has violated a material term of the contract.

(3) Implementation specifications: other arrangements.

(i) If a covered entity and its business associate are both governmental entities:

(A) The covered entity may comply with paragraph (e) of this section by entering into a memorandum of understanding with the business associate that contains terms that accomplish the objectives of paragraph (e)(2) of this section.

(B) The covered entity may comply with paragraph (e) of this section, if other law (including regulations adopted by the covered entity or its business associate) contains requirements applicable to the business associate that accomplish the objectives of paragraph (e)(2) of this section.

(ii) If a business associate is required by law to perform a function or activity on behalf of a covered entity or to provide a service described in the definition of *business associate* in § 160.103 of this subchapter to a covered entity, such covered entity may disclose protected health information to the business associate to the extent necessary to comply with the legal mandate without meeting the requirements of this paragraph (e), provided that the covered entity attempts in good faith to obtain satisfactory assurances as required by paragraph (e)(3)(i) of this section, and, if such attempt fails, documents the attempt and the reasons that such assurances cannot be obtained.

(iii) The covered entity may omit from its other arrangements the termination authorization required by paragraph (e)(2)(iii) of this section, if such authorization is inconsistent with the statutory obligations of the covered entity or its business associate.

(4) Implementation specifications: other requirements for contracts and other arrangements.

(i) The contract or other arrangement between the covered entity and the business associate may permit the business associate to use the information received by the business associate in its capacity as a business associate to the covered entity, if necessary:

(A) For the proper management and administration of the business associate; or

(B) To carry out the legal responsibilities of the business associate.

(ii) The contract or other arrangement between the covered entity and the business associate may permit the business associate to disclose the information received by the business associate in its capacity as a business associate for the purposes described in paragraph (e)(4)(i) of this section, if:

(A) The disclosure is required by law; or

(B) (*1*) The business associate obtains reasonable assurances from the person to whom the information is disclosed that it will be held confidentially and used or further disclosed only as required by law or for the purpose for which it was disclosed to the person; and

(*2*) The person notifies the business associate of any instances of which it is aware in which the confidentiality of the information has been breached.

300   Records and Billing

301   Record making and keeping

This chapter addresses the ways HIPAA affects two major practice activities:

1. Clinical records - creating, maintaining, accessing, and releasing your notes, narratives, and reports. HIPAA offers two kinds of progress notes and dictates controls on what information is disclosed to whom.

2. Billing for your services - generating insurance claims including coding your services, submitting bills, and monitoring payments due and received. HIPAA will completely change the forms, codes, and process of billing insurers for claims.

The present state of clinical records

It appears to me that there are as many record making systems in use by clinicians as there are clinicians. Each has developed a philosophy and methods to record what he or she finds of interest, of future value, or is required to note by some organization or person. Some record almost nothing and others write pages for each session. Some are precise and easily read, others are and telegraphic, opaque, illegible and completely uninformative to anyone else.

While there may be no universally satisfactory format, some minimal standard content is valuable for jogging our memories, informing successor clinicians, communication to those in other healthcare professions, and documenting treatment for legal and ethical needs. These forces and those of licensing laws and commerce are moving us toward standardized content and HIPAA accelerates this by its requirements for the contents of progress notes. Our records, driven by all these forces, are largely just collections of data and not the information to support clinical choices.

Computerized record programs can minimize the overhead of repeated entry of data, speed the accessibility, discourage the omission of needed information, and lessen the burdens of creating narratives by supplying checklists from which to choose the most felicitous phrasings.

Current computer programs emulate the contents paper records. I expect no significant improvements in records systems to come from the computerize the paper approach. Only studies of what information affects treatment outcomes can produce better records and few of these have been done in the mental health area (as far as I know) with no large impact.

The present state of billing for services

Guilfoy (2002) estimates that there are presently 400 ways that the HCFA-1500/UB-92 forms are completed because these were designed around the systems and needs of individual payers and not around computerized records or clinicians' needs (e.g. information to support clinical decision making). As a result of practices like these some 20% of health costs is wasted in unnecessary overhead and another 10% is lost to fraud said the General Accounting Office.

HIPAA is partly intended to restructure the entire health insurance industry's information practices. The Transaction codes for all kinds of financial transactions, providers, claims, beneficiaries, and hundreds of other kinds of information are required as are standardized procedures for communication among payers and providers. Fortunately, clinicians will not need more than an overview understanding of these, as presented in this section, to participate in and benefit from this administrative simplification.

The next few sections will address how HIPAA will affect practitioners' records and billing practices in some detail.

310   Two kinds of clinical notes

Why two kinds of notes?

Before we get to the contents of each some background may help you understand what lies behind HIPAA's concept of "psychotherapy notes." In 1996, in a famous case, *Jaffee v. Redmond*, (116 S.Ct. 1923), the U.S. Supreme Court held that statements made to a therapist during a counseling session were protected against civil discovery under the Federal Rules of Evidence. This was consistent with many states' laws creating a psychotherapist-patient privilege. Among its ramifications was the shaping of HIPAA. The privacy supports of legal privilege were legislated into what was a that time a bill about the portability of health insurance.

A second major influence on HIPAA was the counsel of psychodynamically oriented clinicians who offered comments to the Secretary for Health and Human Services to emphasize the commonality of "process notes."

> ."‥ the **rationale for providing special protection** for psychotherapy notes is not only that **they contain particularly sensitive information,** but also that **they are the personal notes of the therapist, intended to help him or her recall the therapy discussion** and are of little or no use to others not involved in the therapy. Information in these notes is not intended to communicate to, or even be seen by, persons other than the therapist. Although all psychotherapy information may be considered sensitive, we have limited the definition of psychotherapy notes to only that information that is **kept separate by the provider for his or her own purposes.** It does not refer to the medical record and other sources of information that would normally be disclosed for treatment, payment, and health care operations." (Boldface added.) From a response by the Secretary to a comment.

The HIPAA Privacy Rule considers clinical records to be of two main kinds - the familiar progress notes which are not given a name in HIPAA but I am going to call Routine Notes and the **Psychotherapy Notes.** The Secretary says that "These notes are often referred to as process notes, distinguishable from the routine 'progress notes,' 'the medical record,' or 'official records.'"

Since this is a legal distinction therapists can adopt it or not. Below I review the contents and other differences of each kind of note and then offer some advice on reaching a decision on keeping such notes.

A comparison of routine and psychotherapy notes

Routine notes	**Psychotherapy notes**
Definition and Contents	
By exclusion, these contain all the other usual contents of mental health notes. Since these notes are part of the regular record they are used and disclosed for TPO so a managed care plan or insurer may have **all of the following information:**	From § 164.501 Definitions: Psychotherapy notes are health care provider who is a mental health professional documenting or analyzing the contents of conversation during a private

Routine notes	Psychotherapy notes
	counseling[21] session or a group, joint, or family counseling session."
Medication prescription and monitoring	
Counseling session	"These process notes capture the therapist's impressions about the patient, contain details of the psychotherapy conversation considered to be inappropriate for the medical record, and are used by the provider for future sessions. … process contain sensitive information relevant to no one other than the treating provider."
Start and stop times (or duration)	
The modalities of treatment (types)	
Frequencies of treatment furnished	
Summaries[22] of	
Diagnosis	
Functional status	
Treatment plan	
Symptoms	
Prognosis	These note might include sensitive information about others in the clients interactions, the therapist's tentative
Progress to date	
Results of clinical tests[23]	

Comments: So while "Psychotherapy Notes" have special status the huge amount of sensitive information listed on the left does not. To many clients and therapists that leaves quite a lot that is not protected.

Locations

Part of the client's regular healthcare record or chart.	"are separated from the rest of the individual's medical record"
Nothing more specific is offered.	See below.

---

[21] In a clarification the Secretary said that this was to be interpreted to include **psychotherapy**. "In the final rule, we continue to use the term 'counseling' in the definition of 'psychotherapy.' During our fact-finding, we learned that 'counseling' had no commonly agreed upon definition, but seemed to be widely understood in practice. We do not intend to limit the practice of psychotherapy to any specific professional disciplines." HIPAA is completely discipline neutral.

[22] What is a **summary**? It is not defined in the regulations. I think a few sentences would be sufficient and even a code or check-off revealing very little would be possible.

[23] The American Psychological Association (Newman, 2002) suggested to the Secretary that "The privacy of **test data** should also be protected through patient authorization for release… ." "… test data" includes test results, raw test data (generally, the test form itself, the actual answers of the patient on the test form, etc.), reports, and global scores, and 'test materials' include protocols, manuals, test items, scoring keys or algorithms, and any other materials considered secure by the test developer or publisher." "We respectfully submit that psychological test data are exactly the same type of sensitive information as psychotherapy notes to warrant patient authorization for release." This was not formally incorporated into the final rule and may need to be tested in the courts.

HIPAA's easy release of chart information raises issues of **test security and copyright**. Pearson Assessments, a large publisher of tests, has responded with a policy statement. Go to http://www.pearsonassessments.com/ and then click on "HIPAA." Accessed Oct. 10, 2005.

Routine notes	Psychotherapy notes

Conditioning of services

Failure to consent is a reason to deny. services	Failure to authorize the release of psychotherapy notes cannot be a

A health plan, "may not condition the provision to an individual of treatment, payment, enrollment in the health plan, or eligibility for benefits on the provision of an authorization." This includes all Authorizations and so would cover the Authorization needed to share psychotherapy notes. Thus clinicians can prevent the access by some payers to some information. For more on conditioning, see section 420.

Needed to release

Regular, initial, generic Consent for TPO	A special Authorization for See Section 480 for a form.

In the Guidance of December 4, 2002, the Secretary said that a CE can rely on the previously signed Consent and does not need an authorization to "use and disclose psychotherapy notes, without obtaining individual authorization, to carry out its own limited treatment, payment, or health care operations as follows:
(1) Use by the originator of the notes for treatment,
(2) Use or disclosure for the covered entity's own training programs for its mental health professionals, students, and trainees, and
(3) Use or disclosure by the covered entity to defend itself in a legal action or other proceeding brought by the individual."

Re-disclosure

Yes, for TPO.	No re-disclosure by a receiving CE.

The routine redisclosure of PHI is a much looser privacy safeguard than most states' laws and so they are likely to preempt HIPAA and prevent redisclosure unless the local law does not address redisclosure and so HIPAA would prevail.

Access

Clients have rights to access, copy, and amend because it is part of their medical record	No client access. It is allowed but not required; it is a choice by the note's writer.

Discoverability in litigation

Yes	Probably not. but it depends on the type of suit or charges, the venue, and other factors. Consult your legal counsel.

No client authorization is required for disclosure of Psychotherapy Notes when a client brings legal action against his or her therapist. [§ 164.512(e)]. This is logical because the alternative is to have to ask the now-suing client to cooperate and sign an Authorization to release the notes. The regulations only go so far as allowing release of these notes to the therapist's lawyer for preparing a defense. Can these notes then be "discovered" by the other side and so by the client? On Jan. 20, 2005, the Office of Civil Rights offered some guidance on releasing records when in litigation at: http://anxwers.hhs.gov/cgi-bin/hhs.cfg/php/enduser/std_alp.php?&p_cat_lvl1=7&p_cat_lvl2=52.

Implementation of the two-note system

1. The two kinds of Notes must be separated.

How separate does HIPAA mean? It doesn't say any more. In the absence of guidance, you are free to develop your own methods. Develop ways to easily distinguish the two kinds of notes to prevent an accidental disclosure of psychotherapy notes which would be a prosecutable violation of the client's privacy.

Certainly use different sheets of paper (not on the other side of a page) and perhaps different files if in the same file drawer, computer, or networked computer. You might keep psychotherapy notes on paper and by hand and all other information in a computer or use a different name or code so they are not easily confused or accidentally combined.

2. The information in them must be kept nowhere else.

> "The final rule makes it clear that **any notes that are routinely shared with others,** whether as part of the medical record or otherwise, **are, by definition, not psychotherapy notes,** as we have defined them." (Boldface added) From a response by the Secretary to a comment.

> "However, the requirement that psychotherapy notes be kept separate from the medical record and solely for the use of the provider who created them **means that the special protection does not apply to the same information in another location.**" (Boldface added) (From a response by the Secretary to a comment)

> "Because of the restricted definition we have adopted for psychotherapy notes, we do not expect that members of a team will share such information. **Information shared in order to care for the patient is, by definition, not protected as psychotherapy notes.**" (Boldface added) From a response by the Secretary to a comment.

3. The form of the information is irrelevant.

> "We do not require the notes to be in a particular format, such as hand-written. They may be typed into a word processor, for example. Copying the notes into a different format, per se, would not allow the information to be accessed by a health plan." From a response by the Secretary to a comment.

Other points about psychotherapy notes

*   Authorizations to release them will be very rare.

> "We anticipate **these authorizations will rarely be necessary,** since psychotherapy notes do not include information that covered entities typically need for treatment, payment, or other types of health care operations." Response by the Secretary to a comment.

- An Authorization for the release of psychotherapy notes cannot be combined with other Authorizations except those for other psychotherapy notes. [§ 164.508(b)(3)(ii)].

- The minimum necessary rules do not apply to PHI released under an Authorization so it does not apply to psychotherapy notes.

- A CE "may not use or disclose psychotherapy notes for purposes of another covered entity's treatment, payment, or health care operations without obtaining the individual's authorization." Guidance, Dec. 4, 2002.

- Psychotherapy notes can still be released without an Authorization to Social Security Disability and to Workers' Compensation but not to Medicare.

The regulations

All discussion of Psychotherapy Notes is in the Preamble and the Secretary's responses in Guidances not the regulations.

Psychotherapy Notes are described in the Federal Register/ Vol.65, NO. 250: p. 82497; also 82622, 82623; 82652-82654). See Section 1040 for the definition.

311   Deciding to keep or not to keep psychotherapy notes

1. Look at your current records. Find a dozen notes of which you think highly.

    a. Is there material which you believe you believe you must record and yet you don't want it shared with:
        *   the client because it is your working hypotheses and was of value only at one time? Remember, clients have no access to psychotherapy notes unless you give it.
        *   insurance companies or others who are not required to protect its confidentially as carefully as your profession requires you to?
        *   anyone else because it is too sensitive and potentially damaging to the client or to others?
        *   other treaters because they are not and will not be doing the kind of work you are with the client?

    b. But you...
        *   may want to share the information with professional students for training.
        *   find value and meaning in these notes as you review them.

If so, the information should be kept separate in psychotherapy notes.

2. If, on the other hand, you mainly record the formalities of the therapy such as your interventions and the clients responses you may feel comfortable in disclosing this to an insurer or other CE and so you have no need for records beyond the routine progress note.

Here are two possible notes made about treatment of the same client with Anxiety Disorder and Narcissistic Personality Disorder

Routine Note

7/16/05
Sess # 8   45 mins   Individual p/t - cog-behav. using Foa's manual.
Revd HW[24] and diary. 2 panics-used breathing -> shorter duration, milder sx. Praised client. Revd relaxation methods and practiced DMR[25] x 10 mins - 7 SUDS[26]-> 3. SD[27] hierarchy 4, step 6 was achieved at 2 SUDS. Discussed role of dysfunctional thoughts in generating client's depression. Revised HW.

Psychotherapy Note

7/16/05
Sess # 8   45 mins   Individual p/t interpersonal insight-oriented.
Cl consulted Dr. Smith re breast enlargement surg. Deflected excessive praise but will address next time (3rd recurrence). Saw new associate of husb. - triggered fears of loss of attractiveness producing 2 panics. Saw husband's pattern of withdrawal in this week's business trip leading to worry and anxiety.

---

[24] Homework

[25] Deep Muscle Relaxation

[26] Subjective Units of Discomfort

[27] Systematic Desensitization.

3. Another possibility is to keep psychotherapy notes for some clients. Perhaps there is only some information you want to see more fully protected. For those times and contents create and label a psychotherapy note. Doing so for some clients may not have to be explained in a courtroom but doing so for only some sessions may look suspiciously like destroying notes.

4   If you are not getting requests for intrusive case summaries and similar versions of your notes, keep just Psychotherapy Notes for simplicity and provide a summary in a letter.

5. A variation would be to keep only Psychotherapy Notes, don't release them, and in the rare situation when you have to or wish to share PHI, generate a simple Routine Progress note using a checklist form.

Summary: Advantages vs. disadvantages

The main advantages of keeping Psychotherapy Notes are the fact that the client has no access to them, that you don't have to reveal them for clients to use their insurance (non-conditioning), and that you can think for the record in terms both clinical hypotheses and risk management but need not (ever?) reveal this content.

The main disadvantages are that they require maintaining separate records, are possibly to be discoverable in some legal proceedings, and don't protect a great deal of information which must be placed in the routine notes.

312   Format for a routine progress note

(On your letterhead or other identification of the professional creating the note.
Erase the *s)

Case Progress Note   Page _____

Name of client _____ Date ____/ ____/20___

Start _____ Ending _____ times. Duration 90 75 60 50 45 30 15 minutes

Intended schedule: Biweekly Weekly   2 4 6 8 12 weeks PRN

Diagnosis (DSM-IV/ICD) _____ Code # _____

Diagnosis (DSM-IV/ICD) _____ Code # _____

GAF score today _____ Other measures*_____

Target symptoms**   **Change
                                                 since _____ date

_____ ____

_____ ____

_____ ____

_____ ____

_____ ____

Treatment provided**_____

_____

Treatment planned*** _____

_____

Current/Changed medications****   See _____

Prognosis: Guarded Improvement Recovery Fluctuating   _____

Notes**_____

_____

_____

_____

Person completing this form: _____ _____ _____
                                   Signature/Initials   Printed   Title

Notes

* Depending on the case you might use the Y-BOCS for obsessive/compulsions, the Beck Depression or Anxiety Inventories, or dozens of other. All are improvements over the anchorless GAF.

** If you wish to enter any datum on every note, assigning a code makes for less recording time and space. Examine your current notes to decide what might be coded.

For example, you might use this code for degree of Change with:

<< = Much worse
<   = Worse
0   = No change
>   = Improved
>   = Greatly improved

Similarly, if you need to record the "modalities of treatment" you might assign MM to medication monitoring, F to family therapy, C for conjoint, I for individual, and G for group. You could add a sub-code such as sm for stress management, resoc for resocialization/social skills, etc. If you need to record who was present you might code F for father, M for mother, Sn for son Ss for sister, etc. Or you might prefer to use the SOAP format and enter those letters -Subjective, Objective, Assessment, and Plan. For more on using SOAP or SOAPIER notes in psychotherapy see Zuckerman, 2003.

*** You might enter homework, or changes in the plan and record the treatment plan separately and use a code here.

**** Or you might keep track of medications on a separate sheet or indicate who is responsible for medication for this client.

313   Format for a psychotherapy note

(On your letterhead and perhaps an unusually colored paper)

Psychotherapy Note   Page number _____

Name of client _____   Case/ID number _____

NOTICE: This page is a Psychotherapy Note under the HIPAA regulations. It must not be included in or attached to any other part of the client's health care records except other psychotherapy notes. Patients do not have access to these notes and releasing them requires a special authorization.

Date   Codes*

_____

_____

_____

_____

_____

_____

_____

_____

_____

_____

_____

_____

_____

_____

_____

_____

_____

_____

Reminder: Sign and date every entry.

Codes:

320   Billing under HIPAA

One of HIPAA's main goals is to standardize the ways services are designated and how that information is transmitted electronically and so a large part of the legislation is devoted to what are called transaction codes. These **Transactions and Code Sets: Standardization of Electronic Transactions, Code Sets and Unique Identifiers** occupy only about 5 pages of requirements (§ 162) and 4 pages elsewhere (Part C - Administrative Simplification, sections 1171-1176). The discussion is about another 52 pages but the code sets themselves are at least a thousand pages and are the result of the work of dozens of committees and hundreds of professionals over the last five years. The code sets are available in print[28] or online at <http://www.wpc-edi.com> for those who prize complexity, precision and thoroughness. Besides the code sets for diseases and treatments there are code sets for pharmaceuticals and dental care and others.

As you will see the transactions codes and the changes they impose are devilishly complex. Your actual implementation date for electronic transactions will depend on the insurers you bill and they will move toward compliance at their own rates and pull all of us small fish along.

Below is an overview so you can understand what transaction codes are, how they will be used in mental health, and information to help you decide about computerizing your billing.

Not just billing - transactions

The codes address eight insurance-related transactions including:

1. Health claims or equivalent encounter[29] information.
2. Enrollment and disenrollment in a health plan.
3. Eligibility for a health plan.
4. Health care payment and remittance advice[30].
5. Health plan premium payments.
6. Health claim status[31].
7. Referral certification and authorization.
8. Coordination of benefits[32].

If you skipped reading the list go back and re-read the list while considering how much time and energy you and your staff spend now on these aspects of billing. When fully implemented, all of these determinations will be instantaneous, current, and more accurate. Might this save you time, money, and headaches? Also, as you know, managed care organizations have chosen to delay payments to providers by refusing to accept claims that were not **"clean claims"** (complete and in their preferred format). I believe that HIPAA (in section 1175) requires payers to not take longer than they presently do to pay

---

[28] Published by Washington Publishing Company, PMB 161, 5284 Randolph Road, Rockville, MD, 20852-2116 and on line at http://www.wpc-edi.com/hipaa . The code sets are free downloads.

[29] This means visits or what we call sessions.

[30] This is the bookkeeping name. We get EOBs - Explanation of Benefits.

[31] This has to do with delayed payments and similar information about a claim we filed.

[32] When more than one insurer covers the person their benefits are apportioned among those insurers on a priority basis. This is called coordination of benefits and has been a great headache but will now be completely automatic.

claims. If your state does not have a law requiring timely payments, HIPAA will not do this for you. Payments may not get faster but at least they cannot become more delayed more "due to implementing HIPAA."

The goal is to have one and only one code for each procedure and one set of codes for all payers, plans, and providers. All the codes have been created. What will take several years is implementation because some will choose to modify their legacy computer systems, others will use the clearinghouse route (see below), and some will have to design, test, and implement new systems to work at all levels.

DSM or ICD?

HIPAA's requires the ICD-9-CM (*The International Classification of Diseases, Ninth Revision, Clinical Modification*[33]) for all medical conditions. Since the DSM is specialized for psychiatry it has been passed over in favor of the more broadly medical ICD. DSM-V is about five years in the future. It is even conceivable that this country, one of only two industrialized countries not using ICD-10 might adopt it. For more on ICD-10 see <http://www.ahima.org/icd10/index.asp>. I don't know how this will shake out but suggest you start or continue to use ICD.

HIPAA requires the use of diagnoses from the ICD-9 instead of DSM-IV-TR. Changes to the ICD implemented in October 2004 bring the two closer but there are still differences, stemming from the European origins of ICD and its origination in 1980. DSM is, of course, a description of the symptoms and criteria for each disorder. ICD is simply a list of the diagnoses names and numbers. There is no book of just the mental disorders and no small version (except my own *Reference List of ICD-9-CM Diagnoses* at <www.ICD9Codes.info>) but the whole ICD is available from the Centers for Disease Control and other sources on CD, versions for Windows computers and book versions as well.

Treatments and services will continue to be coded using the *CPT*. (*CPT-4: Physician Current Procedural Terminology* published by the American Medical Association, Chicago, and updated yearly). Dozens of publishers supply computerized versions, training programs, and other kinds of support for the *CPT* but you'll mainly use only the dozen current mental health codes.

A new claim form

To collect all this information some ten new claim forms have been created. For mental health the old HCFA-1500 (or UB-92) will be replaced by the **ANSI 837 Professional Form** (or for agencies, the ANSI 837 Institutional Claims and Encounters Form) which uses the American National Standards Institute Accredited Standards Committee standard ANSI X12N format for electronic data. This is not designed to be a paper form although parts may appear as paper from some insurers. The goal was to both avoid paper forms (and their required data entry) and the paper attachments we now staple, clip, and sticky note to claim forms to clarify points (and which have to be read and responded to by an paid employee of the insurer). Remember time is money and costs reduce profits.

To illustrate what this form is about, among its 300+ data elements (fields) are sections to allow coordination of benefits so that the payers could send the claim on to the secondary insurer, and continue until all following payers have received the claim. Neat, huh? There are data elements to ensure unquestionable identification of individuals to end mix-ups with same names and same birthdays, etc. There is a Related Causes code for when the

---

[33] Published by the United Nations World Health Organization and available from many private and non-profit publishers. A version on CD-ROM (stock number 017-022-01534-0) is available for purchase from the Government Printing Office (GPO) at 202-512-1800 or fax 202- 512-2250.

claim is related to an accident or to employment. There are more options for location of service.

Q: Can I no longer use paper billing forms?
A: There will be a transition period where paper will be accepted until electronic claims are fully implemented by most payers and the larger providers. Paper claims are likely to be accepted for much longer because small practices are not required to submit electronically even to Medicare. I imagine that insurers will continue to accept paper claims but pressure providers to move to electronic submissions by adding a surcharge or indicating that they take a lot longer to pay paper claims. Another option for small practices is to use a clearinghouse.

Clearinghouses

Alert readers may recall that the third kind of CEs (after providers and health plans) are clearinghouses. These are the intermediaries who do the hard work of making payers and providers appear to speak the same language. Their staff and computers translate the billing, coverage, verification, and dozens of other codes back and forth. You can arrange to have a clearinghouse convert claims from your paper or old codes to whatever format any payer now wants. This may be both cost effective and simpler, especially for the next few years until the complexities become routinized. If you bill a large number of payers a clearinghouse will cope with each payer's formats for you.

Alternately, some larger payers have developed their own online web-based programs for submitting claims to them and these are usually free. For example, if you submit Medicare bills check with your regional Medicare organization or your state program. Pennsylvania, for example, has developed a free software package for those billing Medicare (see <http://www.dpw.state.pa.us/omap/hipaa/omaphipaacert.asp> Commercial office management programs for clinicians will also handle these issues.

Other Points

Q: "Does the HIPAA Privacy Rule prevent health plans and providers from using debt collection agencies? Does the Privacy Rule conflict with the Fair Debt Collection Practices Act?
A: "The Privacy Rule permits covered entities to continue to use the services of debt collection agencies. Debt collection is recognized as a payment activity within the payment definition. See the definition of "payment" at 45 CFR 164.501. Through a business associate arrangement, the covered entity may engage a debt collection agency to perform this function on its behalf. Disclosures to collection agencies are governed by other provisions of the Privacy Rule, such as the business associate and minimum necessary requirements." Aspects of the Privacy Rule - December 4, 2002. FAQs
<http://www.hhs.gov/ocr/hipaa/privacy.html>

The Centers for Medicare & Medicaid Services (CMS) recently exempted health benefit debit card transactions from the HIPAA requirements of electronic data transfer. This specifically applied to the use of such cards to pay for services from a Flexible Spending Account (FSA) (and, presumably) Health Savings Accounts. This decision is based on earlier decisions that credit and debit card payments to professionals or pharmacies are not subject to these security rules.

Ed's Opinion: Privacy Rules still apply and so I would put a notice in my Brochure for Patients indicating that credit card payments and similar arrangements are more confidential than checks (with names on them) and are protected by business laws and security methods but both are discoverable.

330   The computerized office

You can buy your own billing program but before you choose this route you might consider what else the many available office management programs can do for you. This will review some of these function so that you can see if they correspond with your needs and practices before we return to meeting HIPAA's expectations.

Computer functions for the mental health professional

1. Billing and accounting programs: Accounts receivable (AR), accounts payable, and the generation of all kinds of health insurance claims forms, using DSM, CPT, and other codes, submitting these electronically, making deposit slips, etc.

2. Electronic Records - documentation/record making and keeping.
- Generating narrative reports such as intakes, progress notes, using ICD codes, etc. The advent of dictation programs will speed these developments.
- Generating and updating treatment plans and similar treatment-supporting forms.
- Word processing functions such as medical spelling checker, encryption, abbreviations glossary/thesaurus, keyboard macros, printing special forms, etc. Paperwork such as letters, client lists, office forms, etc.

3. Practice and caseload management such as client reminders, client phone lists, tracking managed care authorizations, scheduling, etc.

4. Business functions such as payroll, or activity reports on your practice.

5. Computer records' security functions such as backups, passwords, and encryption.

6. Clinical functions
- Client education
- Assessment: Test administration, scoring, interpretation, and report generation; decision support.
- Treatment provision
- Outcome assessment
- Clinical monitoring: Collection of data by fax, phone, and keyboard for intake, monitoring, outcomes, etc.

7. Research and professional writing. Desktop publishing and presentation graphics. Education and teaching.

8. Online education. Searching for and reading professional literature, taking CE courses, consultations with colleagues.

If you do find your needs here, what is stopping you from computerizing your practice? Here is the way one consultant sees it:

> Why Do It?
> A better question might be What's stopping you? More efficient record keeping, cleaner claims, integration with the health-care system, and communication with other providers and third-party payers are just a few of the benefits of using EMRs [**Electronic Medical Records**]. Add to that faster turnaround for processing claims, easy data search and retrieval, more accurate data input, easy claims validation and

submission and HIPAA compliance, and the reasons to switch are even more compelling. (Diecidue, 2002)

The last point bears some elaboration. Making your bills HIPAA-compliant by incorporating the transaction codes is very complex so, if you buy a billing program, you will be shifting this work onto the developer or vendor of the program. Of course, you will retain responsibility for the accuracy of the bills and other legal and ethical concerns but you won't have to do the heavy lifting.

If you submit Medicare bills check with your regional Medicare organization or your state program. Pennsylvania, for example, has developed a free software package for those billing Medicare (see <http://www.dpw.state.pa.us/omap/hipaa/omaphipaacert.asp

331   Your National Provider Identifier - NPI

You, whom Managed Care changed from a therapist into a generic "provider," and the HIPAA Privacy Rule turned into the even more wispy CE (Covered Entity), will now be just a number. You will have to get a National Provider Identifier (NPI) number. Don't panic; you will have two full years to do it. If you are not now and don't want to be a CE, ignore this. If you want one for some administrative purposes but are not a CE, you can get one. Employers who are CEs will use their EINs.

Applications for NPIs will be on paper and via the internet[34] There will be accounts with user names and passwords, and telephone support but no fee. Mike Feely, the savvy therapist, and aficionado of bureaucracy suggested VNPIs (Vanity National Provider Identifiers) for a small fee which could go to the National Coalition to fight HIPAA. Can someone look into this, please?

This site offers ways to register for your NPI.
<https://nppes.cms.hhs.gov/NPPES/Welcome.do>

If you need more information check the sites below

<http://www.cms.hhs.gov/hipaa/hipaa2/regulations/identifiers/default.asp> has the official explanations.

<http://www.hipaadvisory.com/regs/natstandardhcprovidid/implementnpi.htm> has the regulations.

<http://aspe.hhs.gov/admnsimp/faqnpi.htm> offers Frequently Asked Questions and answers from the Federal government.

<http://www.hipaadvisory.com/regs/finalprovid/def.htm> contains more than most need to know but for those blessed with endless curiosity ....

---

[34] By the way, *Wired* magazine, the apparent authority, has decided that "email" no longer needs a hyphen nor "internet" an initial capital.

400   Notices, Consents, and Authorizations

410   Introduction to the Notice of Privacy Practices - The NPP

This document, your NPP, and your current Practice Brochure are the foundations of your efforts to inform your clients about how you will protect the privacy of what they tell you or what you discover about them. They advise clients of their rights and promises that you will act responsibly when they entrust you with their personal health information.

The HIPAA regulations about privacy are quite long, detailed, and complex and so present the client with a quite complex set of considerations and alternatives, all to be explained in your NPP. Furthermore, these rules interact with your state and other laws, court decisions, local practices and professional ethics. Also, the official means of protecting privacy interact with your and the client's decisional processes and life circumstances and require some weighing of risks and benefits. Finally, the NPP must present and explain a number of required items if it is not to be considered a legally defective.

I will first note some issues, quote the regulations about the essential components of the NPP, and then note a few other versions. Lastly, I will offer a general version of an NPP written for mental health practitioners. Although the HIPAA regulations (§164.520) do not offer a standard or sample NPP they do offer a long list of required contents, the lack of any one, making the resulting Consent "defective."

Integration with other rules - Crosswalking

The versions of NPPs presented in this book are based on the HIPAA law and have to be modified in light of more stringent other laws as required by HIPAA [§164.520(b)(1)(ii)(C). For more in this cross-walking see section 240 of this book. Please keep in mind that this crosswalking is an evolving process as new laws, court decisions, unintended consequences, and ramifications come to light. Therefore, I recommend that you schedule a re-examination and possible revision of your Notice at six month intervals for the next year or two.

Tailored and shorter versions

While this is an official and legally required document, it should reflect your way of working just as your practice brochure does because it is both an introduction to you and a contract with the client. It should be integrated into your client intake package of forms and client education and orientation (see Zuckerman, 2003, for a very detailed Practice Brochure). DHHS even says "Covered entities are encouraged to provide individuals with the most specific notice possible."

Some of the NPPs required contents will not apply to mental health practices at all (e.g. organ donation) or only under the rarest of circumstances (disease reporting, national security, cause of death inquiries). Therefore, a shorter version of the NPP may be both practical (less reading time, less distraction) and more likely to support informed consent by focusing on the relevant issues. A shortened version would not replace the longer but could be printed on two pages and placed on top of and reference the longer official version. This is called a layered approach. See section 412 for an example.

Your shorter versions can be designed to the population of clients you see in your practice. For example, if your population has lower reading or English language skills a simplified version might be more appropriate along with the offer of a longer version or a fuller (documented) discussion of their questions. If you see a population whose information is likely to be highly sensitive you can emphasize or expand sections (and incorporate local laws) about what information is shared with whom under what conditions.

The versions below have been reorganized and reworded from the way the contents are presented in the regulations to better fit the flow of reading and understanding for clients. Because the required contents are many and interact, I have provided two versions. The first is fairly long but explains the issues and choices in an almost conversational fashion. If you are more comfortable or you expect a particular client will be more comfortable with fuller explanations use this version alone.

The second is much shorter. This version may be better when your local rules are more stringent and protective than HIPAA's but you still need to comply by furnishing a NPP. The shorter version is also suitable if you do not want to offer clients more on paper which might confuse, distract, or alarm them but it should not be used as a substitute for the longer version which you must offer or make available - see below.

Procedures

- The HIPAA Privacy Rule prohibits the NPP and Consent from being combined into a single document. Therefore put your Consent form (in section 430) **on a separate page** and entitle it so that is clear that it is not a continuation of the NPP.
- You should print the NPP in at least 12 point type (like this) or 14 point type for those with weaker vision so that everyone can read it.
- You must **post your entire NPP** in a clear and prominent location. I suppose that in your waiting area would be sufficient. While you might make a large chart you could alternately place the pages in a binder inside sheet protectors or laminate the pages.

You could offer this to each new client and tell them there are copies available from your receptionist or in a rack in the waiting room. This will reduce copying costs and simplify your providing the latest versions to new or returning clients.

- The client must review the NPP and sign a consent "no later than the date of the first service delivery." Ideally, you could supply the NPP before you see the client by making it part of your client introduction package thus giving him or her time to receive what the regulations call adequate notice. In any case, the client should be made to **review the NPP and sign the Consent before you see him or her.**

- CEs are required to "provide a revised notice to individuals then covered by the plan within 60 days of a material revision." See < http://www.hhs.gov/ocr/hipaa/guidelines/notice.rtf.> If you change it you do not need to mail copies to your continuing clients or even furnish it to them unless asked to do so. Of course, you would provide the revised version to new clients. **When you change your NPP** you do *not* have to get a new acknowledgment of receipt of the notice. Note that this rule does not require any kind of acknowledgment or evidence of your having provided the revised version.

- HIPAA requires the NPP be written **in "plain language"** so that an average reader would understand his or her rights. It does not state a reading level. It does not state "in English" nor does it require versions in any other language or alternative form of communication. However, other laws do mandate foreign language versions (e. g. Title VI of the Civil Rights Act of 1964). Without these, the goal of understanding one's rights may not be achieved, the client's confidence in the CE's commitment to privacy would be weakened, and so you should make the effort to provide a version your clients can understand. HSS has recognized these problems and recently provide a website with guidance for rewording and presenting HIPAA information: http://www.hhs.gov/ocr/hipaa/assist.html>. Versions in many languages are available from many organizations which you can find by searching the web.

- If you maintain a **Web Site** for your practice you must "prominently" post your NPP at the site and you must indicate that clients can obtain a paper copy of the NPP and tell them how to do so. If your site offers or explains any of your clinical services (not, I believe, just information, say about disorders) you must direct clients to read your NPP before receiving your service.

The regulations

The text of the regulations reprinted below has been edited for therapists and boldfaced to focus on the issues for therapists.

§ 164.520 Notice of privacy practices for protected health information.

(a) Standard: notice of privacy practices.
 (1) Right to notice. Except as provided by paragraph (a)(2) or (3) of this section, an individual has a right to **adequate notice** of the uses and disclosures of protected health information that may be made by the covered entity, and of the individual's **rights** and the covered entity's legal **duties** with respect to protected health information.

(b) Implementation specifications: content of notice.
 (1) Required elements. The covered entity must provide a notice that is written in plain language and that contains the elements required by this paragraph.
  (i) **Header**. The notice must contain the following statement as a header or otherwise prominently displayed: "THIS NOTICE DESCRIBES HOW MEDICAL INFORMATION ABOUT YOU MAY BE USED AND DISCLOSED AND HOW YOU CAN GET ACCESS TO THIS INFORMATION. PLEASE REVIEW IT CAREFULLY."
  (ii) Uses and disclosures. The notice must contain:
   (A) A description, including at least one example, of the types of **uses and disclosures** that the covered entity is permitted by this subpart to make for each of the

following purposes: **treatment, payment, and health care operations.**

(B) A description of each of the **other purposes** for which the covered entity is permitted or required by this subpart to use or disclose protected health information without the individual's written consent or authorization.

(C) If a use or disclosure for any purpose described in paragraphs (b)(1)(ii)(A) or (B) of this section is prohibited or materially limited by other applicable law, the description of such use or disclosure must reflect the more stringent law as defined in § 160.202.

(D) For each purpose described in paragraph (b)(1)(ii)(A) or (B) of this section, the description must include **sufficient detail** to place the individual on notice of the uses and disclosures that are permitted or required by this subpart and other applicable law.

(E) A statement that other uses and disclosures will be made only with the individual's written **authorization** and that the individual may **revoke** such authorization as provided by § 164.508(b)(5).

(iii) **Separate statements for certain uses or disclosures.** If the covered entity intends to engage in any of the following activities, the description required by paragraph (b)(1)(ii)(A) of this section must include a separate statement, as applicable, that:

(A) The covered entity may contact the individual to provide **appointment reminders** or information about **treatment alternatives** or other heath-related benefits and services that may be of interest to the individual;

(iv) Individual rights. The notice must contain a statement of the individual's **rights** with respect to protected health information and a brief description of how the individual may **exercise these rights**, as follows:

(A) The right to request **restrictions** on certain uses and disclosures of protected health information as provided by § 164.522(a), including a statement that the covered entity is not required to agree to a requested restriction;

(B) The right to receive **confidential communications** of protected health information as provided by § 164.522(b), as applicable;

(C) The right to **inspect and copy** protected health information as provided by § 164.524;

(D) The right to **amend** protected health information as provided by § 164.526;

(E) The right to receive an **accounting of disclosures** of protected health information as provided by § 164.528; and

(F) The right of an individual, including an individual who has agreed to receive the notice electronically in accordance with paragraph (c)(3) of this section, to **obtain a paper copy** of the notice from the covered entity upon request.

(v) Covered entity's **duties**. The notice must contain:

(A) A statement that the covered entity is required by law to **maintain the privacy** of protected health information and to provide individuals with notice of its legal duties and privacy practices with respect to protected health information;

(B) A statement that the covered entity is required to abide by the terms of the notice currently in effect; and

(C) For the covered entity to apply **a change in a privacy practice** that is described in the notice to protected health information that the covered entity created or received prior to issuing a revised notice, in accordance with § 164.530(i)(2)(ii), a statement that it reserves the right to change the terms of its notice and to make the new notice provisions effective for all protected health information that it maintains. The statement must also describe how it will provide individuals with a revised notice.

(vi) **Complaints**. The notice must contain a statement that individuals may complain to the covered entity and to the Secretary if they believe their privacy rights have been violated, a brief description of how the individual may file a complaint with the covered entity, and a statement that the individual will not be retaliated against for filing a complaint.

(vii) **Contact**. The notice must contain the name, or title, and telephone number of a person or office to contact for further information as required by § 164.530(a)(1)(ii).

(viii) **Effective date.** The notice must contain the date on which the notice is first in effect, which may not be earlier than the date on which the notice is printed or otherwise published.

(2) Optional elements.

(i) In addition to the information required by paragraph (b)(1) of this section, if a covered entity elects to limit the uses or disclosures that it is permitted to make under this subpart, the covered entity **may describe its more limited uses or disclosures** in its notice, provided that the covered entity may not include in its notice a limitation affecting its right to make a use or disclosure that is required by law or permitted by § 164.512(j)(1)(i).

(ii) For the covered entity to apply a change in its more limited uses and disclosures to protected health information created or received prior to issuing a revised notice, in accordance with § 164.530(i)(2)(ii), the notice must include the statements required by paragraph (b)(1)(v)(C) of this section.

(3) **Revisions** to the notice. The covered entity must promptly revise and distribute its notice whenever there is a material change to the uses or disclosures, the individual's rights, the covered entity's legal duties, or other privacy practices stated in the notice. Except when required by law, a material change to any term of the notice may not be implemented prior to the effective date of the notice in which such material change is reflected.

(c) Implementation specifications: provision of notice. A covered entity must make the notice required by this section available on request to any person and to individuals as specified in paragraphs (c)(1) through (c)(4) of this section, as applicable.

(2) Specific requirements for certain covered health care providers. A covered health care provider that has a direct treatment relationship with an individual must:

(i) **Provide the notice no later than the date of the first service delivery,** including service delivered electronically, to such individual after the compliance date for the covered health care provider;

(ii) If the covered health care provider maintains a physical service delivery site:

(A) Have the notice available at the service delivery site for individuals to request to **take** with them; and

(B) **Post** the notice in a clear and prominent location where it is reasonable to expect individuals seeking service from the covered health care provider to be able to read the notice; and

(iii) Whenever the notice is **revised**, make the notice available upon request on or after the effective date of the revision and promptly comply with the requirements of paragraph (c)(2)(ii) of this section, if applicable.

(3) Specific requirements for **electronic notice.**

(i) A covered entity that maintains a web site that provides information about the covered entity's customer services or benefits must prominently **post** its notice on the web site and make the notice available electronically through the web site.

(ii) A covered entity may provide the notice required by this section to an individual **by e-mail, if the individual agrees** to electronic notice and such agreement has not been withdrawn. If the covered entity knows that the e-mail transmission has failed, a paper copy of the notice must be provided to the individual. Provision of electronic notice by the covered entity will satisfy the provision requirements of paragraph (c) of this section when timely made in accordance with paragraph (c)(1) or (2) of this section.

(iii) For purposes of paragraph (c)(2)(i) of this section, if the first service delivery to an individual is delivered electronically, the covered health care provider must **provide electronic notice automatically and contemporaneously in response to the individual's first request for service.**

(iv) The individual who is the recipient of electronic notice retains the right to obtain a paper copy of the notice from a covered entity upon request.

(e) Implementation specifications: documentation. A covered entity must document compliance with the notice requirements by retaining copies of the notices issued by the covered entity as required by § 164.530(j).

A list of these contents

A long and formal version of the required contents, entitled *HIPAA Privacy Rule Checklists Section 164.520 Notice of Privacy Practices for Protected Health Information* can be found in the list at <www.nchica.org/HIPAAResources/Samples/Portal.asp> Accessed Sept. 24, 2005.

This checklist can be very helpful if you are designing your own NPP or when struggling to integrate the NPPs contents with your current Brochure for Clients.

Examples of NPPs

Since these NPPs can be posted to CE's websites, doing a Google search (<www.google.com>) with Notice of Privacy Practices will allow you to see how others are coping with this regulation.

Your state mental health department may be constructing standard documents as, for example, Ohio has done. There are many forms at this site. The NPP is a trifold brochure developed by the Department of Mental Health of the State of Ohio. See <http://www.mh.state.oh.us/legislation/hipaa/hipaa.policy.01-050a.pdf> Accessed Sept. 26, 2005.

The American Medical Association has a draft NPP form online at <http://www.ama-assn.org/ama/pub/category/11564.html> Oct. 6, 2005.

Also see the NPP at <www.calhealth.org/Download/priprac.pdf> which has been modified for California laws. Accessed Sept. 26, 2005.

This version is longer but very well written and explains a great deal to clients. Accessed Sept. 25, 2005. <www.nchica.org/HIPAAResources/Samples/EVpDocuments.htm>

This is a brief version from the Counseling & Mental Health Center at The University of Texas at Austin dated July 18, 2002. Accessed Sept. 26, 2005. <http://www.utexas.edu/student/cmhc/privacy.html>

This brief version is from a practice management consulting firm, Conomikes. Accessed Sept. 26, 2005. Available <http://www.conomikes.com/HIPAAPrivacyNotice.htm>

411   The complete Notice of Privacy Practices

I have simplified and condensed the required language for normally educated clients of a typical mental health professional and the small practice. However, please do not adopt it blindly; your NPP should be tailored to the way your office actually works and only promise what you will deliver. The regulations specifically require this and so offer no standard NPP.

- In this version I have used the plural "we" to refer to your practice but you may want to substitute a less formal "I" where appropriate or a more formal practice name. Also, this version does not include disclosures for fundraising but does include some on marketing (see sections 920 and 930 for more information).

- The paragraph in capitals is required to be verbatim and prominently displayed near the top of the page.

- Remove the footnotes when you review and revise this version and fill in the name and address of your Privacy Officer, etc.

- In regard to legally required reports, note that some states use a suspicion standard and others a belief standard in regard to child or other abuse.

- Medicare's HIPAA web site now has a suggested and sample NPP but only *for Medicare clients* which you can see at <www.medicare.gov/privacypractices.asp>. It is about two pages and has a 9-10th grade reading level. If you intend to use it, you will need to add any variations imposed by more stringent laws in your state and adapt it to your office procedures.

- The Substance Abuse & Mental Health Services Administration (SAMHSA) has published new guidance on the Privacy Rule to help alcohol and substance abuse programs and others understand their responsibilities under both the Privacy Rule and 42 CFR Part 2 (confidentiality of alcohol and drug abuse patient records regulation). *The Privacy Rule and Alcohol/Substance Abuse Programs* (June 2004) is available at: <http://www.hipaa.samhsa.gov/Part2ComparisonCleared.htm>

- If you do research and are concerned with privacy see section 470.

(On your letterhead)

THIS NOTICE DESCRIBES HOW MEDICAL INFORMATION ABOUT YOU MAY BE USED AND DISCLOSED AND HOW YOU CAN GET ACCESS TO THIS INFORMATION. PLEASE REVIEW IT CAREFULLY.

Notice of Privacy Practices

Privacy is a very important concern for all those who come to this office. It is also complicated because of the many federal and state laws and our professional ethics. Because the rules are so complicated some parts of this Notice are very detailed and you probably will have to read them several times to understand them. If you have any questions our Privacy Officer will be happy to help you understand our procedures and your rights. His or her name and address are at the end of this Notice.

Contents of this Notice

A. **Introduction - To Our Clients**

B. **What we mean by your medical information**

C. **Privacy and the laws about privacy**

D. **How your protected health information can be used and shared**

1. **Uses and disclosures *with your consent***

    a. **The basic uses and disclosures - For treatment, payment, and health care operations (TPO)**

    b. **Other uses and disclosures in health care**

2. **Uses and disclosures that *require* your Authorization**

3. **Uses and disclosures that *don't require* your Consent or Authorization**

4. **Uses and disclosures where you to have *an opportunity to object***

5. **An *Accounting* of disclosures we have made**

E. **Your rights concerning your health information**

F. **If you have questions or problems**

A.   Introduction - To our clients

This Notice will tell you how we handle your medical information. It tells how we use this information here in this office, how we share it with other professionals and organizations, and how you can see it. We want you to know all of this so that you can make the best decisions for yourself and your family. Because the laws of this state and the laws of federal government are very complicated and we don't want to make you read a lot that may not apply to you, we have removed a few small parts. If you have any questions or want to know more about anything in this Notice, please ask our Privacy Officer for more explanations or more details.

B.   What we mean by your medical information

Each time you visit us or any doctor's office, hospital, clinic, or any other what are called healthcare providers information is collected about you and your physical and mental health. It may be information about your past, present or future health or conditions, or the tests and treatment you got from us or from others, or about payment for healthcare. The information we collect from you is called, in the law, PHI which stands for **Protected Health Information.** This information goes into your **medical or healthcare record** or file at office.

In this office this PHI is likely to include these kinds of information:
- Your history. As a child, in school and at work, marriage and personal history.
- Reasons you came for treatment. Your problems, complaints, symptoms, or needs.
- Diagnoses. Diagnoses are the medical terms for your problems or symptoms.
- A treatment plan. A list of the treatments and any other services which we think will be best to help you.
- Progress notes. Each time you come in we write down some things about how you are doing, what we notice about you, and what you tell us.
- Records we get from others who treated you or evaluated you.
- Psychological test scores, school records, and other reports.
- Information about medications you took or are taking.
- Legal matters
- Billing and insurance information

This list is just to give you and idea and there may be other kinds of information that go into your healthcare record here.

We use this information for many purposes. For example, we may use it:
- To plan your care and treatment.
- To decide how well our treatments are working for you.
- When we talk with other healthcare professionals who are also treating you such as your family doctor or the professional who referred you to us.
- To show that you actually received the services from us which we billed to you or to your health insurance company.
- For teaching and training other healthcare professionals.
- For medical or psychological research.
- For public health officials trying to improve health care in this area of the country.
- To improve the way we do our job by measuring the results of our work.

When you understand what is in your record and what it is used for you can make better decisions about who, when, and why others should have this information.

Although your health record is the physical property of the healthcare practitioner or facility that collected it, the information belongs to you. You can read it and if you want a copy we can make one for you(but may charge you for the costs of copying and mailing, if you want it mailed to you). In some very rare situations you cannot see all of what is in your records.[35] If you find anything in your records that you think is incorrect or believe that something important is missing you can ask us to amend (add information to) your record although in some rare situations we don't have to agree to do that. If you want, our Privacy Officer, whose name is at the end of this Notice, can explain more about this.

C. Privacy and the laws

We are also required to tell you about privacy because of the privacy regulations of a federal law, the Health Insurance Portability and Accountability Act of 1996 (HIPAA). The HIPAA law requires us to keep your Personal Healthcare Information (or PHI) private and to give you this notice of our legal duties and our privacy practices which is called the **Notice of Privacy Practices** (or **NPP).** We will obey the rules of this notice as long as it is in effect but if we change it the rules of the new NPP will apply to all the PHI we keep. If we change the NPP we will post the new Notice in our office where everyone can see. You or anyone else can also get a copy from our Privacy Officer at any time and it will be posted on our website at [web address].

D. How your protected health information can be used and shared

When your information is read by me or others in this office and used by us to make decisions about your care that is called, in the law, **use.** If the information is shared with or sent to others outside this office, that is called, in the law, **disclosure.** Except in some special circumstances, when we use your PHI here or disclose it to others we share only the **minimum necessary** PHI needed for those other people to do their jobs. The law gives you rights to know about your PHI, how it is used and to have a say in how it is disclosed (shared) and so we will tell you more about what we do with your information.

We use and disclose PHI for several reasons. Mainly, we will use and disclose it for routine purposes to provide for your care and we will explain more about these below. For other uses we must tell you about them and have a written Authorization from unless the law lets or requires us to make the disclosure without your authorization. However, the law also says that there are some uses and disclosures that don't need your consent or authorization.

1. Uses and disclosures of PHI in healthcare *with your consent*

After you have read this Notice you will be asked to sign a separate **Consent form** to allow us to use and share your PHI. In almost all cases we intend to use your PHI here or share your PHI with other people or organizations to provide **treatment** to you, arrange for **payment** for our services, or some other business functions called health care **operations.** Together these routine purposes are called TPO and the Consent form allows us to use and disclose your PHI for TPO. Take a minute to re-read that last sentence until it is clear because it is very important. Next we will tell you more about TPO.

1a. For treatment, payment, or health care operations.

We need information about you and your condition to provide care to you. You have to agree to let us collect the information and to use it and share it to care for you properly. Therefore you must sign the Consent form before we begin to treat you because if you do not agree and consent we cannot treat you.

---

[35] You should mention the client's access to Psychotherapy Notes if you have decided to keep them.

When you come to see us, several people in our office may collect information about you and all of it may go into your healthcare records here. Generally, we may use or disclose your PHI for three purposes: treatment, obtaining payment, and what are called healthcare operations. Let's see what these mean.

For treatment

We use your medical information to provide you with psychological treatments or services. These might include individual, family, or group therapy, psychological, educational, or vocational testing, treatment planning, or measuring the benefits of our services.

We may share or disclose your PHI to others who provide treatment to you. We are likely to share your information with your personal physician[36]. If you are being treated by a team we can share some of your PHI with them so that the services you receive will be work together. The other professionals treating you will also enter their findings, the actions they took, and their plans into your medical record and so we all can decide what treatments work best for you and make up a Treatment Plan. We may refer you to other professionals or consultants for services we cannot provide. When we do this we need to tell them some things about you and your conditions. We will get back their findings and opinions and those will go into your records here. If you receive treatment in the future from other professionals we can also share your PHI with them. These are some examples so that you can see how we use and disclose your PHI for treatment.

For payment

We may use your information to bill you, your insurance, or others so we can be paid for the treatments we provide to you. We may contact your insurance company to check on exactly what your insurance covers. We may have to tell them about your diagnoses, what treatments you have received, and the changes we expect in your conditions. We will need to tell them about when we met, your progress, and other similar things.

For health care operations

There are a few other ways we may use or disclose your PHI for what are called health care operations. For example, we may use your PHI to see where we can make improvements in the care and services we provide. We may be required to supply some information to some government health agencies so they can study disorders and treatment and make plans for services that are needed. If we do, your name and personal information will be removed from what we send.

1b. Other uses in healthcare

Appointment Reminders. We may use and disclose medical information to reschedule or remind you of appointments for treatment or other care. If you want us to call or write to you only at your home or your work or prefer some other way to reach you, we usually can arrange that. Just tell us.

Treatment Alternatives. We may use and disclose your PHI to tell you about or recommend possible treatments or alternatives that may be of help to you.

Other Benefits and Services. We may use and disclose your PHI to tell you about health-related benefits or services that may be of interest to you[37].

---

[36] You may want to clarify or constrain this statement.

[37] This is controversial and rare for mental health work. See section 930 for more information.

Research. We may use or share your information to do research to improve treatments. For example, comparing two treatments for the same disorder to see which works better or faster or costs less. In all cases your name, address and other personal information will be removed from the information given to researchers. If they need to know who you are we will discuss the research project with you and you will have to sign a special Authorization form before any information is shared.

Business Associates. There are some jobs we hire other businesses to do for us. In the law, they are called our Business Associates. Examples include a copy service we use to make copies of your health records and a billing service who figures out, prints, and mails our bills. These business associates need to receive some of your PHI to do their jobs properly. To protect your privacy they have agreed in their contract with us to safeguard your information.

2.   **Uses and disclosures that require your *Authorization***

If we want to use your information for any purpose besides the TPO or those we described above we need your permission on an **Authorization form.** We don't expect to need this very often.

If you do authorize us to use or disclose your PHI, you can revoke (cancel) that permission, in writing, at any time. After that time we will not use or disclose your information for the purposes that we agreed to. Of course, we cannot take back any information we had already disclosed with your permission or that we had used in our office.

3.   **Uses and disclosures of PHI from mental health records that don't *require* a Consent or Authorization**

The laws lets us use and disclose some of your PHI without your consent or authorization in some cases. Here are examples of when we might have to share your information.

When required by law
There are some federal, state, or local laws which require us to disclose PHI.
* We have to report suspected child abuse.[38]
* If you are involved in a lawsuit or legal proceeding and we receive a subpoena, discovery request, or other lawful process we may have to release some of your PHI. We will only do so after trying to tell you about the request, consulting your lawyer, or trying to get a court order to protect the information they requested.[39]
* We have to disclose some information to the government agencies which check on us to see that we are obeying the privacy laws.

For Law Enforcement Purposes
We may release medical information if asked to do so by a law enforcement official to investigate a crime or criminal.

For public health activities
We might disclose some of your PHI to agencies which investigate diseases or injuries.

---

[38] Or whatever standard is used in your state.

[39] This involves you, the professional's, asserting, on the client's behalf, their right to privileged communications.

Relating to decedents[40]
We might disclose PHI to coroners, medical examiners or funeral directors, and to organizations relating to organ, eye, or tissue donations or transplants.

For specific government functions
We may disclose PHI of military personnel and veterans to government benefit programs relating to eligibility and enrollment. We may disclose your PHI to Workers Compensation and Disability programs, to correctional facilities if you are an inmate, and for national security reasons.

To Prevent a Serious Threat to Health or Safety [41]
If we come to believe that there is a serious threat to your health or safety or that of another person or the public we can disclose some of your PHI. We will only do this to persons who can prevent the danger.

4. Uses and disclosures where you to have an opportunity to object

We can share some information about you with your family or close others. We will only share information with those involved in your care and anyone else you choose such as close friends or clergy. We will ask you about who you want us to tell what information about your condition or treatment. You can tell us what you want and we will honor your wishes as long as it is not against the law.

If it is an emergency - so we cannot ask if you disagree - we can share information if we believe that it is what you would have wanted and if we believe it will help you if we do share it. If we do share information, in an emergency, we will tell you as soon as we can. If you don't approve we will stop, as long as it is not against the law.

5.   An accounting of disclosures

When we disclose your PHI we may keep some records of whom we sent it to, when we sent it, and what we sent. You can get an accounting (a list) of many of these disclosures.

E.   Your rights regarding your health information

1. You can ask us to communicate with you about your health and related issues in a particular way or at a certain place which is more private for you. For example, you can ask us to call you at home, and not at work to schedule or cancel an appointment. We will try our best to do as you ask.

2. You have the right to ask us to limit what we tell people involved in your care or the payment for your care, such as family members and friends. While we don't have to agree to your request, if we do agree, we will keep our agreement except if it is against the law, or in an emergency, or when the information is necessary to treat you.

---

[40] You might consider omitting this as it is rare for therapists as is the two before it but you should be clear on these points.
[41] You should decide on the phrasing of this point depending on your state's handling of duty to warn situations.

3. You have the right to look at the health information we have about you such as your medical and billing records[42]. You can even get a copy of these records but we may charge you. Contact our Privacy Officer to arrange how to see your records. See below.

4. If you believe the information in your records is incorrect or missing important information, you can ask us to make some kinds of changes (called amending) to your health information. You have to make this request in writing and send it to our Privacy Officer. You must tell us the reasons you want to make the changes.

5. You have the right to a copy of this notice. If we change this NPP we will post the new version in our waiting area and you can always get a copy of the NPP from the Privacy Officer.

6. You have the right to file a complaint if you believe your privacy rights have been violated. You can file a complaint with our Privacy Officer and with the Secretary of the Department of Health and Human Services. All complaints must be in writing. Filing a complaint will not change the health care we provide to you in any way.

Also, you may have other rights which are granted to you by the laws of our state and these may be the same or different from the rights described above. I will be happy to discuss these situations with you now or as they arise.

F.   If you have questions or problems

If you need more information or have questions about the privacy practices described above please speak to the Privacy Officer whose name and telephone number are listed below. If you have a problem with how your PHI has been handled or if you believe your privacy rights have been violated, contact the Privacy Officer. You have the right to file a complaint with us and with the Secretary of the federal Department of Health and Human Services. We promise that we will not in any way limit your care here or take any actions against you if you complain.

If you have any questions regarding this Notice or our health information privacy policies, please contact our Privacy Officer who is _____ and can be reached by phone at _____ or by e-mail at _____

The effective date of this notice is April 14, 2003[43]

---

[42] You should mention the client's access to psychotherapy notes if you have decided to keep them.
[43] Or whatever date your practice became compliant.

412   **The briefer Notice of Privacy Practices**

Because of concerns raised by practitioners that the NPP is too long for routine use, too complex for most contacts, and will be confusing for many, DHHS has stated that a layered notice is acceptable. This means using a shorter version as a top page of the longer version but it cannot substitute for the longer version and must be written in plain language as well. The version below should be suitable and still fit on two sides of a page. The paragraph in capitals cannot be altered and must be displayed prominently and the top of the page.

(On your letterhead)

Notice of Privacy Practices - Brief Version

THIS NOTICE DESCRIBES HOW MEDICAL INFORMATION ABOUT YOU MAY BE USED AND DISCLOSED AND HOW YOU CAN GET ACCESS TO THIS INFORMATION. PLEASE REVIEW IT CAREFULLY.

Our commitment to your privacy

Our practice is dedicated to maintaining the privacy of your personal health information as part of providing professional care. We also are required by law to keep your information private. These laws are complicated, but we must give you this important information. This pamphlet is a shorter version of the full, legally required NPP and you may have a copy of this to read and refer to it for more information. However, we can't cover all possible situations so please talk to our Privacy Officer (see the end of this pamphlet) about any questions or problems.

We will use the information about your health which we get from you or from others mainly to provide you with **treatment**, to arrange **payment** for our services, and for some other business activities which are called, in the law, health care **operations.** After you have read this NPP we will ask you to sign a **Consent Form** to let us use and share your information. If you do not consent and sign this form, we cannot treat you.

If we or you want to use or disclose (send, share, release) your information for any other purposes we will discuss this with you and ask you to sign an Authorization form to allow this.

Of course we will keep your health information private but there are some times when the laws require us to use or share it. For example:

1. When there is a serious threat to your health and safety or the health and safety of another individual or the public. We will only share information with a person or organization who is able to help prevent or reduce the threat.

2. Some lawsuits and legal or court proceedings.

3. If a law enforcement official requires to do so.

4. For Workers Compensation and similar benefit programs.

There are some other situations like these but which don't happen very often. They are described in the longer version of the NPP.

Your rights regarding your health information

1. You can ask us to communicate with you about your health and related issues in a particular way or at a certain place which is more private for you. For example, you can ask us to call you at home, and not at work to schedule or cancel an appointment. We will try our best to do as you ask.

2. You have the right to ask us to limit what we tell people involved in your care or the payment for your care, such as family members and friends.

3. You have the right to look at the health information we have about you such as your medical and billing records[44]. You can even get a copy of these records but we may charge you. Contact our Privacy Officer to arrange how to see your records. See below.

4. If you believe the information in your records is incorrect or missing important information, you can ask us to make some kinds of changes (called amending) to your health information. You have to make this request in writing and send it to our Privacy Officer. You must tell us the reasons you want to make the changes.

5. You have the right to a copy of this notice. If we change this NPP we will post the new version in our waiting area and you can always get a copy of the NPP from the Privacy Officer.

6. You have the right to file a complaint if you believe your privacy rights have been violated. You can file a complaint with our Privacy Officer and with the Secretary of the Department of Health and Human Services. All complaints must be in writing. Filing a complaint will not change the health care we provide to you in any way.

If you have any questions regarding this notice or our health information privacy policies, please contact our Privacy Officer who is _____ and can be reached by phone at _____ or by e-mail at _____

The effective date of this notice is _____ ___ _____.

Also, you may have other rights which are granted to you by the laws of our state and these may be the same or different from the rights described above. I will be happy to discuss these situations with you now or as they arise.

---

[44] You might mention the client's access to psychotherapy notes if you have decided to keep them or you might not.

420   Informed consent, Consents, and Authorizations

We mental health professionals have a long history of protecting client's privacy and have developed concepts such as informed consent and procedures such as releases and requests for records with quite specific elements to limit disclosure of private or irrelevant information. HIPAA ignores this history and starts fresh. Under HIPAA there are only Consents and Authorizations and they don't mean what we have meant by these words. Also, informed consent has been almost eliminated.

These changes are important, quite striking and yet hard to grasp. Russ Newman (2002) has articulated this best and I quote from his response by the American Psychological Association to the DHHS about the Privacy Rule.

> The APA is disappointed with the proposed removal of the patient consent requirement of the rule at 45 C.F.R. § 164.506. ...
>
> Patients have a right to their privacy, and therefore the right to protect the privacy of their records. Patients are afforded the opportunity to exercise their privacy right when they give consent for the use and disclosure of their records for payment, treatment, and health care operations purposes. **Removing consent as proposed essentially shifts "ownership" of records to the entities that use and disclose them for treatment, payment, and health care operations purposes. Under the proposed modification, the patient is merely given the opportunity to acknowledge that he or she has received notice as to how his or her records will be used and disclosed.**
>
> ... under the modification, patients will lose their ability to give permission regarding the use of their records. Entities, but mainly insurers, will gain regulatory recognition of their use and disclosure of patient records. This modification, subtle as it may be in practical effect, appears to undermine the right of patients to the privacy of their records. (Boldface added.)

Sadly, all of these losses were incorporated into the final version of the Privacy Rule.

> The Privacy Rule permits, but does not require, a covered entity voluntarily to obtain client consent for uses and disclosures of protected health information for treatment, payment, and health care operations. Covered entities that do so have complete discretion to design a process that best suits their needs. *OCR Guidance Explaining Significant Aspects of the Privacy Rule - December 4, 2002*

> **Q: What is the difference between "consent" and "authorization" under the HIPAA Privacy Rule?**
> **A:**   Simply, **Consents are for regular uses and disclosures when the PHI is used in treatment, payment, or the other health operations (TPO). Authorizations are for all other uses and disclosures.** Consents are extremely skeletal. Authorizations are specific, time-limited, and informative. "They are intended to provide the individuals with concrete information about, and control over, the uses and disclosure s of protected health information about themselves." OCR, Ibid.

Fortunately, little in HIPAA "preempts" or overrules generally stronger state laws. We still have to get informed and voluntary consent (neither of which is required nor even mentioned in HIPAA) and we also have to integrate some of HIPAA's rules. In the past we had forms we called "Releases" or "Authorization to Release" or "Requests for Records." Where HIPAA applies there are now Consents and Authorizations (I will use capitals for these to indicate the actual form and not the general idea or process).

About Consents

- Consents are what providers routinely will be obtaining.
- Consent forms are worded very generally and do not specify much about the information (PHI) involved, its uses, or the recipients of this information.
- Consents have **no expiration date**. They will be valid at least for an episode of treatment but that is not defined more explicitly.
- Consent can be **oral**. This may be suitable for initiating treatment in some situations but should be followed up as soon as practicable with a written consent.
- Your Consent forms tell clients where they can find more information about your privacy practices (in you NPP).

The main problem with HIPAA's consent getting process for mental health is ethical. Clients are asked to consent (by signing the Consent form) to the use and disclosure of information without knowing (being informed) what the information is because it has not yet been created in the evaluation and treatment process. Perhaps change will be litigated.

Consent and Treatment

Generally, a Consent is required for providing treatment but there are three **exceptions** to this requirement:

1. Providers with an **"indirect treatment relationship"** don't need to obtain another Consent. For example, when you provide services to a client on the orders of another provider as, for example, when you evaluate a client and serve as a consultant to the primary provider (who would be a CE and have done the NPP and Consent) you don't need to subject the client to your NPP and Consent.

2. In special circumstances you don't need consent, written or oral.
   - ❑ In an emergency treatment situation. You should try to get consent as soon as possible however.
   - ❑ When you are required by law to treat the person and have tried to obtain consent.
   - ❑ When disclosure is necessary for law enforcement or other specified government purposes.

3. When there are significant **barriers to communicating** with the person. If, in your professional judgment, the situation indicates the client consented or wanted to consent to receive treatment, and there is no one else to provide consent (a personal representative) you can do so without formal consent. You must attempt to obtain consent and document your efforts. If your client population does not speak English as a first language or is deaf or blind, you should develop alternative methods for gaining consent because other laws require it although HIPAA does not.

Consent is required for providing treatment. If a client refuses to consent, you may refuse to treat them. The regulations say treatment can be "**conditioned**" on consent."

- However, if the client **refuses to sign or simply does not sign for any reason**, and you have made a "good faith effort" to obtain a written Consent (and document your failed efforts in you notes), you may still treat the person because consent can be presumed because they have come for treatment. However, the way this is all written [in § 164.506(a)(1)] suggests that for routine intakes of therapy clients, a signed consent form is expected.

- Consent can also be presumed. HIPAA allows you to use your professional judgment about the client's consenting to your treatment.

I know this is very confusing because it was designed for medical emergencies (How could ambulance crews get consent forms signed?) and for treating those who do not understand the treatment context and consenting (children? the obtunded?). It is also confusing because it involves two uses of the word consent: 1) signing a Consent form which is actually only an acknowledgement of having seen the NPP, and which does not really involve consenting, and 2) our usual understanding of competent, informed and voluntary consent - an ongoing process.

In my opinion, for therapists, seeing voluntary clients, a written signature on the HIPAA Consent form is all that should be done and this is simply pro forma. Consent to treatment must still be voluntary, competent, and informed to be legal and ethical and your Practice Brochure or similar handouts, with a signature, will accomplish these goals.

Procedures

- You do not actually need to obtain consent before beginning to use a client's PHI. You *may* do so but it is not required. You do not need to delay treatment until you have obtained the consent. This rule is designed so that you can use referral information (which is PHI) to contact a client and set up appointment, ask some questions in order to refer them on, or similar clinical activities.
- You might consider mailing your NPP and Consent form to the client before the initial interview as part of your Client Introductory Package (along with your Practice Brochure and any other materials such as problem checklists or goals lists).
- Only treating CEs and not health plans (insurers, managed care organizations, etc.) are required to obtain the signed Consent form.
- If you are treating a family you do not need a Consent from all the dependents who might be in treatment but only the named insured of the policy. This should be modified in light of family dynamics and structure and local laws.

Q: What if claimant seems to not be competent to consent? For example, someone referred for a neuropsychological evaluation with a history of severe head injury or for an intellectual evaluation with a history of IQs below 70.

A1:   People are presumed to be competent until they are adjudicated incompetent. However, this might conflict with your clinical judgment and professional ethics so

A2:   Instead, seek consent from a suitable personal representative of the client. Ask the referrer or family if there is a guardian or legal representative.

A3:   HIPAA allows you to make a good faith effort to get consent and treat the client even if you have not gotten consent.

A4:   It also allows you to presume consent using your professional judgment.

OCR has developed three excellent Fact Sheets you could use for patient education on privacy rights and protection. Two are very colorful and all three are at <http://www.hhs.gov/ocr/generalinfo.html>. Accessed Oct. 12, 2005.

- Authorizations are more specific as to the information to be used or disclosed, to whom, and for what purposes. However, with an authorization, the entire medical record *can* be disclosed.
- If a client does not agree to an Authorization, a CE may not refuse to treat or cover them - **services cannot be conditioned on an Authorization.** This is an important point. Clinically we want to get old records and should. However, HIPAA does not take this into account. HIPAA was designed to protect PHI by restricting its availability. As a result of HIPAA, insurers cannot compel release of more information than is covered by the Consent when they question benefits or payments. However, an insurer can require an Authorization and release of more information for purposes of enrollment. The client can refuse but may not get the insurance coverage.
- Authorizations expire.
- A special Authorization is needed to release Psychotherapy Notes

More on Authorizations is in section 440.

Q: Might I ever need to get both?
A: Yes, sometimes. It will depend on what you intend to do with the PHI. If you have different uses for the information you may need both. If you need it for TPO you need the Consent but if you also intend to disclose the information to an insurer for an application for life insurance, or to treat the client in a research project you will need an Authorization as well.

- If you receive both an Authorization and a Consent and they are in conflict (usually because the Authorization allows less information to be used and disclosed) you should go by the terms of the Authorization and attempt to resolve the issue as guided by § 164.506(e).

> **Q: What about persons at risk of contracting or spreading a disease.**
> **A:**   A covered entity may disclose protected health information to a person who is at risk of contracting or spreading a disease or condition if other law authorizes the covered entity to notify such individuals as necessary to carry out public health interventions or investigations. For example, a covered health care provider may disclose protected health information as needed to notify a person that (s)he has been exposed to a communicable disease if the covered entity is legally authorized to do so to prevent or control the spread of the disease. See 45 CFR 164.512(b)(1)(iv). *OCR Guidance Explaining Significant Aspects of the Privacy Rule - December 4, 2002*

Again, state laws differ but are likely to take precedence because they are more restrictive of disclosure in these circumstances.

430   Consent forms

After clients have been notified of their rights (though reading or having the NPP or having it read or explained to them) a formal acknowledgment of having been informed of your procedures and their rights is sought. In the regulations this is accomplished by signing what is called a Consent but it is not a consent to treatment or an authorization to having one's PHI used or disclosed. It is simply an indication that one has been exposed to the provider's rules for handling PHI. It would more properly be called an assent or acknowledgment. No more is required because, in the logic of DHHS, by seeking treatment, consent to the sharing of information is implied. I believe that is indeed likely that most people expect that their PHI will be easily shared with all those who need to know it to provide treatment to them. HIPAA incorporates this commonsensical view.

- Because clients have to read the current version of you NPP, there is a space on the Consent to indicate what version (by date) of the NPP they have perused.
- The Consent must be visually and organizationally separate from the NPP. Putting it on a separate page should do. And it must be signed and dated separately from any other consents such as for assignment of benefits, an Authorization for participation in a research study, your own Information for Clients brochure, or a more traditional Release/Request for Records, any of which might accompany it.
- You must retain this Consent for six years from the last date it was in effect - the end of treatment.

A sample Consent form

In the next section is a Consent form which I have written in plain language and which you can and should tailor. Note that is must not be a continuous part of the NPP. Put it on a separate page.

On the form, **the fourth paragraph, which is in boldface,** may cause some patients to hesitate or even refuse; they do not want so little control over their information, especially when they do not yet know what information you will be collecting. It may be best to draw every client's attention to this paragraph and explain how you always use an Authorization to release information and do not rely on this Consent so that he or she will know exactly what will be release and to whom.

The regulations

§ 164.506(c) of the HIPAA regulations specifies all the required contents a privacy consent. The form in the next section of this book incorporates all of these.

(c) Implementation specifications: content requirements. A consent under this section must be **in plain language** and:
   (1) Inform the individual that **protected health information may be used and disclosed** to carry out treatment, payment, or health care operations;
   (2) Refer the individual to the **notice** required by § 164.520 for a more complete description of such uses and disclosures and state that the individual has the right to review the notice prior to signing the consent;
   (3) If the covered entity has reserved the **right to change its privacy practices** that are described in the notice in accordance with § 164.520(b)(1)(v)(C), state that the terms of its notice may change and describe how the individual may obtain a revised notice;
   (4) State that:
      (i) The individual has the right to request that the covered entity **restrict** how protected health information is used or disclosed to carry out treatment, payment, or

health care operations;

       (ii) The covered entity is **not required to agree to requested restrictions**; and

       (iii) If the covered entity agrees to a requested restriction, the restriction is binding on the covered entity;

    (5) State that the individual has the right to **revoke the consent** in writing, except to the extent that the covered entity has taken action in reliance thereon; and

       (6) Be **signed by the individual and dated. (Boldface added)**

Other sample Consent forms

North Carolina Healthcare Information and Communications Alliance has a sample form online at <www.nchica.org/HIPAAResources/Samples/EVpDocuments.htm> October 5, 2002.

The Ohio Department of Mental Health has a form, accurately titled and Acknowledgement, and policies on the Internet at: <http://www.mh.state.oh.us/legislation/hipaa/hipaa.manual.html> September, 20, 2005. These combine in- and outpatient settings consents.

A consent to use an **interpreter** is available in English and Spanish at <http://library.ahima.org/xpedio/groups/public/documents/ahima/pub_bok1_009849.html> Sept. 26, 2005.
However, in response to a question (Answer ID 760 at < ttp://questions.cms.hhs.gov/cgi-bin/cmshhs.cfg/php/enduser/std_alp.php?p_lva=&p_li=&p_page=1&p_cat_lvl1=2&p_cat_lvl2=25>) HHS indicated that generally an authorization is not necessary as the interaction is an healthcare Operation. Sometimes interpreters are family and so permission should be sought but can be inferred by the client's continuing cooperation. Sometimes interpreters are business associates and those rules apply (see section 270). The same rules apply to **Telephone Relay Services (TRS)** who translate for the deaf.

A consent form in Spanish is available at <http://www.mda-ltd.com/privacy_notice1.htm> Sept. 30, 2005.

A Google search, at <www.google.com> will uncover dozens of NPPs to meet your needs because they must be on the provider's websites. You should presume that they are all copyrighted and behave ethically and legally.

431   ## Consent to use and disclose your health information

(On your letterhead)

Consent to use and disclose your health information

This form is an agreement between you, _____ and me/us _____. When we use the word you below, it can mean you, your child, a relative, or other person if you have written his or her name here _____ .

When we examine, test, diagnose, treat, or refer you we will be collecting what the law calls Protected Healthcare Information (PHI) about you. We need to use this information here to decide on what treatment is best for you and to provide any treatment to you. We may also share this information with others who provide treatment to you or need it to arrange payment for your treatment or for other business or government functions.

By signing this form you are agreeing to let us use your information here and send it to others. The Notice of Privacy Practices explains in more detail your rights and how we can use and share your information. Please read this before you sign this Consent form.

If you do not sign this consent form agreeing to what is in our Notice of Privacy Practices we cannot treat you.

In the future we may change how we use and share your information and so may change our Notice of Privacy Practices. If we do change it, you can get a copy from our Web Site, www._____, or by calling us at _____, or from our privacy officer.

If you are concerned about some of your information, you have the right to ask us to not use or share some of your information for treatment, payment or administrative purposes. You will have to tell us what you want in writing. Although we will try to respect your wishes, we are not required to agree to these limitations. However, if we do agree, we promise to do as you asked.

After you have signed this consent, you have the right to revoke it (by writing a letter to our Privacy Officer telling us you no longer consent) and we will comply with your wishes about using or sharing your information from that time on but we may already have used or shared some of your information and cannot change that.

_____   _____
Signature of client or his or her personal representative   Date

_____   _____
Printed name of client or personal representative   Relationship to the client

_____
Description of personal representative's authority

_____
Signature of authorized representative of this office or practice

Date of NPP _____   ❑ Copy give to the client/parent/personal representative.

440   **About Authorizations**

We are used to referring to these forms as "Consent to ..." or "Releases of..." or "Requests for Records," but HIPAA creates "Consents" and "Authorizations" for "Use and/or Disclosure" of "Personal Healthcare Information" all of which are both different labels and conceptually different. Basically, a Consent is needed for using and disclosing (releasing, sharing) of PHI for TPO (which is 95% of our releases and requests) while an Authorization is needed for most other uses and disclosures.

Q: When do I need to get an Authorization signed?
A1:   Simple answer: When what you want to do is not covered by the rules for a Consent and the good news is that this ought to be rather rare. Consents cover use and disclosure for TPO, public health and national security, law enforcement, and to the Secretary of DHHS for enforcement.
A2:   The full answer has to address the four kinds of specified Authorizations and the list of other potential uses.

Four variations on the theme of Authorizations

HIPAA indicates that somewhat different Authorizations exist. There are five types but in practice only three forms are needed and one covers 95% of the needs for a release:

1. For internal use and disclosure of PHI by a CE to itself. The Standard format (section 450) can be slightly amended to serve this purpose.
2. For external use and disclosure. This is for sending for or receiving PHI from another CE. The Standard format (section 450) is designed for this common purpose.
3. For use of PHI in research that includes treatment of the individual. See section 470.
4. For the release of psychotherapy notes. See section 480

Section 441 is a chart comparing the contents of each type. The next several sections of this book contain more detailed discussions of each of these and sample forms.

Other situations requiring an Authorization

Besides the situations above, **Authorizations are needed for all other uses and disclosures.** HIPAA suggests these unfamiliar possibilities:
*   "Use for marketing of health and non-health related items and services by the CE."
*   Use and disclosure "for use in marketing life or casualty insurance or banking services." See section 930 of this book
*   "Disclosure by sale, rental or barter."
*   "Use or disclosure for fund-raising." See section 920.
*   "Disclosure to an employer for use in employment determinations" (presumably not prejudicial hiring but who knows).

All of these are explained further in this book but here are some more likely situations encountered by clinicians:
*   When a client asks for copies of his or her child's records. HIPAA is not clear about which form to use so I recommend using the Standard Authorization form.
*   Disclosures to an insurer for its deciding on a person's eligibility for insurance (underwriting). This applies for life and disability insurance but not health insurance.
*   You are requesting records from another provider. This would be covered by the initial signed consent but since, in most cases, state laws are more protective, an Authorization will be required. If your local laws are less stringent and HIPAA applies

you can use the Standard Authorization (in section 460). Alternately, there are some elements that you might simply add to your current request for records form.

- You are treating a client as part of a research project. See section 470.
- Sharing Psychotherapy Notes. Again, this should be very rare because of the contents of these Notes. See sections 310 and 480.

Based on § 164.508 of the regulations we first will review the required contents of all Authorizations, clarify some new concepts such as non-conditioning, revoking, and compounding, and your ability to rely on Authorizations you obtained before HIPAA. The following sections will explain more about each of the types of Authorization and will offer samples of the language you can incorporate into your current release/request for records forms. Finally, a sample form for each kind of Authorization will be offered.

For more on releasing and forms to use in your practice to release and request information, see Zuckerman (2003).

Checklist for the required contents of all Authorizations

All HIPAA-compliant Authorizations must contain these core elements [as described at § 164.508(c)]. Boldface has been added.

- ❏ "A description of the **information** to be used or disclosed that identifies the information in a specific and meaningful fashion."
- ❏ "The name or other specific identification of the **person**(s) authorized to make the requested use or disclosure."
- ❏ "The name or other specific identification of the **person(s) to whom** the covered entity will make the use or disclosure."
- ❏ "An **expiration date** or an expiration event that relates to the individual or the purpose of the use or disclosure"
- ❏ "A statement of the individual's **right to revoke** the authorization in writing and the exceptions to the right to revoke, together with a description of how the individual may revoke the authorization."
- ❏ "A statement that information used or disclosed pursuant to the authorization may be subject to **redisclosure** by the recipient and no longer be protected by this rule."
- ❏ "The **signature** of the individual and date (or), if the authorization is signed by a personal representative of the individual, a description of the representative's authority to act for the individual."
- ❏ "The authorization is written in **plain** language."

You are specifically allowed to add other elements or information to any of the Authorizations as long as these are not inconsistent with the regulations about authorizations in section 164.508. Therefore **you can use your current forms and simply add any elements from this list and the Standard Authorization which are needed.**

Checklist for elements which make a Authorization defective
[From § 164.508 (b)]

- ❏ "The expiration date has passed or the expiration event is known by the covered entity to have occurred."
- ❏ The authorization is missing a core element or elements specific to any of the kinds of authorizations.
- ❏ "The authorization is known by the covered entity to have been revoked."
- ❏ The authorization is improperly combined with other authorizations (see below).
- ❏ "Any material information in the authorization is known by the covered entity to be false."

Revoking an Authorization

HIPAA [§ 164.508(b)(5)] supports current practice in stating that a client may, at any time, in writing, revoke a previously agreed to release form, and it will apply to all future releases but is not retroactive. See 490 for a form for this revocation. The rule does not require extensive forwarding of this revocation to those who have received the information based on the previous Authorization and so unfortunately they may act on the original Authorization and re-disclose PHI unless you make the effort to inform others.

Combining Authorizations

The rules here are complex but will almost never apply to therapists.
1. An authorization for use and disclosure of PHI collected during research involving treatment may be combine only with:
- A consent to participate in that research.
- A Consent to use or disclose PHI for TPO
- An NPP

2. "An authorization under this section, other than an authorization for a use or disclosure of   psychotherapy notes may be combined with any other such authorization under this section, except when a covered entity has conditioned the provision of treatment, payment, enrollment in the health plan, or eligibility for benefits under paragraph (b)(4) of this section on the provision of one of the authorizations." [§ 164.508(b)(3)(iii)

3. An Authorization for psychotherapy notes may be combined only with another Authorization for psychotherapy notes.

Documentation of Authorizations

HIPAA [§164.508(b)(6) and §164.530(j)] requires you to keep and provide a copy to the client of all Authorizations, in paper or electronic form, for six years from the last time it was in effect.

Using "old" Authorizations

The releases (non-HIPAA records release and request forms) you have obtained from clients can still be depended upon to guide use and disclosure of PHI after your practice becomes HIPAA-compliant as long as you follow precisely what they permitted you to do. The rules at § 164.532 Transition Provisions are very detailed. Essentially, you must do what you said you would do in the original release and not do anything you did not say you would do (and so did not get consent for). For example, you may not make any other disclosures than those agreed to in the release.

Some suggested phrasings to add to your current Authorization Form so that it includes the core HIPAA contents for all authorizations

Your present release form no doubt already indicates the information to be released, and the persons or organizations releasing it and receiving it. Here are some potential additions or clarifications.

Use and disclosure

In some circumstances it may be worthwhile to indicate separately the two functions and so you could modify your form this way.

> I hereby authorize _____to (check those that apply):
> ❏   use the following protected health information, and/or
> ❏   disclose the following protected health information to _____.

Specifying the information

HIPAA does not indicate how the information is to be specified so you might consider offering many possibilities on your form such as by date(s) of service, type of service provided, level of detail to be released, origin of information, etc.

Expiration

Because HIPAA allows either a time or event to be used as the expiration point you might add this:

> I understand and agree that this Authorization will be valid and in effect until _____
> [Enter a date or event upon which this Authorization expires.] unless I chose to revoke (cancel) it. I understand that after that date or event, no more of this information can be used or released to the person or organization unless I sign a new Authorization like this one.

HIPAA offers 90/180 days but if your state law requires a shorter period of time, since that would be more protective of client privacy, it would take precedence over HIPAA. Also, recall that Consents (but not Authorizations) do not expire and so appear to be valid at least for the present "episode of treatment" if not forever.

Revocation

> I understand that I can revoke or cancel this authorization at any time by sending a letter to the Privacy Officer of the organization(s) listed above and which is to supply this information. If I do this, it will prevent any releases after the date it is received but can not change the fact that some information was sent or shared before that date.

Redisclosure

This is a <u>BIG CHANGE</u> and appears to be a huge hole in the safeguards of privacy where HIPAA applies. Most state laws are more protective but may be silent on this issue, so do your own preemption analysis (see section 240) for redisclosure. Also, some federal laws limit or prohibit redisclosure so check to see if those apply to your kind of work.

If Psychotherapy Notes or any other PHI is disclosed to non-covered entities, HIPAA does not apply and so it does not prohibit further re-disclosure by them without authorization. **This is a serious breach in the privacy protections.**

> I understand that if the person or organization that receives my information (described above) is not a health care provider or health

insurer the information may no longer protected by federal privacy regulations.

You might reinforce this by adding "... and can be legally redisclosed or ... shared with others without your consent."

Signatures

HIPAA asks that if a substitute signature is used, the basis for the personal representative's authority be explained.

_____   _____
Signature of client or his or her personal representative   Date

_____   _____
Printed name of client or personal representative Relationship to the client

_____
Description of personal representative's authority

I have seen nothing to indicate what wordings would be most appropriate for the last line.

Completeness

This just seems to be a good addition for raising the confidence of the client.

This form was completely filled in before I signed it.

Additional resources

Sample versions of Authorization forms as well as many others may be found at these sites:
*   North Carolina Healthcare Information and Communications Alliance, Inc. <http://www.nchica.org/HIPAAResources/Samples/OtherDocuments.htm> Accessed Sept. 17, 2005.
*   Physicians Practice Accessed Oct, 17, 2005. <http://www.physicianspractice.com./index.cfm?fuseaction=tools.main>

The regulations

§164.508 Uses and disclosures for which an authorization is required.
(c) Implementation specifications: core elements and requirements.
   (1) Core elements. A valid authorization under this section must contain at least the following elements:
      (i) A description of the information to be used or disclosed that identifies the information in a specific and meaningful fashion;
      (ii) The name or other specific identification of the person(s), or class of persons, authorized to make the requested use or disclosure;
      (iii) The name or other specific identification of the person(s), or class of persons, to whom the covered entity may make the requested use or disclosure;
      (iv) An expiration date or an expiration event that relates to the individual or the purpose of the use or disclosure;
      (v) A statement of the individual's right to revoke the authorization in writing and

the exceptions to the right to revoke, together with a description of how the individual may revoke the authorization;

(vi) A statement that information used or disclosed pursuant to the authorization may be subject to redisclosure by the recipient and no longer be protected by this rule;

(vii) Signature of the individual and date; and

(viii) If the authorization is signed by a personal representative of the individual, a description of such representative's authority to act for the individual.

(2) Plain language requirement. The authorization must be written in plain language.

441 Comparison of the contents of the Authorization forms

This comparison included the core elements of any authorization as specified by HIPAA and the contents of the four sorts of Authorizations. There are only three actual forms: Standard, Research and for Psychotherapy Notes needed.

Contents	Uses/Types				
	Core	Internal	External[45]	Research	Psycho-Notes
Description of the PHI	•	•	•	•	•[46]
Releaser	•	•	•	•	•
Receiver	•	•	•	•	•
Expiration	•	•	•	•	•
Revocation	•	•	•	•	•
Redisclosure	•	•	•	•	•
Signature	•	•	•	•	•
Plain language	•	•	•	•	•
Non-conditioning		•	•[47]		•
Purpose(s)		•	•	•	•
Inspect and copy PHI		•		•	•
Can refuse to sign		•	•	•	•
Copy of Authorization given to client	•	•	•	•	
Disclosure of payment		•		•	
How PHI will be used in TPO				•	
Which PHI *not* being used				•	
Reference to NPP and Consent				•	
Reference in § 164.508	(c)	(d)	(e)	(f)	(a)(2)

---

[45] I recommend the use of this version when a client asks for his or her own or child's records.

[46] Use the Standard form and indicate "psychotherapy notes" under the information to be released.

[47] The non-conditioning does not extend to *payment*, only to *treatment* [§164.508(b)(4)(iii)]. It also does not extend to PHI created solely for disclosure to a third party [§ 164.508(b)(4)(iv)] as in doing an evaluation as a consultant.

450   The Standard Authorization

Although described as an internal authorization in the HIPAA regulations I call this the **Standard Authorization**. It is for our usual purposes of requesting and releasing records to others. With slight modifications it meets the needs of **both the internal and external authorization**. See section 460 for more on External Authorizations.

For simplicity in describing the contents of the three actual Authorization forms I will use this Standard Authorization, as the basic form and treat the others as successively modifying this foundation. This is the way the regs proceed.

When might you need an Internal Authorization?

If you are disclosing PHI for other than TPO you need an Authorization and if this PHI is to be used in your own organization, you need to use a internal Authorization. I am not clear about what such uses might be in a small therapy practice but when you investigate how information flows in your practice (by doing your gap analysis) you will see when you might need this form.

Checklist for the additional required contents of the Standard Authorization

The Standard Authorization must include the core elements of an authorization (see section 440) and add the following (boldface added). Each of these is explicated below

- ❑ "A description of **each purpose** of the requested use or disclosure." [Note that this is not required when the PHI is being released to the client but the wording does not have to be removed.]
- ❑ "A statement that the individual may **inspect or copy** the protected health information to   be used or disclosed ...."
- ❑ "A statement that the individual may ... **refuse** to sign the authorization."
- ❑ You (the CE) "**will not condition** treatment, payment, enrollment in the health plan, or eligibility for benefits on the individual's providing authorization for the   requested use or disclosure." See below for clarification.
- ❑ You (the CE) will "provide the individual with a **copy of the signed authorization**."
- ❑ If it is true, the authorization must say that **payment will be made to you**, directly or indirectly, for your disclosing or using the PHI.

Although you probably skipped reading the paragraph above, the third and fourth elements are new to therapists and should be added to the forms we now used to request records.

The "Conditioning" of Authorizations

The principle is that clients should not have to reveal more than basic information as a condition of receiving treatment or insurance. Treatment should not depend or be conditioned on greater revelations. Prohibiting conditioning is designed to prevent fishing expeditions by health insurers and forced exposure of irrelevant personal information.

> "In addition to the general prohibition on conditioning treatment and payment, covered entities are also prohibited (with certain exceptions described below) from conditioning eligibility for benefits or enrollment in a health plan on obtaining an authorization. This prohibition extends

to all authorizations ...(and) is intended to prevent covered entities from coercing individuals into signing an authorization for a use or disclosure that is not necessary to carry out the primary services that the covered entity provides." A. Federal Register /Vol. 65, No. 250 /Thursday, December 28, 2000 /Rules and Regulations p82516

There **are two exceptions** to the prohibiting of conditioning:

❑ When the treatment is for **research** purposes. This is designed so that a researcher can obtain, use and share additional information of relevance to the project.

❑ **When the services are only to create PHI for disclosure to a third party.** This is so that clients can be sent to consulting evaluators to generate PHI for eligibility decision for disability, life, or health insurance. HIPAA says that if the client refuses to sign an Authorization you can deny only those specific services and not treatment or payment.

The standard form includes language about non-conditioning.

Purpose of the use or disclosure

Surprisingly HIPAA does *not* make telling the client the purpose of the Authorization one of the *core* elements but it is nevertheless required for all Authorization forms. Although the purpose statement is not required when the PHI is being released to the client but it is not worth removing the wording from the form for this purpose..

Inspect or copy PHI

Clients have the right to inspect and/or receive a copy the PHI to be used or disclosed. This is a consistent theme of HIPAA and is one of its major guarantees supporting privacy. This is a **BIG CHANGE.**

> I understand that I have the right to look at and have a copy of my protected health information.

Note: If you are modifying the Standard Authorization for use as an Internal Authorization, this element is not required but again it may not be worth removing.

Client's copy

> I understand that I will get a copy of this Authorization form, after I sign it. Copy given to ❑ client or ❑ legal representative.

Payments to you

If you will be paid or receive any kind of compensation, directly or indirectly, for using or disclosing the client's information you have to tell the client. While this rarely applies to therapists, it is a major step toward openness for medical settings. Note: Again, this statement is not required if the disclosure is requested by the client.

> I understand that you/this practice/clinic/etc. will receive compensation for the use or disclosure of my health information The arrangement has been explained to me and I understand and accept it.

The Standard Authorization Form

The form in the next section is likely to need modification for your setting and needs.

Under section 3a you may not be able to use it to get substance abuse treatment records, and you may want to remove some of the options for records to save space

The regulations

§164.508 Uses and disclosures for which an authorization is required.

(d) Implementation specifications: **authorizations requested by a covered entity for its own uses and disclosures**. If an authorization is requested by a covered entity for its own use or disclosure of protected health information that it maintains, the covered entity must comply with the following requirements.

    (1) Required elements. The authorization for the uses or disclosures described in this paragraph must, in addition to meeting the requirements of paragraph (c) of this section, contain the following elements:

        (i) For any authorization to which the prohibition on conditioning in paragraph (b)(4) of this section applies, a statement that the covered entity will not condition treatment, payment, enrollment in the health plan, or eligibility for benefits on the individual's providing authorization for the requested use or disclosure;

        (ii) A description of each purpose of the requested use or disclosure;

        (iii) A statement that the individual may:

            (A) Inspect or copy the protected health information to be used or disclosed as provided in § 164.524; and

            (B) Refuse to sign the authorization; and

        (iv) If use or disclosure of the requested information will result in direct or indirect remuneration to the covered entity from a third party, a statement that such remuneration will result.

    (2) Copy to the individual. A covered entity must provide the individual with a copy of the signed authorization.

451   The Standard Authorization form

(On your letterhead)

Authorization to use and disclose protected health information

1. I am completing this form to allow the use and sharing of protected health information about
Printed name: _____ Date of Birth: _____

2. I authorize this person or organization _____

_____

_____

3a. To use or disclose the following information:
   ❑ Inpatient or outpatient treatment records for physical and or psychological, psychiatric, or emotional illness.
   ❑ Admission and discharge summaries
   ❑ Psychological or psychiatric evaluation(s), reports, assessments, treatment notes, summaries, or other documents with diagnoses, prognoses, recommendations, or testing records, and behavioral observations or checklists completed by any staff member or the patient, or similar documents.
   ❑ Treatment, recovery, rehabilitation, aftercare plans and other similar plans.
   ❑ Social, family, educational, and vocational histories
   ❑ Social work assessments, occupational therapy and vocational reports and evaluations.
   ❑ Progress, nursing, case or similar notes.
   ❑ Evaluations and reports of consultants.
   ❑ Information about how the patient's condition(s) affects or has affected his or her ability to work, and to complete tasks or activities of daily living.
   ❑ Billing records.
   ❑ Academic and educational records, including achievement and other tests' results, reports of teachers' observations, and all other school or special education documents.
   ❑ HIV-related information and drug and alcohol information contained in these records will be released under this authorization unless indicated here – ❑ Do not release these.
   ❑ Complete copy of the medical record.
   ❑ Other: _____

3b. Dates of care included: From _____ to _____ and
   From _____ to _____ and
   From _____ to _____

4. To this person or organization _____

_____

_____

5. The information will be used/disclosed for the following purposes: _____

_____

_____

6. I understand and agree that this Authorization will be valid and in effect until _____ [Enter a date or event upon which this Authorization expires.] I understand that after that date or event, no more of this information can be used or released to the person or organization unless I sign a new Authorization like this one.

7. I understand that I can revoke or cancel this authorization at any time by sending a letter to the Privacy Officer of the organization listed above and which is to supply this information. If I do this, it will prevent any disclosures after the date it is received but can not change the fact that some information may have been sent or shared before that date.

8. I understand that I do not have to sign this authorization and that my refusal to sign will not affect my abilities to obtain treatment from the professional or facility listed at number 2, above, nor will it affect my eligibility for benefits.

9. I understand that I may inspect and have a copy the health information described in this authorization. There may be a cost for this copy or other services. ❏ Does not apply

10. I understand that if the person or entity that receives the information is not a health care provider or health plan covered by federal privacy regulations, the information described above may be redisclosed and no longer protected by those regulations.

11. I understand that the professional or facility listed in number 2, above, will receive compensation for the use or disclosure of my health information The arrangement has been explained to me and I understand and accept it. ❏ Does not apply

12. I affirm that everything in this form that was not clear to me has been explained and I believe I now understand all of it.

_____   _____
13. Signature of client or his or her personal representative   Date

_____   _____
Printed name of client or personal representative   Relationship to the client

_____
Description of personal representative's authority

14. ❏   I acknowledge that I received a copy of this completed form

15. I, a mental health professional, have discussed the issues above with the client and/or his personal representative. My observations of his or her behavior and responses give me no reason to believe that this person is not fully competent to give informed and willing consent

_____   _____   _____
Signature of professional   Printed name of professional   Date

460   The External Authorization

For the discussion of HIPAA I call this an External Authorization to distinguish it from an Authorization created by a CE to use or disclosure of PHI *within* the CE's own organization which I call an Internal Authorization (see section 450 for more) and from the Standard Authorization.

Required contents

This External Authorization must contain all of the core elements [from § 164.508(c)] (section 440) and elements of the Internal Authorization [from § 164.598(d)] (see section 450) but *removes* these two elements form that Standard form.
- Paragraph 11 on the disclosure of payment for releasing information.
- Paragraph 9 on the right to inspect and copy PHI which is the subject of the Authorization.

You can create the External Authorization by removing paragraphs numbered 9 and 11 from the Standard form, use the included checkboxes, or, because it is simpler, leave them in and use the Standard form for both "internal" and "external" authorization.

The Regulations

§164.508 Uses and disclosures for which an authorization is required.

(e) Implementation specifications: **authorizations requested by a covered entity for disclosures by others.** If an authorization is requested by a covered entity for another covered entity to disclose protected health information to the covered entity requesting the authorization to carry out treatment, payment, or health care operations, the covered entity requesting the authorization must comply with the following requirements.
    (1) Required elements. The authorization for the disclosures described in this paragraph must, in addition to meeting the requirements of paragraph (c) of this section, contain the following elements:
        (i) A description of each purpose of the requested disclosure;
        (ii) Except for an authorization on which payment may be conditioned under paragraph (b)(4)(iii) of this section, a statement that the covered entity will not condition treatment, payment, enrollment in the health plan, or eligibility for benefits on the individual's providing authorization for the requested use or disclosure; and
        (iii) A statement that the individual may refuse to sign the authorization.
    (2) Copy to the individual. A covered entity must provide the individual with a copy of the signed authorization.

470   Authorizations for a research participant

This is not the same as the common informed consent for research participation which is still needed for informed and voluntary consent. This is designed to address the situation in which someone receives treatment (and so creates PHI) as part of being a participant in a research project and so becomes a patient as well as a "participant" ("subject" is considered paternalistic and passive).

The good news is that therapists should only very rarely need to obtain this Research Authorization (my term). Because of the complexity of the issues, interactions with other rules, and the rarity of practitioners' need for such and authorization, I have not included a form. However, below I have presented locations at which you may find more information and brief discussions of some of the HIPAA issues.

General points

- HIPAA pertains only to research projects which include providing treatment to a client; all other research is not subject to HIPAA.
- A Research Authorization is *not* required if any of these three commonly occurring **exceptions** exist [§ 164.512(i)]:
  - ❏ A waiver of the need for an Authorization has been given by an Institutional Review Board (IRB) or a Privacy Board.
  - ❏ The PHI is sought only to prepare a research proposal or other similar purpose. This is designed, in part, to cover the soliciting of clients to participate in a research project based on some of their PHI to identify them as appropriate and yet protect this activity from the limitations on using PHI in marketing.
  - ❏ "The use or disclosure is sought is solely for research on the protected health information of decedents."
- Usually a Consent is used to allow use and disclosure of PHI for TPO. However, when the treatment occurs as part of a research project, the required Authorization must explain that the PHI will be used for TPO.

The "Conditioning" of Authorizations

One of the privacy principles in HIPAA is that clients need not reveal more than the absolutely essential and relevant information as a condition of receiving treatment or insurance payments (this is dealt with by the NPP and the Consent). However, treatment received as a part of participating in a research project is an exception to non-conditioning. This is reasonable as the client will receive services and the researcher/treater needs to be obtain and share information about the participant beyond that usually obtained in treatment to accomplish the goals of the research. Clients can also be required to release PHI acquired by a CE before the research study as well as that collected during the study.

Disclosing information

If, because of the nature of the treatment services you will be providing, you will need to provide an NPP and get a Consent signed, you need to indicate that in this Authorization.

The minimum necessary standard does not apply to your disclosures when the client is involved in a research project because all uses and disclosures made under an Authorization are exempt from this standard.

Self-imposed limits on disclosure

You may decide to not make some disclosures which HIPAA allows. If you do so you are to tell the client that you will not use their information for these purposes. They include disclosures (e.g. to family members), requirements to provide information for public health activities, law enforcement and judicial and administrative activities, and information concerning victims of abuse, etc. Alternately, you can describe the information you do not intend to disclose by its contents. See §§ 164.510 and 164.512

Time limits

Although an Authorization has to have time or event limits, the Research Authorization is more like a Consent because it covers the client's treatment. Therefore, the August 2002 changes allow the use of "end of the research study" or even the word "none" for an expiration date.

Combining forms

The regs allow you to combine this Research Authorization with what we would call an "informed consent to participate in the research" form, the Consent to use and disclose PHI for TPO, and/or the NPP.

Resources

HHS' National Institute of Health published *Protecting Personal Health Information in Research: Understanding the HIPAA Privacy Rule* describing how the Privacy Rule applies to research. See http://privacyruleandresearch.nih.gov/pr_02.asp (Revised July 13, 2004) See also Privacy Guidance in *Authorizations for Research and Institutional Review Boards* at http://www.hhs.gov/ocr/hipaa/privguideresearch.pdf. Both accessed Oct. 12, 2005.

The regulations

The regulations are extensive and complex, and interact with many other federal rules so I advise consultation before using just a HIPAA-compliant Authorization. For those who need to know, here are the relevant sections of the HIPAA regulations.

1. §164.508 Uses and disclosures for which an authorization is required.

2. § 164.512 Uses and disclosures for which consent, an authorization, or opportunity to agree or object is not required.

3. There is much more in the Secretary's response to comments. See especially the Standards for Privacy of Individually Identifiable Health Information. I. Section 164.528-- Accounting of Disclosures of Protected Health Information. Final Modifications. Available at <http://www.hipaadvisory.com/regs/finalprivacymod/acct.htm> Accessed Oct. 1, 2005.

480   Authorization to disclose psychotherapy notes

See the section 310 for more on the nature of psychotherapy notes.

First, you do *not* need an Authorization if you will be using or disclosing the notes for only these activities:
- ❏ You created them and use them in your treatment of the client.
- ❏ They will be used or disclosed in training or supervising mental health students or professionals.
- ❏ To defend yourself when the client undertakes a legal action against you.
- ❏ You are *required* to use or disclose them for law enforcement purposes.
- ❏ You are *permitted* to use or disclose them as laws require or for oversight of you, or when needed by a coroner or medical examiner, or when they are needed to avert a serious threat to health or safety.

Second, the psychotherapy notes must:
- ❏ Have been kept separate from the client's regular medical records.
- ❏ Contain "the documentation or analysis of the contents of conversation during a private counseling session or a group, joint, or family counseling session."
- ❏ *Not* contain the information in the routine progress note (see section 310) or which is available elsewhere.

If the above are true you can simply use the Standard Authorization (section 450) and indicate that the information to be released is the psychotherapy notes. I have not provided a separate form.

Note: You are allowed but not required to disclose these notes to the client and no authorization is needed for this disclosure (because it is *your* choice, not the client's).

The regulations

§164.508(a) Uses and disclosures for which an authorization is required.

(2) Authorization required: **psychotherapy notes.** Notwithstanding any other provision of this subpart, other than transition provisions provided for in § 164.532, a covered entity must obtain an authorization for any use or disclosure of psychotherapy notes, except:
   (i) To carry out the following treatment, payment, or health care operations, consistent with consent requirements in § 164.506:
      (A) Use by originator of the psychotherapy notes for treatment;
      (B) Use or disclosure by the covered entity in training programs in which students, trainees, or practitioners in mental health learn under supervision to practice or improve their skills in group, joint, family, or individual counseling; or
      (C) Use or disclosure by the covered entity to defend a legal action or other proceeding brought by the individual; and
   (ii) A use or disclosure that is required by § 164.502(a)(2)(ii) or permitted by § 164.512(a); § 164.512(d) with respect to the oversight of the originator of the psychotherapy notes; § 164.512(g)(1); or § 164.512(j)(1)(i).

490   Form for revoking an authorization

All Authorizations can be revoked and so a form to do so can come in handy.

(On your letterhead or other identification)

Request to revoke an authorization for disclosure of protected health information

To _____   Re _____
          (clinician or entity)   or Case number _____

I hereby revoke and cancel the Authorization to Release/Disclose information from the

health care records described below which I made on _____ to allow the

professional or agency listed above to send records to _____

_____.

The information concerns:

Client's name _____ Date of birth _____

Address_____

and these dates:

from _____ to _____ and

from _____ to _____ and

from _____ to _____ .

Other ways of identifying the information of concern: _____

_____.

I understand that you may have already made disclosures based on my earlier
authorization and so these disclosures cannot be recovered or undone. I hereby release this
clinician/agency from any legal responsibility or liability for disclosing the information I
authorized previously. I also understand that some disclosures are required by law in
some cases and I cannot revoke their release.

_____   _____
Signature of client or his or her personal representative   Date

_____   _____
Printed name of client or personal representative   Relationship to the client

_____
Description of personal representative's authority

500   Disclosing or releasing PHI

To review, the 300 level sections of this book concerned creating PHI and notes, keeping records, and billing. Sections in 400 were about consent and authorization to use and release that PHI. Now we come to the actual steps of taking the information collected and disclosing/releasing it as consented to and authorized.

You may recall that *Consents are needed for use and disclosure of PHI for TPO and that all other uses and disclosures require an Authorization*. (This is too long for a movie title but do you think this has possibilities as a mantra?).

510   Agreements to disclose

HIPAA has fairly complex rules about what kind of agreement, if any is required for different kinds of disclosure. I hope this diagram will make understanding this easier:

Disclosing under HIPAA: Consents and Authorizations I

Requiring a Consent	Not requiring a Consent or Authorization		Requiring an Authorization
Mainly for TPO But see # 1 below	*Mandatory* 1. To client 2. To DHHS for monitoring your compliance with HIPAA	*Permitted*/optional See 2, b,1-12 below The main issues are Duty to Warn, and victims of abuse Situations	Disclosures to - a non-health insurer - of psychotherapy notes - all other situations See sections 420 and 440

Still fuzzy? How about the same information presented differently in this diagram? If you like it, you can photocopy the next page for referencing.

Disclosing under HIPAA: Consents and Authorizations II

The general rule is: Consent is all that is needed for TPO disclosures: everything else needs an Authorization. As you will see, this is not always accurate guidance. This is a bit simplified to omit very unusual situations.

These disclosures ...	Require a ...
For use and disclosure for TPO to other CE's: - other treaters - insurers (MCOs, health plans) - clearinghouses	Consent, unless • You are an indirect treatment provider (evaluating or treating as a consultant) • You can't get consent because of substantial communication barriers
To the client	Neither a Consent nor an Authorization
Of a child's records toa parent	Standard authorization form needed.
To the DHHS	Neither a Consent nor an Authorization
To an non-health insurer	Standard authorization form needed
To client's employer	**Neither a Consent nor an Authorization (really)**
To an employer for some (?) employment decisions	An Standard authorization
To Workers Compensation, Social Security Disability	Neither a Consent nor an Authorization. See section 560
For duty to warn - To client or police, family, etc. - For victims of abuse	Neither a Consent nor an Authorization Neither a Consent nor an Authorization
To law enforcement, public health officials, etc.	Neither a Consent nor an Authorization
Of Psychotherapy Notes	Special authorization needed
All other situations	An Authorization

The details

1. Disclosures requiring consent - Basically for any TPO (Treatment, Payment, and Health Care Operations), which is very broad. There are (as you might have expected) exceptions   to this. If any of these five are true, you don't need a consent

❑ When you are an **indirect treatment provider.** That is, you are treating the client under the orders of another CE or only seeing the client so you can report your findings or results to that CE. This may apply if you do testing and do not otherwise have a treatment relationship with the client.
❑ If client is an **inmate**.
❑ It is an **emergency** and you decide not to obtain consent.
❑ Treatment is required by law and **you tried but failed to obtain consent**
❑ "**Substantial barriers to communication**" have prevented you from obtaining consent

and in your judgment consent can be inferred (and you document this situation). This appears to have been designed to address the need for consent with clients who are aphasic, frontal-lobe damaged, intoxicated, speak no language you understand, etc.

2. **Disclosures not requiring consent** come in two flavors

   a. **Mandatory** (Required) Disclosures without Consent. The HIPAA regulations [§164.502(a)(2)] **require only two** disclosures without consent:
      1. To the individual client (in which case, consent is presumed).
      2. To the DHHS for monitoring and enforcing of the HIPAA regulations.

   b. **Permitted** (your option) disclosures without consent.
   Within certain guidelines found in the rule, providers **may** use and disclose information without client authorization for the following. This is a summary of the quite large and complex § 164.512 which should be consulted for clarification.
      1. Uses and disclosures required by law.
      2. Uses and disclosures for public health activities.
      3. **Disclosures about victims of abuse, neglect or domestic violence.**
      4. Uses and disclosures for health oversight activities.
      5. Disclosures for judicial and administrative proceedings.
      6. Disclosures for law enforcement purposes.
      7. Uses and disclosures about decedents (this concerns the identification of deceased persons, or the cause of death).
      8. Uses and disclosures for cadaveric organ, eye or tissue donation purposes.
      9. Uses and disclosures for research purposes. This is mainly to allow screening of clients information for possible inclusion in research projects. See section 470.
      10. **Uses and disclosures to avert a serious threat to health or safety.**
      11. Uses and disclosures for specialized government functions (national defense and security).
      12. Disclosures for **Workers Compensation** and **employers**. See section 560.

The boldfaced items above are the ones of most relevance to clinicians and each will have to be crosswalked with state law and ethical concerns. The most critical one is number 10 which interacts with both Duty to Warn laws and with ethics codes.

Conflicting consents or authorizations

The HIPAA regulations at 164.506(e) state that when you have both a HIPAA Consent or Authorization and a more restrictive authorization you **may** use the more restrictive one to guide what you disclose to whom. You can also resolve this conflict of consents by talking or writing to the client to determine their preference (and understanding) and perhaps getting a new Authorization.

520 Routine and non-routine disclosures

In my opinion, these distinctions are of little relevance to therapists in small practices. They appear to have been written into the law to simplify the routine and repeated normal disclosures used by large healthcare agencies and large health plans. However, because they are part of the law, they cannot be ignored, explanations are provided below, and the HIPAA Polices and Procedures Manual (in section 800) addresses them.

Overview

The Privacy Rule categorizes your disclosures into three types one a *use,* and two kinds of *disclosures* to others.

1. PHI you **use internally** to your practice. For example, both your billing person and a therapist covering for you when you are out of town need access to (different) PHI.

2. **Routine** disclosures which do not have to be individually reviewed. This is designed to simplify your deciding what to send to whom. For example, a standardized progress note (see section 312) to managed care organizations.

3. **Non-routine** disclosures which have to be reviewed as to whether they match criteria you have set for the what is the minimum necessary PHI to accomplish the task. This is certainly more vague and requires more effort.

Since you will have to understand them, let us look at these categories in more detail.

1. PHI you use internally to your practice.

This is the absolutely ordinary use of information by you and your staff for TPO. You discovered who needed which PHI when you did the gap analysis.

2. Routine disclosures of PHI

These are the ordinary exchanges of PHI between treaters and health insurers.

You *can* automatically release the specific information sought by an Authorization you receive from a CE because CEs are required to seek only the minimum necessary information when requesting PHI and you are allowed to rely on their judgment. This reliance on the requestor is permitted when the request is made by:
  a. A public official or agency for a disclosure permitted under § 164.512 of the rule.
  b. Another covered entity.
  c. A professional who is a workforce member or business associate of the covered entity holding the information.
  d. A researcher with appropriate documentation from an Institutional Review Board (IRB) or Privacy Board.

3. Non-routine disclosures

These will be quite rare but are critical. These disclosures have to be reviewed as to whether they match criteria you have set for what information is the minimum to accomplish the task of the recipient of the PHI. These criteria need to be balanced against each other. For example, if there is knowledge that the individual could be significantly harmed by a disclosure but the provider may not get reimbursed for the care, consider alternatives such as discussing other payment arrangements with the client.

Guidance in Handling Non-Routine Disclosures

In an article designed for larger operations, Amatayakul, et al, (2002) offer the ideas below as Examples of Criteria for Evaluating Non-Routine Disclosures. They could be adapted for inclusion in your policy manual but are offered here for your background understanding of the issues.

1. **Specificity of request:** If request is general, narrow down the disclosure to specific documents or periods of time that would fit the purpose of the request.

2. **Purpose/importance of request:** If there is a clear purpose, disclosures should relate to the purpose. If there is not a clear purpose, it may be necessary to ask for clarification and at the same time ask for what specific disclosures are sought.

3. **Impact to client:**
    a. Negatively in terms of privacy: Could the disclosure potentially harm the client, such as introduce discrimination?
    b. Positively in terms of client care: Would the disclosure help the client?

4. **Impact to covered entity:**
    a. Negatively in terms of compliance: Could the disclosure result in a wrongful disclosure lawsuit? Would, for example, a claim be denied because of failure to produce information?
    b. Positively in terms of ability to provide quality care, obtain reimbursement.

5. **Extent to which disclosure would extend number of individuals** or entities with access to PHI.

6. **Likelihood of re-disclosure.**

7. **Ability to achieve the same purpose** with de-identified information.

8. **Technology available to limit disclosure** of PHI.

9. **Cost of limiting disclosure** of PHI.

10. **Any other factors** believed relevant to the determination.

530 Releasing only the minimum necessary information

Whenever you or any CE uses or discloses PHI, it must make a reasonable effort not to use or disclose more than the minimum necessary PHI (MNPHI - my acronym) to accomplish the intended purpose. These "minimum necessary" standards apply both to your internal **use** of PHI and your external **disclosure** to others.

Why this regulation?

The regulation was a response to a perception that all of people's medical information was too easily accessible to those with no legitimate reason to acquire it.

> ... without the minimum necessary standard, covered entities may be tempted to disclose an entire medical record when only a few items of information are necessary, to avoid the administrative step of extracting or redacting information. *OCR Guidance Explaining Significant Aspects of the Privacy Rule - December 4, 2002*

Using the minimum necessary rule is not simple because

1. There is no definition of minimum necessary information.

> 2. "... the minimum necessary standard is intended to be consistent with, and *not override, professional judgment and standards,* and that covered entities must implement policies and procedures based on their own assessment of what protected health information is *reasonably necessary* for a particular purpose, given the characteristics of their business and their workforce." (Italics added). Ibid

But first, let us consider the rather spacious exceptions and qualifications

1. The minimum necessary requirement **does not apply to disclosures made to a provider for treatment,** to the client, to the Secretary of DHHS, or pursuant to law.

Note: the MNPHI does apply to disclosures for P & O, if not for the T. This is actually a rather nice protection from the wholesale distribution of one's PHI to those outside the helping professions.

2. If the client has signed an **Authorization, those disclosures are exempt for the MNPHI** requirements. The reasoning is that Authorizations specify the information to be disclosed and so a second judgment about what is needed is unnecessary. This exception includes authorizations CEs receive directly from life, disability, or casualty (e.g. auto) insurers pursuant to the client's application for or claim under an insurance policy and federal or state agencies, such as the Social Security Administration (for SSI or Disability) or its affiliated state agencies for benefits.

3. The regulations require CEs, professional members of your workforce, or those of a business associate of yours to **ask for only the MNPHI.** Therefore you are allowed to **trust the requester** of your records to ask for the minimum necessary information. That can certainly be a big exception. I cannot recommend this practice.

Determining the MNPHI

Q: How are covered entities expected to determine what is the minimum necessary information that can be used, disclosed, or requested for a particular purpose?
A: The HIPAA Privacy Rule requires a covered entity to make *reasonable efforts to limit use, disclosure of, and requests for protected health information to the minimum necessary to accomplish the intended purpose.* To allow covered entities the flexibility to address their unique circumstances, the Rule requires covered entities to make their own assessment of what protected health information is reasonably necessary for a particular purpose, given the characteristics of their business and workforce, and to implement policies and procedures accordingly. This is not an absolute standard and covered entities need not limit information uses or disclosures to those that are absolutely needed to serve the purpose. Rather, this is a reasonableness standard that calls for an approach consistent with the best practices and guidelines already used by many providers and plans today to limit the unnecessary sharing of medical information.

The minimum necessary standard requires covered entities to *evaluate their practices and enhance protections as needed to limit unnecessary or inappropriate access* to protected health information. It is intended to reflect and be consistent with, not override, professional judgment and standards. Therefore, it is expected that covered entities will utilize the input of prudent professionals involved in health care activities when developing policies and procedures that appropriately limit access to personal health information without sacrificing the quality of health care. (Italics added) *OCR Guidance Explaining Significant Aspects of the Privacy Rule - December 4, 2002*

So what do I, a therapist, have to do about this?

For a therapist, the MNPHI rule will rarely apply because:

1. Most of our disclosures are for treatment purposes and to other CEs and this is kind of disclosure is exempt.

2. Disclosures to insurers beyond the substantial PHI in Routine notes (see section 310) which are disclosed under a Consent should be rare.

3. There is only one tiny exemption to the no MNPHI restrictions when there is an authorization rule (see #2, above). Releases authorized by a client for PHI to be used internally by the CE need to be evaluated for MNPHI.

4. Other disclosures might be to a small claims court or bill collection agency for long overdue payments or other unusual situations. For these you must make *reasonable efforts* to use or disclose only the MNPHI required to achieve the purpose of the particular use or disclosure. This is certainly common practice among therapists and should not be a burden to most.

5. Requests asking for any and all records should never be filled automatically. Such requests should be reviewed with the requester to determine the specific information needed. Some may ask for less when informed of the costs involved. More typical is the lawyer on a fishing expedition.

Most clients who ask for "all their records" should be contacted and what they are seeking discussed with them. Some may have the fantasy that your records contain some truth or wisdom which was subsequently lost or overlooked. They will be disappointed at finding only notes about your conversations.

6. When records are sought by a school system, consider your local laws as well as FERPA.

Developing your office's policy on MNPHI

Your gap analysis will have revealed what kinds of information you release to whom. The next step is to develop policies about MNPHI releases.

Covered entities must make their own determination of exactly what PHI is reasonably necessary for any particular purpose. You are only required to have a policy about the MNPHI and you are not required to evaluate each case for what to release (Section 164.514(d)(3)). You *could* decide as policy to release the entire record because it is what is" reasonably necessary" to achieve the purpose (164.514(d)(5)) and write a justification for such a release but this is against the intent of the regulations. Also, be very chary about releasing the entire record unless you have specified that kind of release in your policy because disclosing it without such a policy would be a presumptive violation of the rule. However, if your records' information is in a continuous series of entries and with all kinds of information included in your notes, separating out the MNPHI will require rewriting of your records (redaction). You could decide and put into your policy manual, that your normal practice to release the entire record because of the difficulty or cost of redacting (rewriting) it. Keep this in mind when you redesign your records system.

The regulations

The regulations on MNPHI can be found at two places.

§ 164.502 Uses and disclosures of protected health information: general rules.

(b) Standard: minimum necessary.
(1) Minimum necessary applies. When using or disclosing protected health information or when requesting protected health information from another covered entity, a covered entity **must make reasonable efforts** to limit protected health information to the minimum necessary to accomplish the intended purpose of the use, disclosure, or request.
   (2) Minimum necessary does not apply. This requirement does not apply to:
      (i) Disclosures to or requests by a health care provider **for treatment;**
      (ii) Uses or disclosures made **to the individual,** as permitted under paragraph (a)(1)(i) of this section, as required by paragraph (a)(2)(i) of this section, or pursuant to an authorization under § 164.508, except for authorizations requested by the covered entity under § 164.508(d), (e), or (f);
      (iii) Disclosures made to the **Secretary** in accordance with subpart C of part 160 of this subchapter;
      (iv) Uses or disclosures that are **required by law**, as described by § 164.512(a); and
      (v) Uses or disclosures that are required for compliance with applicable requirements of this subchapter.

§ 164.514 Other requirements relating to uses and disclosures of protected health information.
§ 164.514(d)(d)(iii)(B)(d)
   (1) Standard: minimum necessary requirements. A covered entity must reasonably ensure that the standards, requirements, and implementation specifications of § 164.502(b)

and this section relating to a request for or the use and disclosure of the minimum necessary protected health information are met.

(2) Implementation specifications: minimum necessary uses of protected health information.

(i) A covered entity **must identify**:

(A) Those persons or classes of **persons**, as appropriate, **in its workforce** who need access to protected health information to carry out their duties; and

(B) For each such person or class of persons, the category or **categories of protected health information** to which access is needed and any conditions appropriate to such access.

(ii) A covered entity must make reasonable efforts to limit the access of such persons or classes identified in paragraph (d)(2)(i)(A) of this section to protected health information consistent with paragraph (d)(2)(i)(B) of this section.

(3) Implementation specification: minimum necessary disclosures of protected health information.

(i) For any type of disclosure that it makes on a routine and recurring basis, a covered entity must implement policies and procedures (which may be standard protocols) that limit the protected health information disclosed to the amount reasonably necessary to achieve the purpose of the disclosure.

(ii) For all other disclosures, a covered entity must:

(A) **Develop criteria** designed to limit the protected health information disclosed to the information reasonably necessary to accomplish the purpose for which disclosure is sought; and

(B) Review requests for disclosure on an individual basis in accordance with such criteria.

(iii) A covered entity **may rely, if such reliance is reasonable under the circumstances, on a requested disclosure as the minimum necessary for the stated purpose when:**

(A) Making disclosures to public officials that are permitted under § 164.512, if the public official represents that the information requested is the minimum necessary for the stated purpose(s);

(B) The information is requested by **another covered entity;**

(C) The information is requested by a professional who is a member of its workforce or is a **business associate** of the covered entity for the purpose of providing professional services to the covered entity, if the professional represents that the information requested is the minimum necessary for the stated purpose(s); or

(D) Documentation or representations that comply with the applicable requirements of § 164.512(i) have been provided by a person requesting the information for research purposes.

(4) Implementation specifications: minimum necessary requests for protected health information.

(i) A covered entity must limit any request for protected health information to that which is reasonably necessary to accomplish the purpose for which the request is made, when requesting such information from other covered entities.

(ii) For a request that is made on a routine and recurring basis, a covered entity must implement policies and procedures (which may be standard protocols) that limit the protected health information requested to the amount reasonably necessary to accomplish the purpose for which the request is made.

(iii) For all other requests, a covered entity must review the request on an individual basis to determine that the protected health information sought is limited to the information reasonably necessary to accomplish the purpose for which the request is made.

(5) Implementation specification: other content requirement. For all uses, disclosures, or requests to which the requirements in paragraph (d) of this section apply, a covered entity **may not use, discloses or request an entire medical record,** except when the entire medical record is specifically justified as the amount that is reasonably necessary to accomplish the purpose of the use, disclosure, or request.

540 Incidental disclosures

No system for containing PHI will be leak proof. DHHS decided, after receiving many vigorous complaints about how tight rules and elaborate procedures would not really increase the safeguards but only the burden on CE's to develop rules about "incidental disclosures." Appreciators of self-reflexivity take note: rules about when rules can be broken from the big rule maker.

Examples of common practices which might lead to disclosure include talking to a client or family at a bedside while another client was in the room, sign-in sheets on which clients could read the names of previously signed-in clients, calling out client's names in the waiting room or at a pharmacy, etc.

DHHS expects that incidental, unintentional, and accidental uses and disclosures will occur. As a result **incidental uses and disclosures are defined** (in the July 6, 2002 *Guidance* from DHHS) as secondary uses or disclosures that cannot be reasonably prevented, are limited in nature, and occur as a by-product of an otherwise permissible use or disclosure.

FAIR WARNING: Splendid example of legal reasoning coming up:

An incidental use or disclosure is permissible only to the extent that the covered entity has applied reasonable safeguards as required by § 164.530(c), and implemented the minimum necessary standard, where applicable, as required by §§ 164.502(b) and 164.514(d). These create, in terms more familiar to health care professionals, a minimal standard of care. If such "reasonable safeguards" were *not* applied, an incidental use or disclosure is not a permissible use and therefore an unlawful privacy violation. Got it?

And, because this "incidental" standard applies to all permissible uses and disclosures under the privacy rule, it applies to incidental uses and disclosures which occur when performing payment and all health care operations, not just treatment. So, if you tell your billing clerk to bill Mrs. Smith for treating her anxieties and Mrs. Jones overhears you say this, this disclosure of Mrs. Smith's PHI is still "incidental."

Got it? Ready for one more? A section [at §164.528(a)(1)(iii)] says you don't even have to list such incidental disclosures on your Accounting of Disclosures (see section 651). *Phew!* More good news: if you exercised reasonable diligence in your safeguarding of privacy, you will not be subject to "civil monetary penalties" although the Department of Justice can still impose criminal penalties.

To summarize, incidental uses and disclosures are permissible only to the extent that reasonable safeguards have been used and the minimum necessary information standard has been used (where it applies - see section 530). The overall idea is that CE's have to protect PHI with a minimum **standard of care**. If CEs do maintain that standard of care they will be judged to be in substantial compliance even when an violation of permissible uses or disclosure of PHI happens.

Q: Does the HIPAA Privacy Rule require hospitals and doctors' offices to be retrofitted, to provide private rooms, and soundproofed walls to avoid any possibility that a conversation is overheard?
A: No, the Privacy Rule does not require these types of structural changes be made to facilities.

Q: Is a covered entity required to prevent any incidental use or disclosure of protected health information?
A: No. The HIPAA Privacy Rule does not require that all risk of incidental use or disclosure be eliminated to satisfy its standards.

Rather, the Rule requires only that covered entities implement reasonable safeguards to limit incidental uses or disclosures. See 45 CFR 164.530(c)(2). *OCR Guidance Explaining Significant Aspects of the Privacy Rule - December 4, 2002*

A Quiz

Q.   You reveal some PHI about the identified patient during a family therapy session. Is this a violation of the client's privacy?
A: No because you can assume that those present are family members or others involved in the individual's care. See § 164.510(b).

Q.   You reveal some PHI about one member of a therapy group during a session. Is this a violation of the client's privacy?
A: Nope. It is not a violation because this is part of treatment

Q.   To identify your new client in the crowded waiting room you call out her name. Violation?
A: No. An incidental disclosure. But it could have been avoided by changing your procedure. For example, approach and ask, "Hello, I am Dr. Sangfreud. Are you here to see me?"

The regulations

§ 164.530 Administrative requirements.

(c) (1) Standard: Safeguards. A covered entity must have in place appropriate administrative, technical, and physical safeguards to protect the privacy of protected health information.
  (2)
        (i) Implementation specification: Safeguards. A covered entity must reasonably safeguard protected health information from any intentional or unintentional use or disclosure that is in violation of the standards, implementation specifications or other requirements of this subpart.
        (ii) A covered entity must reasonably safeguard protected health information to limit incidental uses or disclosures made pursuant to an otherwise permitted or required use or disclosure.

550   Redisclosure - Releasing information created by others

Generally, law and practice do not allow a clinician to release information in a client's record which has been created by someone else, usually another clinician. The rationale is that it is the property of the creating clinician or organization. However, where HIPAA will apply, the blanket rule is that all information can be shared for treatment purposes. **This is a <u>BIG CHANGE</u> !**

My sense is that medically ill patients who have not been educated into our (mental health) rules generally expect that all those who provide care for them do and should communicate easily and fully (while strenuously keeping the information from leaving the group of professionals). They expect that this open communication would include sending all the records (redisclosure) in one professional's possession on to all others who are providing care. So, HIPAA's allowing free re-disclosure is rather comfortable for clients as well as for the movers and shakers of healthcare in America who do not want to be bothered with obtaining informed consent.

- It seems clear that state and federal laws prohibiting re-disclosure are more protective of privacy and will *not* be preempted by HIPAA. We will continue to operate under the familiar laws. Problems will arise when a state's laws are silent on redisclosure because then HIPAA will prevail. You must know your local laws.

- You should try to keep the potential for re-disclosure in mind whenever you prepare to send any part of your records to another CE, especially in another state. Your records can be redisclosed to almost anyone who provides almost any kind of services because TPO is a big house with many unsuspected rooms.

- (Quick Review) If PHI is being released normally (for treatment and to a CE) under a Consent or under an Authorization, the minimum necessary information rules do not apply. If the PHI is being released for Payment or healthcare Operations, they *do* apply (see section 530) and so you can limit what might be redisclosed.

- Because clients generally have access to their own records, PHI created by you but in the hands of another provider may be shared with the client or his or her legal representative. Psychotherapy notes are an exception, I believe. Since an Authorization is required to share them, even for TPO, when shared under such an Authorization, the receiving CE must treat them as not accessible to the client because they are still psychotherapy notes.

560 HIPAA and Workers' Compensation, Social Security Disability, etc.

Clinicians are often asked to supply information to insurers to evaluate claims for benefits under various kinds of insurance besides the more routine payments from health insurers for the services they have performed on clients. Since this is PHI, HIPAA is involved. Let's see how.

First, to simplify matters, to what kind of insurance does HIPAA *not* apply?

> **Q:** **Are the following types of insurance covered under HIPAA: long/short term disability; workers compensation; automobile liability that includes coverage for medical payments?**
>
> **A:** No, the listed types of policies are not health plans. The HIPAA Administrative Simplification regulations specifically exclude from the definition of a health plan any policy, plan, or program to the extent that it provides, or pays for the cost of, excepted benefits, which are listed in section 2791(c)(1) of the Public Health Service Act, 42 U.S.C. 300gg-91(c)(1). See 45 CFR 160.103. As described in the statute, excepted benefits are one or more (or any combination thereof) of the following policies, plans or programs:
>   - Coverage only for accident, or disability income insurance, or an combination thereof.
>   - Coverage issued as a supplement to liability insurance.
>   - Liability insurance, including general liability insurance and automobile liability insurance.
>   - Workers' compensation or similar insurance.
>   - Automobile medical payment insurance.
>   - Credit-only insurance.
>   - Coverage for on-site medical clinics [at a worksite or school or some residential facilities]
>   - Other similar insurance coverage, specified in regulations, under which benefits for medical care are secondary or incidental to other insurance benefits. *OCR Guidance Explaining Significant Aspects of the Privacy Rule - December 4, 2002* (Bracketed words added).

Therefore you can release PHI to these organizations without regard to HIPAA's rules for disclosure to CEs because they are not CEs.

Disclosing PHI

While HIPAA applies to state Medicaid programs (because they are considered health plans) their rules appear to be more stringent and so you can rely on what they have asked for.

The Privacy Rule permits covered entities to disclose, *without authorization*, protected health information to workers' compensation insurers, State administrators, employers, and other persons or entities involved in workers' compensation systems. This includes programs established by the Black Lung Benefits Act, the Federal Employees' Compensation Act, the Longshore and Harbor Workers' Compensation Act, and the Energy Employees' Occupational Illness Compensation Program Act. See 45 CFR 164.512(*l*). These are all for obtaining benefits or payment for services and the kinds of information sought is structured by the state laws. In addition, CEs may disclose any PHI to these organizations when the clients has *signed an Authorization*.

MNPHI

The HIPAA rules in this area [§ 164.512(l)] are still structured in terms of the minimum necessary standard but the standard is, for these releases, essentially redefined as: Whatever state laws allow or state officials ask for.

- "The minimum necessary standard does not apply to disclosures that are required by State or other law or made pursuant to the individual's authorization." Ibid.
  You can rely on their Authorization (request) to define what is the minimum necessary.

- "For disclosures of protected health information made for workers' compensation purposes under 45 CFR 164.512(*l*), the minimum necessary standard permits covered entities to **disclose information to the full extent authorized by State or other law.** In addition, where protected health information is requested by a State workers' compensation or other public official for such purposes, **covered entities are permitted reasonably to rely on the official's representations that the information requested is the minimum necessary** for the intended purpose. See 45 CFR 164.514(d)(3)(iii)(A)."

- "For disclosures of protected health information for **payment** purposes, covered entities may disclose the type and amount of information necessary to receive payment for any health care provided to an injured or ill worker." Ibid.

Other issues

1. Clients do not have the right to request that you restrict the PHI you disclose to Workers Compensation when the PHI is required by the law.

> **Q:** **My State law says I may provide information regarding an injured workers' previous condition, which is not directly related to the claim for compensation, to an employer or insurer if I obtain the workers' written release. Am I permitted to make this disclosure under the HIPAA Privacy Rule?**
> **A:** A covered entity may disclose protected health information where the individual's **written authorization** has been obtained, consistent with the Privacy Rule's requirements at 45 CFR 164.508. Thus, a covered entity would be permitted to make the above disclosure if the individual signed such an authorization. Ibid

2. Releasing PHI to employers is allowed.

> **Q:** **Can a CE disclose PHI from pre-employment physicals, drug tests, or fitness-for-duty examinations to an individual's employer without an authorization?**
> **A:** Yes, in three circumstances: 1) your services were provided at the request of the employer, or; 2) your services were an evaluation to determine whether the individual has a work-related illness or injury, or; 3) the employer had to keep such PHI records because of Occupational Safety and Health Administration (OSHA), the Mine Safety and Health Administration (MSHA), or the requirements of a similar State law. Ibid

You must provide the individual with written notice that the information is to be disclosed to his or her employer. Also, nothing in the Rule prohibits an employer from conditioning employment on an individual providing an authorization for the disclosure of such information.(Ibid.) In light of this you should have a thorough discussion with a client before doing any evaluation.

570 Consulting under HIPAA

We mental health professionals do many kinds of consulting and some may interact with HIPAA.

> **Q:** **Are health care providers restricted from consulting with other providers about a patient's condition without the patient's written authorization?**
> **A:** No. Consulting with another health care provider about a patient is within the HIPAA Privacy Rule's definition of "treatment" and, therefore, is permissible. In addition, a health care provider (or other covered entity) is expressly permitted to disclose protected health information about an individual to a health care provider for that provider's treatment of the individual. See 45 CFR 164.506. OCR Guidance Explaining Significant Aspects of the Privacy Rule - December 4, 2002. FAQs

Q: **So, which kinds of consultation will need what kinds of releases?**
A1: **Inpatient and residential facilities**

Ancillary staff member at inpatient facility?
Consent was obtained by the facility and you are providing treatment.

Attending privileges but not staff member?
Consent was obtained by the hospital and you can operate under that if you and the hospital have formed an Organized Health Care Arrangementl. You can use and disclose only PHI generated in this episode of treatment. Note that if, after discharge, the ex-inpatient comes to see you as a new out-patient you will have to do your own NPP and Consent.

A2: **Consulting with peers**

About your own difficult case?
This comes under the Treatment part of TPO and so no further release is needed.

With other professionals in your group practice?
No new consent is needed because you are all part of the same CE (if you are). Also, since this is true you don't need a Business Associate (BA) agreement with them.

A3: **Evaluating a client upon referral**

Referral by a professional who is treating the client?
HIPAA calls this an "indirect treatment relationship" since you too are providing part of treatment (even though you will not see the client in a continuing relationship), and so no further consent is needed. This would also be true if you were an employee of the referring professional or agency. You might make sure they have done the NPP and Consent-signing on their client or else do you own.

Referral by a school system of which you are not an employee?
HIPAA specifically defers to FERPA and its rules on access and privacy. If you are in private practice providing evaluations under contract with a school or billing clients for your services this makes the situation more complex. If you are providing evaluations which are both health care and educational this adds to the complexity. I cannot speak to this with authority and suggest you consult your local experts.

Referral by a court, Social Security Disability, or other governmental agency
Social Security and Workers Compensation are specifically excluded from HIPAA. Other agencies may not be, so you should ask them if they are HIPAA compliant or excepted from HIPAA. If they are compliant, you are providing an evaluation which is part of Treatment and so you don't need another consent.

A4:   Discussing a client with non-peer professionals such as a

Pharmacist?
Part of treatment so no new consent needed.

Case manager, Intensive Case Manager, etc.?
These are representatives of a CE (either a provider or a health plan) and so they come under either treatment or payment. No new consent is needed but it would be a good idea to refer to this kind of possibility in your NPP because clients may not routinely be aware of this kind of disclosure of their PHI.

Home-health worker, Wraparound service provider (Behavior Specialist Consultant, Therapeutic Support Staff, Mobile Therapist, Clinical Supervisor) or similar caregiver?
This type of discussion would be use and disclosure for treatment.

Nurse, dentist, podiatrist, chiropractor?
This type of discussion would be a disclosure for treatment.

Psychologist, social worker, counselors, psychiatrist, physician?
This type of discussion would be a disclosure for treatment.

Alternative medicine practitioner?
These practitioners provide treatment but are not recognized in the original Medicare law on which HIPAA is based. I believe that it would be legally appropriate and ethical to get an Authorization from the client before sharing PHI with any of these practitioners.

My recommendations when doing and evaluation

If you cannot be absolutely certain that they were Notified and Consented when first seen by the referrer, discuss these points with them:

- You were referred to me by _____ for the purpose(s) of _____ .

- The results of my evaluation will be sent to your primary provider and/or the person or agency who referred you to me.

- I will not keep a record of this evaluation's results so if you ever need copies please seek it from the person or organization who referred you.

- We will meet once or perhaps a few times to complete the evaluation but we will not have an ongoing treatment relationship and I will not become your doctor and you will not be my patient.

580 Oral communications

Very often we discuss a client's situation and so disclose PHI in a conversation with the client or with another treating professional in an area or under circumstances which are not completely private. We do not have a consent or authorization to disclose the client's PHI to those nearby who might overhear. Have we violated the HIPAA rules? The answer is "Yes. However ... "

1. HIPAA does not require a guarantee of privacy. You do not need to rebuild your office to be soundproof because HIPAA takes account of costs and benefits. However, you should be aware and cautious. Routinely disclosing because of laziness or carelessness will be seen as a violation.

2. Be aware of who "needs to know" when sharing information in a group situation. The secretary filing or typing or whatever in the same room as your discussion with a fellow treater does not need and should not receive the same information. Move to a private area or show your fellow the information on paper or find another way to preserve confidentiality.

3. DHHS recognizes some disclosures as incidental, secondary, unpreventable, limited in nature, and occurring as a by-product of an otherwise permitted disclosure. (See section 540.) However, these will be considered violations if you have not taken reasonable safeguards such as taking some precautions to not be overheard (e.g. stepping away, keeping your voice down) and disclosing only the minimum information necessary (e.g. not using the client's name or other clearly identifying information).

If you use a **Telecommunications Relay Services (TRS)** programs to communicate with a patient who is deaf or any other reason, the Federal Communications Commission (FCC) decided (July 2004) that this does not violate the HIPAA Privacy Rule and you don't need to have a Business Associate (BA) agreement with the TRS. Read more at http://www.hipaadvisory.com/action/faqs/fcc.htm>. Accessed Sept. 24, 2005. See also, the note on page 104 for a decision by HHS.

590   Verifying the identity of those seeking PHI

When someone asks you to disclose a client's PHI, the regulations require you to verify both the identity of the requester and their authority to acquire the information.

Therapists have always been careful about these disclosures because they are aware of the sensitive nature of much of their information. The HIPAA materials are quoted below to give you an indication of how this issue is framed and how important it is considered by the size of the regulations.

In the Preamble (pages 82546-7) to the regulations relating to *Section 164.514(h) Verification of Identity and Authority of Persons Requesting Protected Health Information,* the Secretary has this to say:

> The covered entity must establish and use written policies and procedures (which may be standard protocols) that are reasonably designed to verify the identity and authority of the requestor where the covered entity does not know the person requesting the protected health information. **The knowledge of the person may take the form of a known place of business, address, phone or fax number, as well a known human being.** .... additional verification is only required where this regulation (or other law) requires additional proof of authority and identity.

> We do not mandate particular identification requirements (e.g., driver's license, photo ID), but rather leave this to the discretion of the covered entity. The covered entity must also establish and document procedures for verification of identity and authority of personal representatives, if not known to the entity. For example, a health care provider can require a copy of a power of attorney, or can ask questions to determine that an adult acting for a young child has the requisite relationship to the child.

> In some circumstances, identity or authority will be verified as part of meeting the underlying requirements for disclosure. For example, a disclosure under § 164.512(j)(1)(i) **to avert an imminent threat to safety** is lawful only if made in the good faith belief that the disclosure is necessary to prevent or lessen a serious and imminent threat to the health or safety of a person or the public, and to a person reasonably able to prevent or lessen the threat. If these conditions are met, no further verification is needed. In such emergencies, the covered entity is not required to demand written proof that the person requesting the protected health information is legally authorized. Reasonable reliance on verbal representations are appropriate in such situations. (Boldface added)

Because the regs are quite detailed, it will be very important to rely on DHHS' assurance that **covered entities are expected to do only what is reasonable.**

§ 164.514 Other requirements relating to uses and disclosures of protected health information.

(h)

(1) Standard: verification requirements. Prior to any disclosure permitted by this subpart, a covered entity must:

(i) Except with respect to disclosures under § 164.510, verify the identity of a person requesting protected health information and the authority of any such person to have access to protected health information under this subpart, if the identity or any such authority of such person is not known to the covered entity; and

(ii) Obtain any documentation, statements, or representations, whether oral or written, from the person requesting the protected health information when such documentation, statement, or representation is a condition of the disclosure under this subpart.

(2) Implementation specifications: verification.

(i) Conditions on disclosures. If a disclosure is conditioned by this subpart on particular documentation, statements, or representations from the person requesting the protected health information, a covered entity may rely, if such reliance is reasonable under the circumstances, on documentation, statements, or representations that, on their face, meet the applicable requirements.

(A) The conditions in § 164.512(f)(1)(ii)(C) may be satisfied by the administrative subpoena or similar process or by a separate written statement that, on its face, demonstrates that the applicable requirements have been met.

(B) The documentation required by § 164.512(i)(2) may be satisfied by one or more written statements, provided that each is appropriately dated and signed in accordance with § 164.512(i)(2)(i) and (v).

(ii) Identity of public officials. A covered entity may rely, if such reliance is reasonable under the circumstances, on any of the following to verify identity when the disclosure of protected health information is to a public official or a person acting on behalf of the public official:

(A) If the request is made in person, presentation of an agency identification badge, other official credentials, or other proof of government status;

(B) If the request is in writing, the request is on the appropriate government letterhead; or

(C) If the disclosure is to a person acting on behalf of a public official, a written statement on appropriate government letterhead that the person is acting under the government's authority or other evidence or documentation of agency, such as a contract for services, memorandum of understanding, or purchase order, that establishes that the person is acting on behalf of the public official.

(iii) Authority of public officials. A covered entity may rely, if such reliance is reasonable under the circumstances, on any of the following to verify authority when the disclosure of protected health information is to a public official or a person acting on behalf of the public official:

(A) A written statement of the legal authority under which the information is requested, or, if a written statement would be impracticable, an oral statement of such legal authority;

(B) If a request is made pursuant to legal process, warrant, subpoena, order, or other legal process issued by a grand jury or a judicial or administrative tribunal is presumed to constitute legal authority.

(iv) Exercise of professional judgment. The verification requirements of this paragraph are met if the covered entity relies on the exercise of professional judgment in making a use or disclosure in accordance with § 164.510 or acts on a good faith belief in making a disclosure in accordance with § 164.512(j).

Notes

600   Clients' rights to control their PHI

610   The opportunity to object to the use or disclosure of one's PHI

The regulations say that the CE can use or disclose a client's PHI without consent or authorization if they were told (in the NPP) that this would happen and were given the "opportunity to agree to or prohibit or restrict the disclosure." This sounds like a real protection but it turns out that this is mainly about limiting what information is given to hospital directories [§ 164.510(a)]. Obviously this part does not much apply to therapists.

However, there is a second application of this ability to restrict disclosures. The client has to be given an opportunity to object when PHI is shared with family members and others[48] who "are involved in[49]" his or her care, when the client is present. When the client is not present, the CE can use professional judgment to decide what to share and with whom.

Requests for restricting the use and disclosure of one's PHI

As we will see, there is no effective way for a client to restrict the sharing of his or her PHI in this legislation.

1. A client may not request limitations on PHI used:
    a. where no consent, authorization, or opportunity to object is required.
    b. for oversight and evaluating compliance with the law.

2. CEs must offer the client the opportunity to *request* restriction on the use and disclosure of their PHI but the CE does not have to *comply* with the client's wishes unless the CE wants to do so. It is expected that the CE will very rarely comply with restrictions and simply inform the client of its policies as stated in its NPP.

3. If the CE agrees to some limitations, these are not enforceable by the client under HIPAA. Clients may, of course, ask to terminate a restriction they sought and which was agreed to but the CE may unilaterally and without notice terminate any agreed on limitations. This termination of an agreement cannot take effect on uses or disclosures until the client is informed. The CE may use or disclose any PHI acquired after the termination and notification in any way permitted by HIPAA.

The regulations

I do not address here the use of PHI for a facility directory, meaning the list that is consulted when you visit someone in a hospital or similar facility and that clergy use to make rounds. See § 164.510(a)(1) for this information.

---

[48] "Such persons involved in care and other contact persons might include, for example: **blood relatives; spouses; roommates; boyfriends and girlfriends; domestic partners; neighbors; and colleagues.** Inclusion of this list is intended to be illustrative only, and it is not intended to change current practices with respect to: (1) involvement of other persons in individuals' treatment decisions; (2) informal information-sharing among individuals involved in a person's care; or (3) sharing of protected health information to contact persons during a disaster." Preamble, page 82522. Also "In § 164.510(b) we do not require verification of identity for persons assisting in an individual's care or for notification purposes." Preamble, page 82547.

[49] It does not say "provide" care to the client.

For your references, below are the most relevant parts of **§ 164.510 Uses and disclosures requiring an opportunity for the individual to agree or to object.**

(b) Standard: uses and disclosures for involvement in the individual's care and notification purposes.

(1) Permitted uses and disclosures.

(i) A covered entity may, in accordance with paragraphs (b)(2) or (3) of this section, **disclose to a family member, other relative, or a close personal friend of the individual,** or any other person identified by the individual, the protected health information directly relevant to such person's involvement with the individual's care or payment related to the individual's health care.

(ii) A covered entity may use or disclose protected health information **to notify, or assist in the notification of (including identifying or locating), a family member,** a personal representative of the individual, or another person responsible for the care of the individual of the individual's location, general condition, or death. Any such use or disclosure of protected health information for such notification purposes must be in accordance with paragraphs (b)(2), (3), or (4) of this section, as applicable.

(2) Uses and **disclosures with the individual present.** If the individual is present for, or otherwise available prior to, a use or disclosure permitted by paragraph (b)(1) of this section and has the **capacity** to make health care decisions, the covered entity may use or disclose the protected health information if it:

(i) Obtains the individual's agreement;

(ii) Provides the individual with the opportunity to object to the disclosure, and the individual does not express an objection; or

(iii) Reasonably infers from the circumstances, based the exercise of professional judgment, that the individual does not object to the disclosure.

(3) **Limited uses and disclosures when the individual is not present.** If the individual is not present for, or the opportunity to agree or object to the use or disclosure cannot practicably be provided because of the individual's incapacity or an emergency circumstance, the covered entity may, in the **exercise of professional judgment,** determine whether the disclosure is in the best interests of the individual and, if so, **disclose only the protected health information that is directly relevant to the person's involvement with the individual's health care.** A covered entity may use professional judgment and its experience with common practice to make reasonable inferences of the individual's best interest in allowing a person to act on behalf of the individual to pick up filled prescriptions, medical supplies, X-rays, or other similar forms of protected health information. (Boldface added.)

611 **Form to request limitations on disclosure of one's PHI**

(On your letterhead)

Form to request restrictions on communication and/or disclosure of my personal healthcare information

I request the following restrictions to the use or disclosure of my personally identifiable health information: _____

_____

_____

_____

_____

_____
Printed Name (Client)

_____   _____
Signature of client or his or her personal representative   Date

_____   _____
Printed name of client or personal representative   Relationship to the client

_____
Description of personal representative's authority

❑ Accepted

❑ Refused

Reason(s): _____

_____

_____

_____   _____   _____
Printed name of Privacy Officer   Signature   Date

620   Client's requests for alternative communication channels

Therapists are used to this but HIPAA puts into law the practice of offering clients a more private ways to communicate about appointments or other issues than calling or sending mail to them at work or at home.

You, as a CE, must permit clients to request to receive communications from you which might contain PHI by alternative means or at alternative locations. You may not require an explanation of the client's reasons for this request. You must make reasonable accommodations to do this. You do not *have* to do this - it is your choice.

You may require the client to make this request in writing but need not. For therapists an oral request should be sufficient if you then make a note in the chart. You should examine the ways you communicate with clients outside the office and decide what you could do to prevent breaches of their confidentiality if you disregarded their request. For example, make a note of changes about their wishes in your Rolodex if you use one to make calls to clients about their appointments or on your billing form if you send bills to them.

If you need to, for one client's special situation, or where you think it might become sticky, you can use the form below for them to request confidential communication in writing.

The regulations

This is an edited version of the regulations focusing on small psychotherapy practices.

§ 164.522 Rights to request privacy protection for protected health information.
(b)
    (1) Standard: confidential communications requirements.
      (i) A covered health care provider must permit individuals to request and must accommodate reasonable requests by individuals to receive communications of protected health information from the covered health care provider by alternative means or at alternative locations.
    (2) Implementation specifications: conditions on providing confidential communications.
      (i) A covered entity may require the individual to make a request for a confidential communication described in paragraph (b)(1) of this section in writing.
      (ii) A covered entity may condition the provision of a reasonable accommodation on:
        (A) When appropriate, information as to how payment, if any, will be handled; and
        (B) Specification of an alternative address or other method of contact.
      (iii) A covered health care provider may not require an explanation from the individual as to the basis for the request as a condition of providing communications on a confidential basis.

621 Form to request alternative communication channels

(On your letterhead)

Request for other ways of communicating with me

I do not need to provide any reason and simply request the following alternatives to or limitations on communicating with me by you or this practice:

1. Please telephone me ONLY at this number(s): _____

When you call please follow these directions: _____

_____

_____

Please do NOT telephone me at this number(s): _____

_____

2. Please direct all postal mail to this address: _____

_____

Please do NOT send postal mail to this address: _____

3. You may e-mail to me at this address: _____

_____   _____
Signature of client or his or her personal representative   Date

_____   _____
Printed name of client or personal representative   Relationship to the client

_____
Description of personal representative's authority

❑ Accepted
❑ Refused

Reason(s)for decision: _____

_____

_____

_____   _____   _____
Printed name of Privacy Officer   Signature   Date

630　　Clients' access to their records

HIPAA's change are mostly small but this is a <u>BIG CHANGE</u> and will have wide impact. Because few states' laws specifically address access in mental health and most set some limitations, HIPAA, which sets fewer barriers to access, will preempt them. **You are going to have to allow clients more access to your/their records.**

How access works

Section § 164.524, of HIPAA gives clients not only access to their records but rights to copies of them and to amend their records [§ 164.526] (see section 560). This part of the regulations is quite detailed and long (see later) so I have rewritten them in ordinary language, cut some parts irrelevant to therapists, and reorganized them for clarity.

1. Such access is not wide open; there are two **exceptions** and they are important. Clients do not have access to:
    a. Psychotherapy notes
    b. Information "compiled in reasonable anticipation of, or for use in, a civil, criminal, or administrative action or proceeding."

2. Generally you must **allow access** or obtaining of a **copy** of the records or both.
    a. You must provide the records within 30 days of the receipt of the request for records unless you don't have the records on-site and then you can take up to 60 days to comply. If you still can't comply, you can add another 30 days if you provide an explanation to the client of the reasons for the delay and a date you will comply. You can extend the time this way only once.
    b. You must provide the PHI in the form requested, if readily available, or if not, in a hard copy or another form if the client agrees to this. Does this mean the notes have to be legible or have to be rewritten (redacted) to be legible? This is unclear at present but may be clarified by DHHS in the future.
    c. You must arrange a convenient time and place for inspection or obtaining a copy or negotiate fees for mailing a copy. You can talk to the client to make these arrangements.
    d. Instead of access you can provide a summary or an explanation of the PHI but only if the client agrees in advance to this and to pay any fees you impose.
    e. You can charge for the copy or the summary or explanation but the fees must be cost-based and agreed to beforehand.

Note: **The new APA Code of Ethics** (effective June 30, 2003) permits psychologists **to withhold records for non-payment** of fees except in an emergency. However, HIPAA does not recognize this exception which is a barrier to access and so, even in states, where the APA Code is incorporated into the licensing law, HIPAA will prevail (in my opinion). Consider the implications. Perhaps you should not write up a report until paid or never allow a client to run up a significant debt to you.

3. **You can deny access** or partially deny the request (offer access to less PHI than is requested) and can do so under a variety of situations. The regulations organize these into "reviewable" and "unreviewable grounds for denial" of access.

    a. The **unreviewable** grounds are:
        - They are excepted, as above in 1.
        - The records are of an inmate and obtaining such records would interfere with the operations or safety of the correctional institution.
        - The PHI was obtained in the course of research that includes treatment (see

section 470) and the patient agreed to a temporary suspension of this access.
- The access is illegal under the Privacy Act, 5 U.S.C. § 552a.
- The information was obtained from someone not a health are provider and this person was promised confidentiality, and the patient's viewing of the PHI would reasonably reveal the source of the information.

b. The **reviewable** grounds all include a licensed health care professional [meaning you, and not a secretary, but not more specifically defined] who evaluates the access and uses professional judgment to determine that access is:
- "reasonably likely to endanger the life or physical safety of the individual or another person "or
- "reasonably likely to cause substantial harm to another person (not a health care provider) who is referred to in the PHI," or
- "reasonably likely to cause substantial harm" to the individual or another person if the client's personal representative gains access to the information.

c. If you deny access for any these reasons the client has the right to have your decision **reviewed by a licensed health care professional** (whom you select) who did not participate in the initial denial decision and whose decision is binding on you. Such review must be timely, the client must be informed of the decision promptly, and you must take appropriate actions quickly. If you deny the request in whole or in part for any reason you must do so **in writing**, in plain language, and timely fashion.

While there is a form for this in section 631, I assume that such circumstances will be rare and that the denial might better come in the form of a detailed and well-reasoned set of statements. A denial must contain the basis for the denial, and, if it is a reviewable denial, a statement of the client's right to a review and how to exercise this right. It must also describe how to complain to you or the Office of Civil Rights and offer the name, title, and phone number of the contact person (your Privacy Officer).

If you decide on a partial denial of access, you must make the other PHI available to the client. And, of course, you must keep documentation of this access or denial but it does not have to be listed in the Account of disclosures (see section 652).

Q: Who pays and how much for copies?
A: The October 2, 2002 guidance from DHHS says you can charge reasonable fees for labor, supplies, and postage *but* you cannot change the client for the costs of searching for and retrieving the records. You can charge a fee for preparing a summary or explanation of the PHI if the client has agreed to the summary and the price instead of the actual records.

Q: What if what they are seeking is not in my records?
A: You can't just ignore the request. If you don't have it but know where it is, you have to tell the client. If you don't know, tell them that.

Q: What if they can't read my notes or may very likely misinterpret what is in them?
A: If you have not been keeping separate notes (Routine and Psychotherapy Notes), you could provide someone to translate them for the client but that might introduce errors and misunderstandings. If handwritten, you could rewrite them or type them up but this is not what is sought and takes a lot of time. You can offer them a summary which you could prepare and charge them for (if they agreed to this option beforehand). A discussion with you or the privacy officer before proceeding is probably the best course.

The regulations

§ 164.524 Access of individuals to protected health information.

(a) Standard: access to protected health information.

(1) Right of access. Except as otherwise provided in paragraph (a)(2) or (a)(3) of this section, an individual has a right of access to inspect and obtain a copy of protected health information about the individual in a designated record set, for as long as the protected health information is maintained in the designated record set, except for:

(i) Psychotherapy notes;

(ii) Information compiled in reasonable anticipation of, or for use in, a civil, criminal, or administrative action or proceeding; and

(iii) Protected health information maintained by a covered entity that is:

(A) Subject to the Clinical Laboratory Improvements Amendments of 1988, 42 U.S.C. 263a, to the extent the provision of access to the individual would be prohibited by law; or

(B) Exempt from the Clinical Laboratory Improvements Amendments of 1988, pursuant to 42 CFR 493.3(a)(2).

(2) **Unreviewable** grounds for denial. A covered entity may deny an individual access without providing the individual an opportunity for review, in the following circumstances.

(i) The protected health information is excepted from the right of access by paragraph (a)(1) of this section.

(ii) A covered entity that is a correctional institution or a covered health care provider acting under the direction of the correctional institution may deny, in whole or in part, an inmate's request to obtain a copy of protected health information, if obtaining such copy would jeopardize the health, safety, security, custody, or rehabilitation of the individual or of other inmates, or the safety of any officer, employee, or other person at the correctional institution or responsible for the transporting of the inmate.

(iii) An individual's access to protected health information created or obtained by a covered health care provider in the course of research that includes treatment may be temporarily suspended for as long as the research is in progress, provided that the individual has agreed to the denial of access when consenting to participate in the research that includes treatment, and the covered health care provider has informed the individual that the right of access will be reinstated upon completion of the research.

(iv) An individual's access to protected health information that is contained in records that are subject to the Privacy Act, 5 U.S.C. § 552a, may be denied, if the denial of access under the Privacy Act would meet the requirements of that law.

(v) An individual's access may be denied if the protected health information was obtained from someone other than a health care provider under a promise of confidentiality and the access requested would be reasonably likely to reveal the source of the information.

(3) **Reviewable** grounds for denial. A covered entity may deny an individual access, provided that the individual is given a right to have such denials reviewed, as required by paragraph (a)(4) of this section, in the following circumstances:

(i) A licensed health care professional has determined, in the exercise of professional judgment, that the access requested is reasonably likely to endanger the life or physical safety of the individual or another person;

(ii) The protected health information makes reference to another person (unless such other person is a health care provider) and a licensed health care professional has determined, in the exercise of professional judgment, that the access requested is reasonably likely to cause substantial harm to such other person; or

(iii) The request for access is made by the individual's personal representative and a licensed health care professional has determined, in the exercise of professional judgment, that the provision of access to such personal representative is reasonably likely to cause substantial harm to the individual or another person.

(4) Review of a denial of access. If access is denied on a ground permitted under

paragraph (a)(3) of this section, the individual has the right to have the denial reviewed by a licensed health care professional who is designated by the covered entity to act as a reviewing official and who did not participate in the original decision to deny. The covered entity must provide or deny access in accordance with the determination of the reviewing official under paragraph (d)(4) of this section.

(b) Implementation specifications: requests for access and timely action.

(1) Individual's request for access. The covered entity must permit an individual to request access to inspect or to obtain a copy of the protected health information about the individual that is maintained in a designated record set. The covered entity may require individuals to make requests for access in writing, provided that it informs individuals of such a requirement.

(2) Timely action by the covered entity.

(i) Except as provided in paragraph (b)(2)(ii) of this section, the covered entity must act on a request for access no later than 30 days after receipt of the request as follows.

(A) If the covered entity grants the request, in whole or in part, it must inform the individual of the acceptance of the request and provide the access requested, in accordance with paragraph (c) of this section.

(B) If the covered entity denies the request, in whole or in part, it must provide the individual with a written denial, in accordance with paragraph (d) of this section.

(ii) If the request for access is for protected health information that is not maintained or accessible to the covered entity on-site, the covered entity must take an action required by paragraph (b)(2)(i) of this section by no later than 60 days from the receipt of such a request.

(iii) If the covered entity is unable to take an action required by paragraph (b)(2)(i)(A) or (B) of this section within the time required by paragraph (b)(2)(i) or (ii) of this section, as applicable, the covered entity may extend the time for such actions by no more than 30 days, provided that:

(A) The covered entity, within the time limit set by paragraph (b)(2)(i) or (ii) of this section, as applicable, provides the individual with a written statement of the reasons for the delay and the date by which the covered entity will complete its action on the request; and

(B) The covered entity may have only one such extension of time for action on a request for access.

(c) Implementation specifications: provision of access. If the covered entity provides an individual with access, in whole or in part, to protected health information, the covered entity must comply with the following requirements.

(1) Providing the access requested. The covered entity must provide the access requested by individuals, including inspection or obtaining a copy, or both, of the protected health information about them in designated record sets. If the same protected health information that is the subject of a request for access is maintained in more than one designated record set or at more than one location, the covered entity need only produce the protected health information once in response to a request for access.

(2) Form of access requested.

(i) The covered entity must provide the individual with access to the protected health information in the form or format requested by the individual, if it is readily producible in such form or format; or, if not, in a readable hard copy form or such other form or format as agreed to by the covered entity and the individual.

(ii) The covered entity may provide the individual with a summary of the protected health information requested, in lieu of providing access to the protected health information or may provide an explanation of the protected health information to which access has been provided, if:

(A) The individual agrees in advance to such a summary or explanation; and

(B) The individual agrees in advance to the fees imposed, if any, by the covered entity for such summary or explanation.

(3) Time and manner of access. The covered entity must provide the access as requested

by the individual in a timely manner as required by paragraph (b)(2) of this section, including arranging with the individual for a convenient time and place to inspect or obtain a copy of the protected health information, or mailing the copy of the protected health information at the individual's request. The covered entity may discuss the scope, format, and other aspects of the request for access with the individual as necessary to facilitate the timely provision of access.

(4) Fees. If the individual requests a copy of the protected health information or agrees to a summary or explanation of such information, the covered entity may impose a reasonable, cost-based fee, provided that the fee includes only the cost of:

(i) Copying, including the cost of supplies for and labor of copying, the protected health information requested by the individual;

(ii) Postage, when the individual has requested the copy, or the summary or explanation, be mailed; and

(iii) Preparing an explanation or summary of the , if agreed to by the individual as required by paragraph (c)(2)(ii) of this section.

(d) Implementation specifications: denial of access. If the covered entity denies access, in protected health information whole or in part, to protected health information, the covered entity must comply with the following requirements.

(1) Making other information accessible. The covered entity must, to the extent possible, give the individual access to any other protected health information requested, after excluding the protected health information as to which the covered entity has a ground to deny access.

(2) Denial. The covered entity must provide a timely, written denial to the individual, in accordance with paragraph (b)(2) of this section. The denial must be in plain language and contain:

(i) The basis for the denial;

(ii) If applicable, a statement of the individual's review rights under paragraph (a)(4) of this section, including a description of how the individual may exercise such review rights; and

(iii) A description of how the individual may complain to the covered entity pursuant to the complaint procedures in § 164.530(d) or to the Secretary pursuant to the procedures in § 160.306. The description must include the name, or title, and telephone number of the contact person or office designated in § 164.530(a)(1)(ii).

(3) Other responsibility. If the covered entity does not maintain the protected health information that is the subject of the individual's request for access, and the covered entity knows where the requested information is maintained, the covered entity must inform the individual where to direct the request for access.

(4) Review of denial requested. If the individual has requested a review of a denial under paragraph (a)(4) of this section, the covered entity must designate a licensed health care professional, who was not directly involved in the denial to review the decision to deny access. The covered entity must promptly refer a request for review to such designated reviewing official. The designated reviewing official must determine, within a reasonable period of time, whether or not to deny the access requested based on the standards in paragraph (a)(3) of this section. The covered entity must promptly provide written notice to the individual of the determination of the designated reviewing official and take other action as required by this section to carry out the designated reviewing official's determination.

(e) Implementation specification: documentation. A covered entity must document the following and retain the documentation as required by § 164.530(j):

(1) The designated record sets that are subject to access by individuals; and

(2) The titles of the persons or offices responsible for receiving and processing requests for access by individuals.

631 Form to request access to one's health information

(On your letterhead)

Form to request access to personal healthcare information

A. Client's name _____ Date of birth _____

Client's Address _____

Telephone_____ Other identification(s) _____

Date(s) or the part of client's record to be accessed _____

_____

Type(s) of information to be accessed _____

_____

_____

B. I have consulted with the privacy officer about these records and information and have
decided that I want (select one)
- ❑ to read and review the original records or photocopies of them.
- ❑ to read and review the original records or photocopies of them with a professional.
  Time and place to do the above _____ .
- ❑ to receive a photocopy of these records
- ❑ to receive a summary of the information in these records.
- ❑ to receive a written explanation of the information in these records.
- ❑ other _____
- ❑ I want this copy mailed to me at the above address or at _____

C. Costs (select one)
- ❑ I have been advised of the cost of copying, postage, or providing a summary or
  explanation and have agreed to pay $ _____ .
- ❑ I have revised my request. See a version of this form dated _____.

_____   _____ _____
Signature of client or legal representative   Printed name   Date

_____
Description of personal representative's authority

D. Decision a of the health care provider:
1. ❑ I will comply with this request. I will provide these records in the form requested
       within 30 days of receiving this request.

2. ❑ I deny this request for the reason(s) listed below. You may not appeal my decision.
     - ❑ The information you are seeking is not in my records.
       - ❑ I do not know who has this information.
       - ❑ I believe that this information is in the possession of _____

❑ I choose not to allow you access to my Psychotherapy notes.
❑ The information was or is compiled in reasonable anticipation of, or for use in, a civil, criminal, or administrative action or proceeding.
❑ The information was obtained as part of a research program you agreed to participate in and you agreed to a temporary suspension of your right to access thisinformation.
❑ The information is not available to the client for inspection as permitted by federal law. For example, the access is illegal under the Privacy Act, 5 U.S. C. § 552a.
❑ The information was obtained from someone who is not a healthcare provider and they were promised confidentiality, and your viewing of this information would reasonably reveal the source of this information.
❑ Other reason_____ .

3. ❑ I will partly comply with this request. I have removed parts of the record and will allow access to the remaining parts. My reasons for removing those parts are that:
❑ I choose not to allow access to my psychotherapy notes.
❑ The information was or is compiled in reasonable anticipation of, or for use in, a civil, criminal, or administrative action or proceeding.
❑ The information was obtained as part of a research program you agreed to participate in and you agreed to a temporary suspension of your right to access this information.
❑ The information is not available to the client for inspection as permitted by federal law. For example, the access is illegal under the Privacy Act, 5 U.S. C. § 552a.
❑ The information was obtained from someone who is not a healthcare provider and they were promised confidentiality, and your viewing of this information would reasonably reveal the source of this information.
❑ Other reason_____ .

4. ❑ I deny this request for the reason(s) listed below. As a licensed healthcare professional, it is my professional judgment that your access to this information is reasonably likely to
❑ endanger your life or physical safety or that of another person.
❑ cause substantial harm to another person, who is not a healthcare provider but is referred to in the record.
❑ cause substantial harm to the individual or to another person if your personal representative is allowed access.
❑ Other reason(s) _____ .

If you disagree with my decision made for the reasons in section 4, above, you may have my decision reviewed by a licensed healthcare professional who did not participate in this decision. I will obey the decision of this person. This decision will be made within 30 days of receipt of this form, you will be notified within 15 days after that, and I will act on the decision also within15 days of being told of it. To arrange this review, check the box below. You may also file a complaint about my decision with the Secretary of the DHHS. Our privacy officer will assist you in doing this. If you have any questions or want to know more, please contact the Privacy Officer.

_____   _____
Signature of Health Care Practitioner   Date

Privacy Officer: Name _____ Phone _____
Address _____

❑ I, the client, disagree with your, the healthcare professional's, decision and want an independent review.

640   The right to amend one's PHI

As part of the openness of records which is designed to inform clients of what is in their records, clients generally are given the right, under HIPAA [§ 164.526(c)(1)], to modify their records somewhat. They cannot "correct" or "change" the record but can ask to "amend" it. This means that they can add their information and have this addition linked to the relevant parts of your records. They don't have a right to have any information removed.

As you might expect there are **exceptions** [§164.526(d)] to this right of amendment. You don't need to amend their records if:

- ❑ **You didn't create the PHI** and the client has not provided "a reasonable basis to believe that the originator of protected health information is no longer available to act on the requested amendment."
- ❑ The PHI of concern is **not in your records;** it "is not part of the designated record set."
- ❑ The PI II of concern is **not PHI** which is available for the client's inspection under § 164.524 (see section 630, client access to records, for more on this).
- ❑ You believe **the information is accurate and complete.**

As you can see, there won't be many situations in which you will have to amend your records but the steps are described below so you can refer to them if necessary. The regulations are extensive and complex because this is an important issue.

Procedure

The procedures in the regulations are very detailed. I have grouped them into six sequential steps and rephrased them into ordinary language.

Time one   You receive a request from a client to **examine** his or her own or child's records.

The Privacy Officer has examined the request, evaluated the client's goals, and responded with a copy of the records or a discussion with the client. (This disclosure does *not* have to be documented in the Account of Disclosures but should be in the chart. See Medical Record Access Log, section 650). The client has been notified in the NPP or told by the Privacy Officer that they can amend the record and has completed the form (see section 641) to request amendment.

Time Two   You receive a **Request**[50] for Amendment.

You must act on it within 60 days of receipt. If you can't act within 60 days you must tell the client the reasons for the delay, and the date you will act on it. If you do so, you can extend the date by 30 days but only once.

Time Three   You act on the Request

1. **If you comply with the request** wholly or in part you must::
   a. Identify the record or records of concern in your possession.
   b. Decide on what form of amending you will use: a paragraph of explanation, client-

---

[50] Throughout this book I have used a initial capital to identify a document or form.

provided pages, additional documents, or whatever seems most appropriate.
- c. Provide some link from the records to the amendment. A note on the original record stating that more information can be found at the site of the additions, later in the chart, and under the date you made the addition, should be sufficient.
- d. Tell the client of the amendment and the link.
- e. Get the client's agreement (with a consent or authorization or both, depending on who has the information) to have you notify all persons who need to know of the
- f. Make reasonable efforts, in a reasonable time frame, to provide the amended record to those people whom the client identifies as having received this part of their record and also those whom you identify as having received this PHI (including your business associates) and who might rely on it to the detriment of the client.

2. On the other hand, **if you deny the request,** wholly or in part, you must:
- a. Provide, in a timely manner, to the client, a Denial (letter), written in plain language, which explains your reasons.
- b. You must also, at this time, explain how, if the client disagrees, he or she can file a Disagreement (in writing and usually to the Privacy Officer) detailing why he or she disagrees with the denial. You can limit the size of this Disagreement.
- c. Your Denial letter must also explain that if he or she does not submit this **Disagreement**, the client may still request that you attach his or her Request for Amendment and your denial statements whenever you disclose the PHI of concern (see below, time five) and that you will do so. (HIPAA requires that you do this.)
- d. The Denial must also explain how to complain to the Secretary (see § 160.306) and/or to you by supplying the name or title, and phone number of a contact person (your Privacy Officer).

Time Four   After this interchange, your next steps are these:

1. You can prepare a written **Rebuttal** to the client's statement of Disagreement and if you do, you must provide it to the client.

2. You have to attach to the records of concern which are in your possession the following:
- a. The client's Request for Amendment.
- b. Your Denial (letter) of the request.
- c. The client's Disagreement statement or letter (if the client wrote one).
- d. Your Rebuttal (if you made such).

3. You have to keep some documentation of who was responsible for handling such requests for amendment and all the other papers for six years after this sequence.

Time Five   When you make disclosures

1. Whenever you disclose this part of the client's PHI you must include the four appended documents (see Time 4, #2, a-d) *or* an accurate summary of the above.

2. If the client did not submit a statement of Disagreement, you can include the first two *or* an accurate summary of the above but only if they have requested you to do so.

3. But what if their PHI is sent electronically and you cannot include these documents? You *may* send them separately.

Time Six   When you learn of an Amendment

Whenever you receive notice from another CE that there is an amendment to PHI which you have received, you must add the amendment to it in a timely manner, inform any others you know to have this PHI, and perhaps inform the client.

The regulations

§ 164.526 Amendment of protected health information.

(a) Standard: right to amend.
    (1) Right to amend. An individual has the right to have a covered entity amend protected health information or a record about the individual in a designated record set for as long as the protected health information is maintained in the designated record set.

    (2) Denial of amendment. A covered entity may deny an individual's request for amendment, if it determines that the protected health information or record that is the subject of the request:
        (i) Was not created by the covered entity, unless the individual provides a reasonable basis to believe that the originator of protected health information is no longer available to act on the requested amendment;
        (ii) Is not part of the designated record set;
        (iii) Would not be available for inspection under § 164.524; or
        (iv) Is accurate and complete.

(b) Implementation specifications: requests for amendment and timely action.
    (1) Individual's request for amendment. The covered entity must permit an individual to request that the covered entity amend the protected health information maintained in the designated record set. The covered entity may require individuals to make requests for amendment in writing and to provide a reason to support a requested amendment, provided that it informs individuals in advance of such requirements.
    (2) Timely action by the covered entity.
        (i) The covered entity must act on the individual's request for an amendment no later than 60 days after receipt of such a request, as follows.
            (A) If the covered entity grants the requested amendment, in whole or in part, it must take the actions required by paragraphs (c)(1) and (2) of this section.
            (B) If the covered entity denies the requested amendment, in whole or in part, it must provide the individual with a written denial, in accordance with paragraph (d)(1) of this section.
        (ii) If the covered entity is unable to act on the amendment within the time required by paragraph (b)(2)(i) of this section, the covered entity may extend the time for such action by no more than 30 days, provided that:
            (A) The covered entity, within the time limit set by paragraph (b)(2)(i) of this section, provides the individual with a written statement of the reasons for the delay and the date by which the covered entity will complete its action on the request; and
            (B) The covered entity may have only one such extension of time for action on a request for an amendment.

(c) Implementation specifications: accepting the amendment. If the covered entity accepts the requested amendment, in whole or in part, the covered entity must comply with the following requirements.
    (1) Making the amendment. The covered entity must make the appropriate amendment to the protected health information or record that is the subject of the request for amendment by, at a minimum, identifying the records in the designated record set that are affected by the amendment and appending or otherwise providing a link to the location of the amendment.

(2) Informing the individual. In accordance with paragraph (b) of this section, the covered entity must timely inform the individual that the amendment is accepted and obtain the individual's identification of and agreement to have the covered entity notify the relevant persons with which the amendment needs to be shared in accordance with paragraph (c)(3) of this section.

(3) Informing others. The covered entity must make reasonable efforts to inform and provide the amendment within a reasonable time to:

(i) Persons identified by the individual as having received protected health information about the individual and needing the amendment; and

(ii) Persons, including business associates, that the covered entity knows have the protected health information that is the subject of the amendment and that may have relied, or could foreseeably rely, on such information to the detriment of the individual.

(d) Implementation specifications: denying the amendment. If the covered entity denies the requested amendment, in whole or in part, the covered entity must comply with the following requirements.

(1) Denial. The covered entity must provide the individual with a timely, written denial, in accordance with paragraph (b)(2) of this section. The denial must use plain language and contain:

(i) The basis for the denial, in accordance with paragraph (a)(2) of this section;

(ii) The individual's right to submit a written statement disagreeing with the denial and how the individual may file such a statement;

(iii) A statement that, if the individual does not submit a statement of disagreement, the individual may request that the covered entity provide the individual's request for amendment and the denial with any future disclosures of the protected health information that is the subject of the amendment; and

(iv) A description of how the individual may complain to the covered entity pursuant to the complaint procedures established in § 164.530(d) or to the Secretary pursuant to the procedures established in § 160.306. The description must include the name, or title, and telephone number of the contact person or office designated in §164.530(a)(1)(ii).

(2) Statement of disagreement. The covered entity must permit the individual to submit to the covered entity a written statement disagreeing with the denial of all or part of a requested amendment and the basis of such disagreement. The covered entity may reasonably limit the length of a statement of disagreement.

(3) Rebuttal statement. The covered entity may prepare a written rebuttal to the individual's statement of disagreement. Whenever such a rebuttal is prepared, the covered entity must provide a copy to the individual who submitted the statement of disagreement.

(4) Record keeping. The covered entity must, as appropriate, identify the record or protected health information in the designated record set that is the subject of the disputed amendment and append or otherwise link the individual's request for an amendment, the covered entity's denial of the request, the individual's statement of disagreement, if any, and the covered entity's rebuttal, if any, to the designated record set.

(5) Future disclosures.

(i) If a statement of disagreement has been submitted by the individual, the covered entity must include the material appended in accordance with paragraph (d)(4) of this section, or, at the election of the covered entity, an accurate summary of any such information, with any subsequent disclosure of the protected health information to which the disagreement relates.

(ii) If the individual has not submitted a written statement of disagreement, the covered entity must include the individual's request for amendment and its denial, or an accurate summary of such information, with any subsequent disclosure of the protected health information only if the individual has requested such action in accordance with paragraph (d)(1)(iii) of this section.

(iii) When a subsequent disclosure described in paragraph (d)(5)(i) or (ii) of this section is made using a standard transaction under part 162 of this subchapter that does not permit the additional material to be included with the disclosure, the covered entity may separately transmit the material required by paragraph (d)(5)(i) or (ii) of this section, as applicable, to the recipient of the standard transaction.

(e) Implementation specification: actions on notices of amendment. A covered entity that is informed by another covered entity of an amendment to an individual's protected health information, in accordance with paragraph (c)(3) of this section, must amend the protected health information in designated record sets as provided by paragraph (c)(1) of this section.

(f) Implementation specification: documentation. A covered entity must document the titles of the persons or offices responsible for receiving and processing requests for amendments by individuals and retain the documentation as required by § 164.530(j).

641   Form to request amendment of one's PHI

(On your letterhead)

Form to request an amendment of or addition to my personal healthcare information

Client's name _____ Date of birth _____

Client's Address _____

Telephone_____ Other identification(s) _____

This is page ___ of ____ pages

Date(s) or the part of client's record to be amended _____

_____

Type(s) of information to be amended _____

_____

Please explain how the record is incorrect or incomplete _____

_____

_____

What should the record say to be more accurate or complete? _____

_____

_____

_____

Would you like this amendment sent to those to whom we have disclosed information in the past? If so, please write below the name and address of the organization(s) or individual(s): _____

_____

_____

_____   _____
Signature of client or his or her personal representative   Date

_____   _____
Relationship to the client   Description of personal representative's authority

Decision a of the health care practitioner:

❑ I will comply with this request.

❑ I deny this request because the PHI :
    ❑ was not created by this organization
    ❑ is accurate, in my judgment.
    ❑ is complete, in my judgment.
    ❑ is not available to the client for inspection as permitted by federal law.
    ❑ is not part of client's designated record set.
    ❑ Other reason _____

_____

❑ I will partly comply with this request. I indicate which parts I will amend and not amend. _____

_____

_____

_____

If you, the client, disagree with my decision, please check the box here ❑.

You may write a Letter of Disagreement to the Privacy Officer stating your reasons for disagreeing and your letter will be included whenever we disclose this part of your records.

If you do not write this letter you can ask us to send this Request for Amendment along with our reasons for denying your Request whenever we send this part of your medical records to anyone. If you have any questions or want to know more, please contact the Privacy Officer.

_____   _____
Signature of Health Care Practitioner   Date

Privacy Officer: Name _____ Phone _____

Address _____

650   Medical record disclosures log

The Security Rule requires very complex controls on access to *electronic* records but a small office won't have to do too much. If you use an electronic medical records system it will likely include some ways to keep track of disclosures you made of client's records. If you are a solo practitioner you may use just a word processor to create and keep your records and so will need to make some efforts to secure them – See section 700. However, to release them you will print them out and so they will be paper records.

If you use paper records the Security Rule won't apply but the Privacy rule still does and so you need to keep a paper record of some of the disclosures you have made. You should, to protect yourself, and keep track of what is going on with client records, note at least the information sought on the form below. If you ever receive a request for an accounting of the disclosures you have made you can easily generate the accounting from the information on this form.

I recommend generating this form when you receive the first request for a particular client's records because it keeps all this information in one place, out of the sequential progress notes (where it is likely to be released and so open the door to possible accusations of privacy violations for releasing more than the minimum necessary PHI, etc.), and assures that all necessary information is recorded.

- Add codes to this form as appropriate for your practice.

- Place the form in the front of the chart where it will be seen by anyone seeking to make copies of the records and so will be used.

- Attach copies of the Authorizations (requests to release records) to the back of this form.

651   **Form for a medical record disclosure log**

(On your letterhead)

Medical record disclosure log

Client: _____   File number _____

What PHI was disclosed?[*]	To whom?	For what purpose?	When?	By whom?
_____	_____	_____	_____	_____
_____	_____	_____	_____	_____
_____	_____	_____	_____	_____
_____	_____	_____	_____	_____
_____	_____	_____	_____	_____
_____	_____	_____	_____	_____
_____	_____	_____	_____	_____
_____	_____	_____	_____	_____
_____	_____	_____	_____	_____
_____	_____	_____	_____	_____
_____	_____	_____	_____	_____
_____	_____	_____	_____	_____
_____	_____	_____	_____	_____
_____	_____	_____	_____	_____
_____	_____	_____	_____	_____
_____	_____	_____	_____	_____
_____	_____	_____	_____	_____
_____	_____	_____	_____	_____

This is page ___ of _____ pages.

* Codes: F = Financial, Billing, Collections, Payments.   INT = Intake or evaluation
          PN = Routine Progress Notes   PTN = Psychotherapy Notes   WR = Whole Record

652 An accounting of disclosures

The needed account

First, don't panic. Under HIPAA you *don't* have to keep a record of *all* the disclosures you make or records you release. Not even most of them. You only have to keep an account of those you release for a purpose *other than TPO*. Since the vast majority of records clinicians release are for treatment, payment or healthcare operations, the list you have to keep should be very small.

Second, there are a number of **exceptions** to what the list of disclosures might contain. You do not have to tell the client of disclosures you made:
- ❑ to carry out TPO
- ❑ to the individual him or herself.
- ❑ for law enforcement or national security purposes, or to correctional institutions.
- ❑ when a law enforcement official or a health oversight agency asks you to suspend the individual's right temporarily. See § 164.528(a)(2)(1)] for more details.
- ❑ to your business associates.

Rationale

You can see how the goal of protecting privacy through openness led to this requirement. However, such a small burden can be protective of you as well. Recall that once PHI is released under HIPAA it is almost beyond your control. HIPAA does not contain restrictions on re-release (see section 550 on re-disclosure) beyond that of other CE's or business associates although other federal and state laws will very likely take precedence here. If a client complains about an unauthorized disclosure you will need to show that it did not come from you by providing a list of all your disclosures and their authorizations. I recognize that this scenario is unlikely and the procedure hardly foolproof but this is what this law requires and can work in your best interest.

Contents of the account

The accounting of other disclosures must contain the following:
- ❑ The date of disclosure.
- ❑ The name and address of the organization or person to whom you sent the records.
- ❑ A brief description of the PHI disclosed.
- ❑ "A brief statement of the purpose of the disclosure that reasonably informs the individual of the basis for the disclosure, or in lieu thereof, a copy of the individual's authorization or the request for a disclosure..." which would contain such information.

You must also maintain:
- ❑ A copy of any accounting you furnished to the individual if you have done so.
- ❑ A list of the names and "titles of the persons or offices responsible for receiving and processing requests for an accounting by individuals.

Under HIPAA you have to maintain these for six years after sending the records. If during this six year period you made multiple disclosures to the same person or entity for the same purpose or based on a single authorization, you need only record the above information for the first disclosure, summarize the series of disclosures and add the date of the last disclosure to your accounting. You must keep this accounting and a record of the titles of the person responsible for handling requests for an accounting (this normally would be your Privacy Officer). For the kinds of record therapists usually release it is simpler to keep a record of all releases by just keeping the Authorizations used.

Providing the accounting when requested

- An individual has the right to learn what disclosures you made in the last six years or a since you care began (but no further back than April 14, 2003 for us CEs).

- You can generate this account by referring to the Medical Record Disclosures Log (see Section 571).

- You must act on the request within 60 days of receipt. If you can't act within 60 days you must tell the client the reasons for the delay, and the date you will act on it. If you do so, you can extend the date by 30 days but only once.

- You can't charge for the first accounting in any 12 month period but if other accountings are requested within 12 months you can charge a reasonable, cost-based fee, if you have told the client the fee and allowed them to withdraw or alter their request.

The form

The form in section 654 allows you to make multiple copies of the second page to accommodate more disclosures. You need only enter the numbers for each disclosure in sequence.

A quiz

Do I need to make an entry into a client's medical record disclosure log in these situations?

Q: When I read a record to answer a client's question?
A: No. This is not a disclosure of information but a use.

Q: When I call another provider to discuss a client's condition?
A: No. This disclosure is for treatment, and the Privacy Rule does not require that you keep any account of at all of disclosures for TPO.

Q: When I disclose information to an representative of a health insurance company to pursue a claim or clarify a bill?
A: No. This is a disclosure for payment.

Q: When my secretary looks in a client's chart to call them to remind them of an appointment?
A: No. This is a use, not a disclosure, of information. However, your NPP should have told the client that you might call them to remind them of appointments.

The regulations

§ 164.528 Accounting of disclosures of protected health information.

(a) Standard: right to an accounting of disclosures of protected health information.

(1) An individual has a right to receive an accounting of disclosures of protected health information made by a covered entity in the six years prior to the date on which the accounting is requested, except for disclosures:

(i) To carry out treatment, payment and health care operations as provided in § 164.502;

(ii) To individuals of protected health information about them as provided in § 164.502;

(iii) For the facility's directory or to persons involved in the individual's care or other notification purposes as provided in § 164.510;

(iv) For national security or intelligence purposes as provided in § 164.512(k)(2);

(v) To correctional institutions or law enforcement officials as provided in § 164.512(k)(5); or

(vi) That occurred prior to the compliance date for the covered entity.

(2)

(i) The covered entity must temporarily suspend an individual's right to receive an accounting of disclosures to a health oversight agency or law enforcement official, as provided in § 164.512(d) or (f), respectively, for the time specified by such agency or official, if such agency or official provides the covered entity with a written statement that such an accounting to the individual would be reasonably likely to impede the agency's activities and specifying the time for which such a suspension is required.

(ii) If the agency or official statement in paragraph (a)(2)(i) of this section is made orally, the covered entity must:

(A) Document the statement, including the identity of the agency or official making the statement;

(B) Temporarily suspend the individual's right to an accounting of disclosures subject to the statement; and

(C) Limit the temporary suspension to no longer than 30 days from the date of the oral statement, unless a written statement pursuant to paragraph (a)(2)(i) of this section is submitted during that time.

(3) An individual may request an accounting of disclosures for a period of time less than six years from the date of the request.

(b) Implementation specifications: content of the accounting. The covered entity must provide the individual with a written accounting that meets the following requirements.

(1) Except as otherwise provided by paragraph (a) of this section, the accounting must include disclosures of protected health information that occurred during the six years (or such shorter time period at the request of the individual as provided in paragraph (a)(3) of this section) prior to the date of the request for an accounting, including disclosures to or by business associates of the covered entity.

(2) The accounting must include for each disclosure:

(i) The date of the disclosure;

(ii) The name of the entity or person who received the protected health information and, if known, the address of such entity or person;

(iii) A brief description of the protected health information disclosed; and

(iv) A brief statement of the purpose of the disclosure that reasonably informs the individual of the basis for the disclosure; or, in lieu of such statement:

(A) A copy of the individual's written authorization pursuant to § 164.508; or

(B) A copy of a written request for a disclosure under §§ 164.502(a)(2)(ii) or 164.512, if any.

(3) If, during the period covered by the accounting, the covered entity has made multiple disclosures of protected health information to the same person or entity for a single purpose under §§ 164.502(a)(2)(ii) or 164.512, or pursuant to a single authorization

under § 164.508, the accounting may, with respect to such multiple disclosures, provide:

(i) The information required by paragraph (b)(2) of this section for the first disclosure during the accounting period;

(ii) The frequency, periodicity, or number of the disclosures made during the accounting period; and

(iii) The date of the last such disclosure during the accounting period.

(c) Implementation specifications: provision of the accounting.

(1) The covered entity must act on the individual's request for an accounting, no later than 60 days after receipt of such a request, as follows.

(i) The covered entity must provide the individual with the accounting requested; or

(ii) If the covered entity is unable to provide the accounting within the time required by paragraph (c)(1) of this section, the covered entity may extend the time to provide the accounting by no more than 30 days, provided that:

(A) The covered entity, within the time limit set by paragraph (c)(1) of this section, provides the individual with a written statement of the reasons for the delay and the date by which the covered entity will provide the accounting; and

(B) The covered entity may have only one such extension of time for action on a request for an accounting.

(2) The covered entity must provide the first accounting to an individual in any 12 month period without charge. The covered entity may impose a reasonable, cost-based fee for each subsequent request for an accounting by the same individual within the 12 month period, provided that the covered entity informs the individual in advance of the fee and provides the individual with an opportunity to withdraw or modify the request for a subsequent accounting in order to avoid or reduce the fee.

(d) Implementation specification: documentation. A covered entity must document the following and retain the documentation as required by § 164.530(j):

(1) The information required to be included in an accounting under paragraph (b) of this section for disclosures of protected health information that are subject to an accounting under paragraph (a) of this section;

(2) The written accounting that is provided to the individual under this section; and

(3) The titles of the persons or offices responsible for receiving and processing requests for an accounting by individuals.

653 **Form to request an Account of Disclosures**

(on your letterhead)

**Form to request an accounting of disclosures of my
Protected Health Information**

Date of Request: _____ Record No.: _____

Name: _____ Date of Birth: _____

Address: _____

_____

Time period

I would like an accounting of all disclosures of my PHI you made from _____ to
_____. The maximum is six years before this request and no further back that April
14, 2003.

Cost

I understand that there is ❑ no charge for this accounting or ❑ a fee of $ _____
because this is a second or later request within twelve months and I will pay the feet.

Response time for my request

I have been informed that I will receive either the requested accounting or an explanation
of the causes of the delay within 30 days.

_____   _____
Signature of client or his or her personal representative   Date

_____   _____
Printed name of client or personal representative   Relationship to the client

_____
Description of personal representative's authority

<u>For office use only</u>
Date we received this request _____
Date the Account sent: _____
Name of privacy officer who processed this request_____

654   Form for an Account of Disclosures

(On your letterhead)

An account of disclosures of my protected healthcare information

Client's name _____ Case number _____

Instructions

1. **Staff DO NOT need to make an entry on this form when:**
   - ❑ The disclosure was made or is to be made to carry out TPO - treatment, payment, or health care operations
   - ❑ The disclosure is or was made to:
     - ❑ the client for his or her own purposes
     - ❑ law enforcement personnel or national security purposes
     - ❑ correctional institutions.
     - ❑ a business associate.
   - ❑ This disclosure was one of many made to the same person or entity. Just enter the first disclosure and the dates of subsequent disclosures.
   - ❑ The disclosures occurred prior to the date the clinician of entity became compliant with HIPAA (usually April 14, 2003).
   - ❑ The date of the last disclosure was more than six years before the date of the present request.

2. **Consult with the Privacy Officer before releasing this account.**

Date accounting was requested _____ 30 days later will be _____

Fee for providing this accounting The first copy in any twelve month period is free. Additional copies will be charged $ _____ . If a fee is imposed, tell the client in advance of providing this accounting and let them cancel or modify their request for the accounting.

Name of person providing this account _____

Title of person _____ Date sent to client _____

1. Date _____

PHI Sent to _____

Address _____

What PHI was disclosed? _____

Why was this needed? _____

. Date _____

PHI Sent to _____

Address _____

What PHI was disclosed? _____

Why was this needed? _____

. Date _____

PHI Sent to _____

Address _____

What PHI was disclosed? _____

Why was this needed? _____

. Date _____

PHI Sent to _____

Address _____

What PHI was disclosed? _____

Why was this needed? _____

. Date _____

PHI Sent to _____

Address _____

What PHI was disclosed? _____

Why was this needed? _____

. Date _____

PHI Sent to _____

Address _____

What PHI was disclosed? _____

Why was this needed? _____

❑   End of this accounting of disclosures or Disclosures continue onto page ___

Page___ of ___

660   Complaints and reports of privacy violations

Note: Take any and all complaints or reports of problems seriously. They can be the harbinger of a ethics complaint, licensing board action or worse. Act immediately.

As part of your NPP you mentioned that there is a method available for clients to lodge complaints or report violations of their or others privacy. While these are not necessarily the same things it is simpler and more convenient to combine them and have them addressed by the Privacy Officer. Also, having such a mechanism is part of good client relations and a valuable sentinel for heading off more serious problems.

Timeliness

"This complaint must be filed within 180 days of when the complainant knew or should have known that the act had occurred. The Secretary may waive this 180-day time limit if good cause is shown. See 45 CFR 160.306 and164.534. OCR will provide further information on its web site about how to file a complaint (www.hhs.gov/ocr/hipaa/)." *OCR Guidance Explaining Significant Aspects of the Privacy Rule - December 4, 2002*

[OCR is the Office of Civil Rights of the Department of Health and Human Services.]

Sample complaint form

In the sample complaint form below I have combined a variety of problems which might arise and deliberately avoided the use of the word "complaint." Filing this form is the second step, after talking to the Privacy Officer, in resolving a complaint.

Anonymous reporting

While HIPAA does not require anonymity be offered, it is always a good policy and the form below incorporates it.

Online complaint filing

The third step in resolving a compliant of a privacy violation is filing with the Office of Civil Rights, which is responsible for investigating complaints of HIPAA privacy violations. A form and Fact Sheet are available in English and Spanish at <http://www.hhs.gov/ocr/generalinfo.html. Filing can be done from: <http://www.hhs.gov/ocr/privacyhowtofile.htm>. Both were accessed Oct. 12, 2005.

Complaints on paper can be sent to Privacy Complaints, P. O. Box 8050, U. S. Department of Health and Human Services, Centers for Medicare & Medicaid Services, 7500 Security Boulevard, Baltimore, Maryland 21244-1850.

The regulations

Section § 164.520 (b)(1)(vi) and (vii) require that you provide a mechanism for reporting privacy violations and Section § 164.530 addresses the requirement for complaints about your policies and procedures.

§ 164.520 Notice of privacy practices for protected health information.
(b) Implementation specifications: content of notice.

(1) Required elements. The covered entity must provide a notice that is written in plain language and that contains the elements required by this paragraph.

(vi) Complaints. **The notice must contain a statement that individuals may complain to the covered entity and to the Secretary if they believe their privacy rights have been violated,** a brief description of how the individual may file a complaint with the covered entity, and a statement that the individual will not be retaliated against for filing a complaint.

(vii) **Contact**. The notice must contain the name, or title, and telephone number of a person or office to contact for further information as required by § 164.530(a)(1)(ii).

§ 164.530 Administrative requirements.
(d)

(1) Standard: **complaints** to the covered entity. A covered entity must provide a process for individuals to make complaints concerning the covered entity's policies and procedures required by this subpart or its compliance with such policies and procedures or the requirements of this subpart.

(2) Implementation specification: documentation of complaints. As required by paragraph (j) of this section, a covered entity must **document all complaints received**, and their **disposition**, if any.

(g) Standard: refraining from intimidating or **retaliatory** acts. A covered entity may not intimidate, threaten, coerce, discriminate against, or take other retaliatory action against:

(1) Individuals. Any individual for the exercise by the individual of any right under, or for participation by the individual in any process established by this subpart, including the filing of a complaint under this section;

(2) Individuals and others. Any individual or other person for:

(i) Filing of a complaint with the Secretary under subpart C of part 160 of this subchapter;

(ii) Testifying, assisting, or participating in an investigation, compliance review, proceeding, or hearing under Part C of Title XI; or

(iii) Opposing any act or practice made unlawful by this subpart, provided the individual or person has a good faith belief that the practice opposed is unlawful, and the manner of the opposition is reasonable and does not involve a disclosure of protected health information in violation of this subpart.

661 Complaint form

(On your Letterhead)

Is there a problem?

If you are not satisfied with your experiences in our office we want to hear from you so that we can provide our services to you in ways that we both find satisfactory.

If you have a problem with anything about our practice, first, speak with one of our staff. If the problem is with your insurance, bills, or payment, talk to _____ who is our _____ . If the problem is with your therapy, talk to your therapist or Case Manager. If you believe there has been some kind of violation of the confidentiality or the privacy of your records speak to our Privacy Officer, _____ and let us clarify and fix the situation. If you don't know whom to talk to about a problem ask our Privacy Officer for advice.

If you are not satisfied or the problems still continues please fill out this simple form and I assure you it will be investigated, we will try our best to fix it, and to repair any damage that has been done. Also, I promise you that we will not in any way limit your care here or take any actions against you if you bring a problem to our attention. Also, you do not have to put your name on this form if you do not want to. Thank you.

Client's name _____ Date of birth _____

Identification No. _____ Telephone number _____

Client's address _____

What is or was the problem? _____

_____

_____

What would you like to see done about the problem? _____

_____

_____

_____   _____
Signature of client or his or her personal representative   Date

_____   _____
Printed name of client or personal representative   Relationship to the client

_____
Description of personal representative's authority

Note: A response must be made within 30 days from when you, the Privacy Officer receive this form if a name is given on the form. Indicate action taken on a separate page.

_____   _____   Version #___
Privacy Officer   Phone

700 HIPAA's Security Rule

701   Rationale and necessity of the Security Rule

The intent of the rule (Part 142 - Security and Electronic Signature Standards of the HIPAA law) is to assure the access to EPHI is limited to only those authorized (by the patient) and to protect it from an interesting variety of threats. Previously, there was no minimum standard for the protection for PHI stored or distributed electronically over telecommunication systems. In 1997, the National Research Council reported widespread weaknesses in healthcare security measures such as user authentication, access controls, audit trails, controls of external communication links and access, physical security, systems back up, and disaster recovery. The final Security Rule was published in the *Federal Register* February 20, 2003.

BIG POINT: The American Psychological Association's Practice Organization (APAPO) views the psychologist's fully addressing the issues raised by the Security Rule, making good decisions about these rather technical and legal issues, and especially documenting the choices made and their rationales (by writing a HIPAA Policy and Procedures Manual – HP&PM) as **absolutely essential** to the continued legitimate functioning of psychologists. They believe that were a privacy breech (an unauthorized disclosure) to be reported, the HIPAA investigators (from the Federal Office of Civil Rights) would first and foremost want to see the clinician's HP&PM. (Personal communications, July 2005.)

Therefore, besides the usual educational efforts of CE courses and articles in APA journals, the PO, with APAIT, has developed a *HIPAA Security Rule Online Compliance Workbook*. It will, after describing each safeguarding procedure in the Security Rule, offer some guidance and options, and help the user borrow or write the text for a tailored HP&PM. It also offers a sample disaster plan and some other related resources. For more on this see <http://www.apapractice.org/apo/hipaa/course.html>. It is available to APAPO members and APAIT subscribers for $100 with 4 CE credits and at higher cost to others.

•   CMS has published 6 pamphlets in the *HIPAA Security Series* which offer quite specific information for compliance with the HIPAA Security Rule. A reading of these 100 pages will make you quite an expert.
<http://www.cms.hhs.gov/hipaa/hipaa2/education/default.asp#SecurityEd>.

702 Some aspects of the Security Rule make compliance easier

Before you toss this book aside feeling overwhelmed by these demands consider these points.

1. **The Privacy and Security Rules interact**. As a result, much of what you do for the Privacy Rule will protect you for the Security Rule. The rules are interdependent and need to be simultaneously considered in all decisions. **Privacy is the goal; the methods of achieving it are security** or less tersely, "Security applies to the spectrum of physical, technical and administrative safeguards that are put in place to protect the integrity, availability and confidentiality of information." (Gue, 2002). Or from a different perspective "... while the Privacy Rule outlines the process for obtaining authorized disclosures of protected health information, the Security Rule focuses on preventing unauthorized disclosure. A separate set of steps must be taken to ensure compliance with both. " (APA Practice Organization, by Legal and Regulatory Affairs Staff, No date.)

2. The security rule does not distinguish between internal communications and communications that are external to a CE (as does the Privacy Rule). It covers both transmitting PHI and *storing* it, **so even if you** haven't transmitted them but only write your records on a word processor, or store them on disks, you must comply with the Security Rule (and so with all the rest of HIPAA). **Essentially, you must comply with both.**

3. While the privacy rule applies to all PHI, the security rule's standards **apply only to PHI that is in an electronic form (EPHI) - not PHI on paper!** But no champagne yet for you who gingerly use your computers only as super typewriters.

4. Note that for clinicians the Security Rule **became final on April 21, 2005** so that at this point you will have to implement them as part of your becoming HIPAA-compliant whenever you decide to do so.

5. The rules and regulations are **not rigidly prescriptive and flexibly allow you to choose** from many means to provide the necessary security of records. Structurally, there are **standards** which are more abstract and then **implementation specifications** which are more specific. Standards can be adopted flexibly..

> § 164.306 Security standards: General rules.
> (b) Flexibility of approach.
>   (1) Covered entities may use any security measures that allow the covered entity to **reasonably and appropriately** implement the standards and implementation specifications as specified in this subpart.
>   (2) In deciding which security measures to use, a covered entity must take into account the following factors:
>   (i) The size, complexity, and capabilities of the covered entity.
>   (ii) The covered entity's technical infrastructure, hardware, and software security capabilities.
>   (iii) The costs of security measures.
>   (iv) The probability and criticality of potential risks to electronic protected health information.

The implementation specifications are of two types - "required" and "addressable" (more on this later). The procedure for considering and responding to each addressable IS gives you options.

§ 164.306 (d).
    a. "**Assess** whether each implementation specification is a **reasonable and appropriate safeguard** in its environment, when analyzed with reference to the likely contribution to protecting the entity's electronic protected health information; and" then
    b. Either implement the specification if it is "**reasonable and appropriate**" or
    c. If it is not "reasonable and appropriate" do these:
        "(1) **Document** why it would not be reasonable and appropriate to implement the implementation specification; and
        (2) Implement an **equivalent alternative** measure if **reasonable and appropriate.**"

Note the use of the phrase to "reasonably and appropriately implement the standards." This allows you to choose how much effort time and money to invest in safeguards.

6. Safeguards need be only "reasonable and appropriate" efforts to protect against both intentional and accidental violations. **You do not have to protect your records against all possible threats but only those most likely, realistic, and current in your present judgment.**

7. Also, the standards are "**technologically neutral**" so that you can select hardware and software which best suits your needs.

8. As you will see most of the security requirements applicable to small practices are **just good sense**. You *should* backup your data, limit access with passwords, arrange your workspaces so that patients cannot see your computer screens, protect you computers against viri and other attacks, etc.

9. **Preemption applies here too.** "The statute requires generally that the [HIPAA] security standards supersede contrary provisions of State law including State law requiring medical or health plan records to be maintained or transmitted in written rather than electronic formats." Ibid. I interpret this to mean that all state medical/health/mental health/substance abuse records will have to be computerized.

10. CMS will publish a seventh **pamphlet** in the *HIPAA Security Series* to address the needs of small practices. It was unpublished as of Oct. 12, 2005 but do check at: <http://www.cms.hhs.gov/hipaa/hipaa2/education/default.asp#SecurityEd>.

710   Complying with the Security Rule

Okay, I believe you don't want to think about this. You are already fully occupied with helping demoralized and defeated clients, running a complex business in a tough market, and maybe even being a member of a family and community in your spare time. Complying with HIPPAA looks hard; it is complex and full of unknown risks. And, it's written in a language (legal jargon and bureaucratese) where English words have other meanings. The jargon has precise meanings arrived at through history and litigation. All the materials I have seen start with the HIPAA law as written and try to explain it to us non-lawyers There is no overlap of legal jargon with clinicians' jargon and so the words are opaque and even with intense reading barely translucent.

I struggled with this law and it finally dawned on me: the lawyers' approach to the issues and solutions is lot like what we do with a new client: we do an assessment (gap analysis): gather the facts and history, identify the dynamics (risk analysis) involved at different levels (individual, family, etc, needs and wishes, rewards and cues, etc. design appropriate goals, and propose and negotiate a basic treatment plan (risk management plan). The plan has to fit the resources available, not be in conflict with other goals and plans, be tried and lastly, be revised. Since we actually are *good* at this it won't be too hard. Really. Relax. Let me show you how this plays out in HIPAA's risk analysis and risk management.

A Review: Gap Analysis' data -> Risk Analysis -> Risk Management Plan +
HIPAA Policies and Procedures Manual

Section 250 is designed to allow you to collect data on how your office handles PHI/EPHI: who, how, and where it is created, received, stored and distributed and disclosed. This supports the Risk Analysis - to identify potential threats to and vulnerabilities of information systems and the associated risk - which in turn will be the basis for your Risk Management plan. No government agency offers a compliance-guaranteeing method but a commonly relied on a publication (*NIST SP 800-30*) offers steps. The quotes below are from this and the *HIPAA Security Series* pamphlet number 6 to which I have added comments.

711   Risk Analysis

The Security Rule requires CEs to do a Risk Analysis, that is to "[c]onduct an accurate and thorough assessment of the potential risks and vulnerabilities to the confidentiality, integrity, and availability of electronic protected health formation held by the covered entity." § 164.308(a)(1)(ii)(A). What does this actually require?

1. **Identify the scope of the risk analysis** which "is the potential risks and vulnerabilities to the confidentiality, availability and integrity of all EPHI that a covered entity creates, receives, maintains, or transmits. This includes EPHI in all forms of electronic media: hard drives, floppy disks, CDs, DVDs, Smart Cards, Personal Digital Assistants (PDAs), transmission media, or portable electronic storage media (generically, removable media). This is actually designed to limit the work you must do.

2. **Gather data** on where the EPHI is stored, received, maintained or transmitted. This is the data for the gap analysis. A CE "could gather relevant data by: reviewing past and/or existing projects; performing interviews; reviewing documentation; or using other data gathering techniques. The data on EPHI gathered using these methods must be documented. (See §§ 164.308(a)(1)(ii)(A) and 164.316(b)(1).)" A small office with paper records and only some electronic billing would find this very easy to do.

3. Identify and document **potential threats and vulnerabilities** "to the confidentiality,

availability and integrity of the EPHI. As discussed earlier, the potential for a threat to trigger or exploit a specific vulnerability creates risk. Therefore, identification of threats and vulnerabilities are central to determining the level of risk."

CEs can start with a categorized list of **threats** (such as natural, human, and environmental) and also identify threats unique to the circumstances of their environment. CEs should focus the list of threats to those that are reasonably anticipated. In fact. human threats will be of greatest concern. Sources include "employees (the most common source), ex-employees, hackers, commercial rivals, terrorists, criminals, general public, vendors, customers and visitors. Anyone that has the access, knowledge and/or motivation to cause an adverse impact on the covered entity can act as a threat."

CEs should create a list of **vulnerabilities**. "Sources of information to identify non-technical vulnerabilities may include previous risk analysis documentation, audit reports or security review reports. Sources of information to identify technical vulnerabilities may include assessments of information systems, information system security testing, or publicly available vulnerability lists and advisories" on the internet and the CEs outside vendors or contractors.

4. **Assess current security measures**. "Security measures can be both technical and non-technical. Technical measures are part of information systems hardware and software. Examples … include access controls, identification, authentication, encryption methods, automatic logoff and audit controls. Non-technical measures are management and operational controls, such as policies, procedures, standards, guidelines, accountability and responsibility, and physical and environmental security measures." "The output of this step should be documentation of the security measures a covered entity uses to safeguard EPHI."

5. Determine the **likelihood** of threat occurrence. One set of categories is this.
"• High Likelihood – a high probability exists that a threat will trigger or exploit one or more vulnerabilities. This might be due to the existence of multiple organizational deficiencies, such as the absence, inadequacy or improper configuration of security controls, or due to geographic location (such as, within a flood zone).
• Medium Likelihood – a moderate probability … due to the existence of a single organizational deficiency, such as the lack of security measures.
• Low Likelihood – a low probability … due to the existence of a single organizational deficiency, such as improper configuration of security controls. "

"The output of this step should be documentation of all threat and vulnerability combinations with associated likelihood ratings that may impact the confidentiality, availability and integrity of EPHI of a covered entity"

6. Determine the potential **impact**. "The most common outcomes include, but are not limited to: unauthorized access to or disclosure of EPHI, permanent loss or corruption of EPHI, temporary unavailability of EPHI, financial losses, and the loss of physical assets. Consideration of these outcomes will also be the basis for "prioritizing risk mitigation activities."

7. Determine the **level of risk** based on the conclusions from the previous two steps– likelihood of threats and their impact. The above cited publication suggests a risk level matrix based on these two sources of data, i. e. high, medium, and low risk levels.

8. Identify **security measures** and finalize documentation. For each rated entry, specific actions and a timeline are to be assigned so that the risk can be reduced. Lastly, of course, all this must be written down. "The evaluation, prioritization, modification, and implementation of security measures identified in this step is part of the risk management process, addressed in the next section"

712   Risk management

This "includes the implementation of security measures to reduce risk to reasonable and appropriate levels to, among other things, ensure the confidentiality, availability and integrity of EPHI, protect against any reasonably anticipated threats or hazards to the security or integrity of EPHI, and protect against any reasonably anticipated uses or disclosures of EPHI that are not permitted or required under the HIPAA Privacy Rule."

1. **Develop and Implement a Risk Management Plan**. "The purpose of a risk management plan is to provide structure for the covered entity's evaluation, prioritization, and implementation of risk-reducing security measures." "The risk analysis ...will provide ... the information needed to make risk prioritization and mitigation decisions." "Cost is one of the factors a covered entity must consider when determining security measures to implement. However, cost alone is not a valid reason for choosing not to implement security measures that are reasonable and appropriate."

2. **Implement Security Measures** "… these projects or activities should each have an identified scope, timeline and budget."

3. **Evaluate and Maintain Security Measures**. "Security measures implemented to comply with standards and implementation specifications adopted under § 164.105 [(the Organizational Requirements)] and this subpart [(the Security Rule)] must be reviewed and modified as needed to continue provision of reasonable and appropriate protection of [EPHI] as described at § 164.316." § 164.306(e). "The Security Rule does not specify how frequently to perform risk analysis and risk management."

"In Summary: Risk analysis and risk management are the foundation of a covered entity's Security Rule compliance efforts."

713   The regulations of the Security Rule with commentary

The extensive quotations from the regulations which follow is designed both for quick skimming (read just the **boldfaced** words) and to show you how comprehensive the rule is and so what you must consider to become compliant with the Security Rule. Note that the list below is rearranged, condensed, and sometimes reworded from the published regulations. I have added definitions and clarifications as well as comments to try to bridge the jargon chasm between clinicians and lawyers/bureaucrats/technologists. The comments are addressed to you, the employer, senior staff, Security Officer, or solo practitioner.

The rule recognizes that the fields of information technology and the electronic medical record are rapidly evolving but that some kinds of safeguards must be universally adopted and others cannot be specified by law but will be developed in the process of working computer programs and EPHI. Therefore the Security Rule separates the computerized functions and procedures for securely handling EPHI - called **implementation specifications** or **IS** - into two kinds: 1. Those methods considered to be broadly and likely permanently needed are called **required** in HIPAA, and, 2. Those which are equally essential for security but whose methods and approach to solution can vary with computer programs, organizational needs, local history or other variables. These latter are called **addressable** ISs. Implementing them is **not optional**; only the methods for doing so are open to your judgment and choice. I count 27 specifications as required and which must be implemented as written and 22 as "Addressable." These are no less important, enforced, or complicated than those "required"

Each **Implementation Specification (IS)** is marked as (**Required**) and I have used words like must, have to, and should. Specifications whose methods you have to weigh are marked as (**Addressable**) and I have used words like addressed, dealt with, considered, and the like. I have added boldface for easier locating of topics. And lastly, each IS has been numbered (like this **1, 2, 3**) on the far left side for reference and clarity.

The Security Rule addresses **four areas** with Implementation Specifications (IS) in each. There are the three Administrative, Physical, and Technical Safeguards and the Policies and Procedures Documentation Requirements. We will tackle them in order and con brio. Reading regulations can be fun. Fun. Fun.

Area 1   Administrative safeguards.   § 164.308(a)

These administrative procedures are the documented (written), formal practices to manage the selection and execution of security measures.

(1)(i) Security management process
1   (A) **Risk analysis** (Required). How is PHI/EPHI created, stored, and used in your office? [See section 250 of this book] What risks is EPHI exposed to? (See above)
2   (B) **Risk management** (Required). You must manage – with a plan – the risks you discover.
3   (C) **Sanction policy** (Required). What negative actions will you take against employees who fail to comply with your security policies and procedures.
4   (D) **Information system activity review** (Required). Regularly review records of computer activity, as recorded in audit logs, access reports, and security incident tracking reports, all generated by the computer.

5   (2) Identify **the security official** (Required) who is responsible for implementing the Security Rule. This does not have to be the Privacy Officer.

(3)(I) **Workforce** security.
6   (A) **Authorization and/or supervision** (Addressable) of workforce members who will and do work with PHI.
7   (B) **Workforce clearance procedure** (Addressable) determines that everyone who access PHI is appropriate by criteria you decide such as training or work title.
8   (C) **Termination procedures** (Addressable) for preventing access to PHI when the person is no longer employed by you.
•   Comments: Besides the usual selection processes of hiring such as background, reference, and credential checks HIPAA expects you to remove the access to PHI of those employees you dismiss or otherwise stop employing. You must have a plan for removing their access to records but it may be as simple as collecting keys and passcards and removing their user accounts (IDs) from access lists on the computers.

(4)(i): Information **access management**.
9   (A) (This does not apply to therapists)
10   (B) **Access authorization** (Addressable). How will you enable only some staff to access PHI.
11   (C) **Access establishment and modification** (Addressable) through policies and procedures you establish, document, review, and modify a user's access to a workstation, transaction, program, or process. For example, some staff are given access to only some information and others to all PHI.

(5)(i): **Security awareness and training.**

12 (A) **Security reminders** (Addressable). Periodic notices to staff to attend to security practices.

13 (B) **Protection from malicious software** (Addressable). Procedures for guarding against, detecting, neutralizing, and reporting viri, Trojan horses, spyware, etc. (The inclusive term for these is "malware.")

14 (C) **Log-in monitoring** (Addressable). Recording who uses the computer system and when.

15 (D) **Password management (**Addressable). Limiting who accesses the computer to only those authorized by you with a technology like passwords.

• Training is mentioned in the title but has no IS so that it can be flexible. The contents might include security awareness, updates on viri, worms, and similar intruders, reporting of access failures, etc. Privacy issues can be integrated into and combined with security training. Retraining and reminders should also be parts of your operation. And, *all* personnel should be included.

(6)(i): **Security incident procedures.**

16 (ii) **Response and Reporting** (Required). Identify and respond to suspected or known security incidents (like loss of information to a virus). Mitigate, to the extent practicable, the harmful effects of security incidents that you learn about and as soon as practicable. Document security incidents and their outcomes. You must have methods for discovering these unauthorized disclosures or threats of disclosure.

(7)(i) **Contingency plan** for responding to an emergency or other occurrence (for example, fire, vandalism, system failure, and natural disaster) that damages systems that contain PHI.

17 (A) **Data backup plan** (Required). Schedule systematic full and incremental backups of PHI. Test the backups. Store the data safely, probably off-site.

18 (B) **Disaster recovery plan** (Required) includes procedures to restore any lost of data. See section 740 of this book.

19 (C) **Emergency mode operation plan** (Required) to enable continuation of critical business processes with continued protection of the security of PHI.

20 (D) **Testing and revision procedures** (Addressable) of contingency plans.

21 (E) **Applications and data criticality analysis** (Addressable). Evaluate the relative importance of specific computer programs and data in supporting the contingency plan, above.

22 (8) **Evaluation.** (Required) Perform a periodic technical and non-technical evaluation of the extent to which an your office's security policies and procedures meet the requirements.

23 § 164.308(b)(1) **Business associate contracts** (Required). The requirements parallel those of the Privacy rule discussed in section 270. Three more sections of the regulations add three more required ISs (numbers **43, 44**, and **45**): 164.314(a)(i), (a) 2 (i) and (a) 2 (ii). They are not included here because they rarely apply to therapists.

Area 2   Physical safeguards   § 164.310

(a)(1) **Facility access controls to** limit physical access to computers and buildings to those properly authorized persons.

24 (a)(2)(i) **Contingency operations** (Addressable) so you can get, use, and share PHI in the event of an emergency.

25 (ii) **Facility security plan** (Addressable) to safeguard the facility and the equipment therein from unauthorized physical access, tampering, and theft.

26   (iii) **Access control and validation procedures** (Addressable) to ensure and limit a person's access to facilities based on their role or function, including visitor control, and control of access to software programs for testing and revision.

27   (iv) **Maintenance records** (Addressable) document repairs and modifications to the physical components of a facility which are related to security (for example, hardware, walls, doors, and locks).

28 (b) **Workstation use.** (Required)

29 (c) **Workstation security** (Required) restricts actual access to the computers authorized users.

(d)(1) **Device and media control** of the receipt and removal of hardware and electronic media that contain PHI into and out of a facility, and the movement of these items within the facility.

30   (2)(i) **Disposal** (Required) of media with PHI.

31   (ii) **Media re-use** (Required). Complete erasure of PHI before re-use of media.

32   (iii) **Accountability** (Addressable). Maintain a record of the movements of hardware and electronic media and any person responsible therefore.

33   (iv) **Data backup and storage** (Addressable). Create a retrievable, exact copy of electronic protected health information, when needed, before movement of equipment.

- For all of this section D i-iv, see section 750.

Area 3   Technical safeguards

These are the processes that protect and monitor information access and that prevent unauthorized access to data that is transmitted over a network
§ 164.312

(a)(1) **Access control** allows computer use of PHI to only those persons or software programs that have been granted access rights. The PHI must also be protected, when it is stored, from intruders trying to access your computers through external communication points.

34   (2)(i) **Unique user identification** (Required). No shared, reused, or duplicate IDs.

35   (ii) **Emergency access procedure** (Required) for obtaining EPHI in an emergency.

36   (iii) **Automatic logoff** (Addressable) procedures that terminate an computer session after a predetermined time of inactivity so that no one else can casually read what is on screen.

37   (iv) **Encryption and decryption** (Addressable) of PHI stored and used. Note that encryption is not *required* only addressable.

- Comment: Different levels of access to PHI should depend on a user's job's needs. Possibilities include context-based access (for example, different access for the billing department than the clinician's offices), role-based access (different access to billers and clinicians), or identity-based (different access to Joe in billing than to Mary the therapist) so that only those employees who have a business need may access such information. The system must also allow emergency access.

38 (b) **Audit controls** (Required) record and examine activity on computers that contain or use EPHI.

- An audit trail is information about who accessed the PHI or altered it by editing, adding or deleting information and when. The trail of dates and actions can then be examined or audited.

39 (c)(1) **Integrity.** (2) **Mechanism to authenticate electronic protected health information** (Addressable) to corroborate that PHI has not been altered or destroyed in an unauthorized manner.

40 (d) **Person or entity authentication** (Required) to verify that a person or organization seeking access to EPHI is really the unique one he, she, or it claims to be.
• **User identification** and authentication is to prevent the incorrect identification of an entity who is accessing secure data. If your practice uses a networked computer system each person authorized to have access should have a unique identifier. Passwords, tokens (cards, dongles, keys), and biometric measurements such as fingerprints and retinal images are identifiers.

(e)(1) **Transmission security** measures guard against unauthorized access to PHI that is being transmitted over an electronic communications network.
41 (2)(i) **Integrity controls** (Addressable) ensure that electronically transmitted PHI is not improperly modified without detection until disposed of.
42 (ii) **Encryption** (Addressable) of EPHI is not *required* but you must implement a mechanism to encrypt EPHI whenever deemed necessary. See also IS #37, above. I think there are two ISs because the methods and procedures for encrypting transmission will be different from those of storage and use.
• **Data authentication** and the verification of integrity concern assuring that the data received is the same as the data sent; that it has not been accidentally corrupted or altered during storage or more likely, during transmission. This is what the lawyers call a document's probative value - whether it can be relied on to be authentic. So called "electronic" or "digital signatures" increase the capability of uniquely identifying who created, sent, and received PHI via electronic transmittal systems. HIPAA does not require such electronic signatures but see section below.

Area 4   Policies and procedures and documentation requirements § 164.316

You have to write down your policies and procedures. This will constitute your HIPAA P&PM.
46 (a) **Policies and procedures.** (Required). You must "... implement reasonable and appropriate policies and procedures to comply with the standards .... This standard is not to be construed to permit or excuse an action that violates any other standard, implementation specification, or other requirements of this subpart. A covered entity **may change its policies and procedures at any time, provided that the changes are documented and are implemented** in accordance with this subpart."

(b) (1) **Documentation** of the policies and procedures implemented to comply with this subpart must be kept in written form (which may be electronic); and
(ii) If an action, activity or assessment is required by this subpart to be documented, maintain a written record of the action, activity, or assessment. subpart; and
47 (f)(2)(i) **Time limit** (Required). Retain the documentation required by paragraph (b)(1) of this section for **6 years** from the date of its creation or the date when it last was in effect, whichever is later.
48 (ii) **Availability** (Required). Make documentation available to those persons responsible for implementing the procedures to which the documentation pertains.
49 (iii) **Updates** (Required). Review documentation periodically, and update.

From what I understand, risk management as required is the incorporation of these standards and ISs into document which is called both a risk management plan and a HIPAA Policies and Procedures Plan or Manual. For this see section 800.

720   The office's communication methods

Office machines

"Copy machines, fax machines, and telephones, even those that contain memory and can produce multiple copies for multiple people are not intended to be included in the term 'computer.' Therefore, because 'paper-to-paper'[51] faxes, person-to-person telephone calls, video teleconferencing, or messages left on voice-mail were not in electronic form before the transmission, those activities are not covered by this rule. See also the definition of 'electronic media' at § 160.103." From the Comments on the Final Security Rule.

While this excludes most of these communication methods from the Security Rule, they are still covered by the Privacy Rule. Rather than list them here as well, most of the ideas about maintaining privacy when using telephones, answering machines, and faxes they have been incorporated into the checklist in section 760.

Telephones

• Use a telephone in ways you cannot, or are very unlikely to, be overheard. Stepping away form a public desk, covering the mouthpiece with your hand, using a phone in a private office, and similar precautions are necessary. Don't take risks; interrupt the call to move to a more private location.

Leaving messages on a client's answering machine or voice mail

HIPAA warns us to be very cautious in our communications which might contain direct or indirect PHI. An example is the concern over what information to leave on a client's answering machine where the messages can be picked up by other than the client. Current advice includes:
• Obtaining the client's authorization as to the number on which confidential messages can be securely left. See section 620.
• Messages to other numbers should be so vague as to prevent linking a client with his or her medical condition. Phrases such as "response to your question" or "a call about your concern" might be used.
• It might be best to leave only a message suggesting when the client can return your call most conveniently.
• Offer your phone number only when the client does not have it and don't indicate any clinician's or practice's name. Use phrases such as, "Please call me at 123-456-7890" when you believe the client will recognize your voice.

Faxes, faxing, and fax machines under HIPAA

Faxes are almost instantaneous, less expensive than regular mail (postal, land, or "snail mail"), and create a reliable paper record. However, fax machines which not specifically labeled as secure offer very little privacy protection. While the message goes out in sounds over telephone lines and so is hidden in the other millions of calls, faxes don't guarantee the identities of the sender or recipient of the fax or that the content was not altered after it was sent (i.e. that some of it was lost or removed or that another message mixed in accidentally or deliberately). However, faxes have the legal protections afforded to private telephone messages.

While paper-to-paper faxes are not subject to the Transaction or Security Rules, the Privacy Rule requires you to make significant efforts to assure the privacy of faxed PHI. It requires

---

[51] This suggests that faxing from your computer and to another's computer *would* be covered by the Security Rule. Putting a pretty fine point on it, eh?

administrative procedures, *physical* safeguards, and *technical* security services, that maintain the integrity, confidentiality, and availability of the PHI and prevent unauthorized access.

Physical and technical safeguards

- Mark the number of pages sent on each cover sheet and count the number of pages received and match it with the number sent to assure that none are misplaced.
- If your fax machine is accessible to anyone who should not see PHI consider a machine with separate "mailboxes" with password protection. Unless a code is entered the pages will not print out.
- Newer equipment can be set to send faxes only to a list of numbers known to be secure. If a fax transmission is attempted to a machine not on their list of secure numbers, a message is sent instead telling the recipient that a confidential fax is available but will not be released until a stated procedure is followed by a human (E. g. having their fax call for the fax residing on your machine – this is called poling) that assures that the fax is secure.
- Faxing from a computer to another computer can use encryption programs and there are companies which will make this kind of secure and encrypted faxing quite easy.
- Require that the Privacy Officer enter all the phone numbers of recipients of your faxes. Require that all outgoing faxes be sent to numbers the machine has in its memory and that no one fax by entering a different or new number. Thus few faxes will be misdirected due to erroneous dialing.

Administrative safeguards

- Remind your regular recipients to inform you if their fax number changes. Try to find a routine way to assure that this will be done. Perhaps send a yearly fax broadcast assuring them that your number has not changed and containing some other relevant materials about you and your practice?
- Your fax machine should keep several logs and print out reports about whether faxes were actually sent and received, lists of the names and numbers stored on the machine, etc. Reporting can be set to cover time periods up to a week or say, thirty messages. You can associate each phone number used with a person, office, or business associate to understand you current usage patterns.
- The Privacy or Security Officer should review the logs, investigate suspicions calls, write up a variance report (which you will keep as part of documenting HIPAA compliance), and take some actions to reduce such variances in the future such as revising policies, training if the problems were due to human error, etc.
- If you fax to your business associates, require, in their contracts, that they place their fax machines in secure areas or otherwise assure confidentiality.

Security safeguards

When ever you send a fax or an email there is a risk of its being misdirected so you might place a confidential notice paragraph on your fax cover sheet. You can copy those other use or construct your own version and it appears the essential elements are:
1. A notification that the material is sensitive.
2. An indication that its distribution and use are restricted by specific laws.
3. A request that, if it were incorrectly sent or received, that
   a. the sender be notified;
   b. that it not be distributed or used, and
   c. that it be destroyed or returned.
4. A message of appreciation and gratitude for the recipient's assistance.

Here is a sample Confidentiality Notice:

> The documents accompanying this transmission contain confidential health information that is legally privileged. This information is intended only for the use of the individual or entity named above. If you are not the intended recipient, you are hereby notified that any disclosure, copying, distribution, or action taken in reliance on the contents of these documents is strictly prohibited. If you have received this information in error, please notify the sender immediately and arrange for the return or destruction of these documents.
>
> We promise to return this courtesy to you and others when we receive misdelivered faxes.

More such notices are in section 960.

Because HIPAA requires you to mitigate any unauthorized disclosure, attend promptly and fully to any misdirected faxes. Assure that the fax is returned or destroyed, investigate the source of the error, and make appropriate corrections by training or other means.

Photocopying machines

- Shred all imperfect or extra copies of PHI.
- Count the pages you copy or check to see that the last page copied was not left on the machine.
- Use different colored paper in the copier for records released to the patient, school systems, and a business associate.
- Make up a page sized clear plastic overlay to be used on the copier's glass before the records are copied. It can be used to add the date, a legal confidentiality statement, etc.

E-mail

- Simply do not use email for any kind of PHI unless you have implemented encryption.

Printing from your computer

- Your word processor can often make a watermark in large type across the page at an angle when you print out the PHI to be disclosed. Or perhaps it can add a confidentiality statement as a footer on every page.
- When you print out PHI from your records you could set the page layout to an odd size or print it sideways (landscape) to distinguish an authorized disclosure from the much more common releases for TPO.
- Slightly higher tech would be to buy software (either a stand-alone program or a function in a clinical records program) for digital signatures which would guarantee the date the record was created, who created it, and that it had not been altered. Using this automatically with all clinical records would not be difficult

730   Controlling the accessibility of PHI

Selecting passwords

A basic privacy protection method is simply to reduce access to computerized records. Records must be protected from unauthorized access by staff, strangers, clients, and hackers who consider it a challenge to break into someone else's computer. Currently "passwords," "passcodes," and "passphrases" are the most commonly used methods but are likely to be replaced by bodily components like fingerprints or retinal prints. For example, an inexpensive fingerprint reader is available (9/05) from Microsoft but it strangely comes with no guarantees.

Below are some guidelines borrowed from the literature on passwords. You might also consider using password software which can generate secure passwords, check a proposed password against a list of commonly selected passwords and other standards, and also provide password aging with reminders to change your password. Similarly, "keychain" programs for passwords can simplify the processes involved.

General advice on passwords

- Access codes based on the initial letters of long phrases or titles or which use the phrases themselves are called passphrases and are safer than simpler and shorter passwords (PWs).
- Depending on the size of your office staff and other individual factors, tiered PWs may makes sense so that, for example, the billers have access to specific computer programs while managers have access to those and to other programs. PWs can be used to allow groups of employees different access. For example, clinicians need access to parts of a patient's files that those doing scheduling do not.
- Never tell anyone your password. No one ever needs to use it to "do maintenance," "fix a problem we are having," "run a test," "replace your old password" or any of the other tactics hackers will use. This so common it even has a name– "social engineering."
- Avoid letting anyone look over your shoulder when you are entering your password. They can't read the little asterisks but they could see how many characters your passwords contains or watch your fingers type.
- Change all passwords immediately if you even suspect that they have been disclosed.
- Don't use the same password for long periods of time. Change your password on a regular basis; certainly less than a year even if it is a very strong password.
- If possible, arrange that after three unsuccessful attempts to enter a password the user is denied access until the password is reset by a system administrator.

Don'ts about selecting a password

- Don't use your user name or any variation of it as a PW. Don't use your real name, maiden name, mothers maiden name ,or the names of your spouse, child, or pets. Even unusual names are likely to be known by those most likely to misuse your files - people who know you.
- Don't use other numbers such as phone numbers, Social Security numbers, addresses, π, birthdates, etc. All are easily discovered.
- Don't use all numbers or all letters, or even repeating characters.
- Don't use common keyboard sequences such as !@#$%^ or nm,./ or trewq just because they are easy to type. Crackers know that too.
- Don't use leading or trailing blanks or more than two consecutive identical characters.
- Don't ever write your password near your computer or in any logical place. Most are

on Post-it Notes® in drawers.
- Don't choose passwords that are familiar words or famous or popular phrases. Don't use full ordinary words. These are too easily guessed or broken by crackers using dictionary programs.
- Try to never re-use a password but if you must, do not reuse any of the last four you previously used.
- A replacement password should be at least three characters different from the last one.

Try to obey at least most of these rules.

Do's about selecting a password

- When selecting a PW, try to make it difficult for a hacker to guess what you have chosen. This seems obvious but most PWs are almost obvious to anyone who knows you or can learn about you online. If you have eliminated their educated guesses (the crackers's shortcut), then a password cracking program will try all the words in many dictionaries (called the brute force approach). Foreign words are apparently not much better as they are not recommended.
- The hardest passwords to guess are completely random. But they are also the hardest to remember and restoring lost passwords are the largest use (waste) of computer support staffs.
- Passwords should contain a minimum of six characters. Ten makes them very had to break.
- Include a combination of numbers and letters, for example, Sylvia Plath's "bell+jar" or Peter, Paul, and Mary's "PP&M" or Hamlet's "2bornot2b" or even "2beeoarnot2bea". Try to add characters like &, %, ~, or +.
- Make up a sentence unique to you and take the first letter of each word for your password. For example, Ha! Did you really think I would give away *my* password?
- Choose creative alternative spellings for phrases like those used on license plates such as Henry Dana's novel "2yrsB4thmst." *Don't* use your license plate number.
- Eliminating vowels from your phrase will not decrease its readability but will make it harder to break because vowels are so common. The most common letters in English are etoainshrdlu, in order of decreasing frequency. Use longer words joined without the vowels such as Elvis' lvmtndr.
- Alternate or use logical combinations of upper and lower case letters. For example, Dave Eggers's *A Heartbreaking Work of Staggering Genius* could become AhWoSg.

As you can see, coming up with a good password can be challenging. Being creative, and doing the unexpected will make it difficult for others to guess your password.

Encryption

It seems obvious that all patient data should be encrypted to keep it from being read, used, altered, shared, or exploited by the unauthorized. Encryption involves applying a key (a rule for how to mix up the original data - the plaintext) so that a new version (ciphertext) of the information is created (by this encrypting) which makes no sense until the key is used again (decryption) to restore the original version. Usually the key is a password and so encryption has the weaknesses of passwords described above although with a strong (unguessable, random, long and complex enough) PW current encryption methods are unbreakable except by those with great resources. Social engineering and breaking and entering (E.g. Daniel Ellsberg's psychiatrist's office) are much easier and more common.

HIPAA's Security Rule does not require encryption of email or other PHI transmitted electronically because of its current complexity and limited availability but it is still an addressable specification. This means you should try to adopt it as soon as practicable and use alternatives now when transmitting PHI. There are services which hold e-mails you send and receive on their servers and limit access with passwords. The service costs about $30 a month. See, for example: Caveo Secure Messaging System at <http://www.caveoinc.com/> will explain a lot. Do a Google search using "secure messaging."

On the other hand, encrypting stored PHI is more practical and certainly advisable. Below are some resources although a discussion of current methods and their advantages and disadvantages is well beyond both this book and its author.

If you want to understand encryption with the elegant and secure Public-key cryptography methods there is a fine one page article at <http://www.hipaadvisory.com/tech/Cryptography.htm> (accessed Sept. 30, 2005). The classic and standard method is called PGP (for Pretty Good Privacy) and was developed and, for many years, courageously defended against nearsighted government opposition by Phil Zimmerman. The International PGP Home Page at <http://www.pgpi.org/> will get you up and running in only a few minutes at no cost with documentation and links to everything PGP. PGP Corporation at <http://www.pgp.com/> offers products for securing mail, palm computers, and Macs and Windows desktops, and all kinds of networks.

Encryption programs

This is an alphabetical list of the text encryption programs widely available as of September, 2005. All have free demo versions. I cannot recommend any as I simply don't know enough.

Cryptainer LE	< http://www.cypherix.co.uk/cryptainerle/index.htm?adv=ec_ep>
CryptosystemME6	<http://hermetic.nofadz.com/crypto/me5.htm>
DriveCrypt	<http://www.drivecrypt.com/drivecrypt.html>
MINCE	<http://bluefive.pair.com/mince.htm>
FineCryp	<http://crypto-systems.com/>
SafeHouse	<http://www.pcdynamics.com/SafeHouse/>
Private Encryptor	<http://www.tropsoft.com/privateencryptor/>

There are hundreds of programs out there ranging from free to a thousand dollars and a Google or Froogle search will find lots for any kind of computer or any kind of data. While the HIPAA standards are "technology neutral" in not requiring any particular technology it turns out that only one method currently meets the nonrepudiation test and that is the public key/private key method for encryption.

Warning: Geek Rambling Ahead: How strong is a 128-bit key? For starters, a 128-bit key has 3.4 x 1038 possible values. That's 1021 times stronger than a 56-bit DES key. The famous DES Cracker machines built in the late 1990's could recover a 56-bit key in a matter of hours. If this time could subsequently be reduced to one second (meaning trying 255 keys per second), then it would take that same machine approximately 149 thousand-billion (149 trillion) years to crack a 128-bit key. To put this into perspective, the universe currently is believed to be less than 14 billion years old. That is why social engineering and burglary are popular ways of obtaining PWs.

Electronic (Digital) Signatures

An electronic signature is any electronically conveyed symbol which is attached to a document and created by a person who intended to use it to sign the document. It can be a name, a digital picture of a signature, or even a sound such as one's voice.

We are so used to signing things and seeing other's signatures that we rarely consider that these are ways of identifying a particular person and linking that person to the document thus certifying that the document we read is the same as the one that was signed. In cyberspace none of these is necessarily true for an e-mail or a letter or other document. We cannot know if there is even a real person, if the name is theirs, if they indeed intended to authenticate a document with their signature, or if the document has been altered since they signed and sent it. (Recall the famous cartoon of one dog at a computer telling another that :"On the net no one knows I'm a dog.")

Without this trust, information should not be shared. The Security Rule does not require any specific methods such digital signatures but makes person or entity authentication a required specification leaving to the user the decisions about methods to be employed. The minimal functions of an electronic signature assure the document you receive has not been altered (message integrity) accidentally or deliberately, the signer is authentically the person involved (user authentication, not forgery), and that the signature is theirs an that they intended to sign it (non-repudiation or non-deniability).

Adopting a digital signature program is some work and cost which has kept this kind of identification out of widespread use among individuals. Note however that every secure website you visit uses this technology to protect your purchasing and financial information.. Also, the American Medical Association offers free "Internet IDs" which are "certificates" which are functionally equal to digital signatures to all member physicians (see <http://www.ama-assn.org/ama/pub/category/3133.html>).

Unless you see a specific need for a digital signature in your practice or one is required by some other organization you are associated with, wait until you next upgrade your computer records system add encryption and digital signatures.

Other ideas for security

- Your computers could be accessed by cleaning staff or anyone else present in your office when you are not. Gordon Herz, PhD of Madison, Wisconsin, has a very clever idea. He uses a wireless mouse and keyboard for his computers and locks these up when he closes his office. Very few people know how to access a computer without these devices and few thieves come so equipped but make sure there are no other computers nearby.

- There is the obvious possibility that repair personnel will have access to the PHI stored on your computers. How can you protect your clients' PHI from this access? Encryption is one answer and HIPAA provides another. It requires us to have business associate contracts with those who receive our PHI. The contract requires the repair facility to take measures to ensure the privacy of the PHI. See section 270 on business associates

740   Coping with disasters

Disasters include fire and water damage, vandalism and burglary, natural disasters and computer system failure. HIPAA requires that you have a plan for maintaining the privacy and security of your records during and after a disaster, ways to continue to operate in the face of a disaster, and methods to recover from any the losses due to the disaster. Obviously, this can get quite complex, but for a small office, my suggestions are the plans detailed in the HIPAA Policies and Procedures Manual, section 875 and below.

1. **Loss of electric power** is a common source of miseries. All personal computers' CPU's, monitors, external drives, and Internet connections should have Uninterruptible Power Supplies (UPS) whose batteries will assure sufficient running time for the user to save recent changes and close current programs when electricity from the mains is lost. Simple UPSs cost around $30-50. The more expensive ones offer protection for brownout (voltage reductions due to high demand) and surges (sudden and extreme increases in voltage or amperage as would be due to lightning) and protection for your phone/fax lines. Buy larger units than you need. They will last for 5-7 years and the batteries should be a replaceable kind. The larger ones also can be programmed to automatically save what you are working on and shut down your computer so you can leave your computer running a program when you are out of the office.

2. **All client data of any kind must be backed up.** Good backup programs will use the least storage space by backing up only recently changed files (called an "incremental backup"), can be set to run unattended (at 3 AM on Tuesday), and will back up to your choice of media (tape, CD-ROM, DVD, hard drives, removable drives, etc.).

Backups to DVDs can hold about 7 gigs (1.379 bazillion pages) but are currently the most expensive hardware (about $60 and $1.00 per disk). Tape backup is even more spacious (but more expensive). Backups to removable hard disks (like Zip drives) and to flash memory is a little less reliable. Backups to CD, either CD-R ("recordable" but only once) or CD-RW (rewritable a thousand times) is cheapest (about $30 and $.10 a disk for 650 megs - 300,000 simple pages) and most durable. You will need many pieces of a medium to do an overlapping multiple backup but the plans are included with all the programs.

As to size needed: I have 15 years of writing, dozens of complex programs, photos. etc. on my Mac and use about 8 gigs. Only videos and music use a lot of storage space. If you have only word processing you may find you can carry all your current records on a flash drive about two inches long and costing $20-50 depending on capacity. Keep all your life documents on your keychain (password protected, of course). Ain't tech great?

3. All programs have the burden of arranging **off-site storage** except backups over the internet. These services encrypt files so access at the storage site is prevented. Subscribers to .Mac have such storage included and others can find these services online for around $20 a month. Other options are to take home your records every night or week or take them to a bank's safe deposit box.

4. **Burglary and vandalism** are disasters too. Backups will help you keep going but won't prevent the thief from reading your records - an unauthorized disclosure if there ever was one. Passwords will do unless the thief is also a hacker. Only encryption will save you then. See section 730 for more.

750 Disposal and destruction of PHI

PHI on Paper

Be aware that all kinds of paper may have PHI - telephone logs, excuses for missing work or school, extra copies of forms or letters, bad photocopies of PHI which went into the trash, and no doubt others.

Some general guidelines

- Don't write it down. Just don't record sensitive but therapeutically-irrelevant information.
- Write as little as possible. An indirect reference, some abbreviations, a cross-reference, or some other method can reduce the amount of information in your records.
- Lock it up or destroy it. Make it a rule to either file any paper with PHI under lock and key, shred it, or take it home when you close up your office for the day.
- Shred it. Thanks to both deceit and paranoia, cheap shredders are now available which for small practices which may need to destroy only a dozen pages a day or at a time. Look for ones which do a cross cut. Some will destroy credit cards or even CDs as well. They are noisy and so you might want to consider their location. Shredders that sit on a waste baskets are now available for $25 so that you can buy one for each desk location and place one next to where you open your mail.

Erasing computer files

Dragging a file to the Trash or Recycle Bin does not remove it even after you "empty" the trash. This only deletes the name of the file from your most obvious directory. It is *not* gone from the hard drive and programs like Norton Utilities can easily recover it. Remember Fawn Hall and Oliver North?

What will get rid of it? An erasing program overwrites each bit of data with a single value. This single overwrite is sufficient for most personal users because few file recovery programs can find the data in its entirety. However, the Department of Defense has a much more severe standard called 5220.22. This involves three separate overwrites, first with zeroes, then with ones and finally with a random character between two and nine. It is widely believed that no commercial or black-market file retrieval products can retrieve a file after this process but there are also a lot of conspiracy nuts who disagree.

There are many available inexpensive programs and they come in two flavors: wipers and scrubbers (also called shredders or burners). **Wipers** recycle leftover bits and pieces on a drive. They overwrite the data in the "empty"(or presently unallocated to any file or record) spaces between files, like Windows' temporary files, swap files, ancient drafts of documents, and internet caches and leave the complete files you created intact. All of these products are for Windows and show an icon on your desktop into which you can drag a file you want deleted. The most common is WipeInfo, by Symantec, and is part of the Norton SystemWorks utility suite and is quite user-friendly. The program Eraser, written by a Finnish developer, Sami Tolvanen, is not as visually pleasing as some of the other tools but is just as effective and is free from <www.tolvanen.com/eraser>. WashAndGo2.0, by Abelssoft will warn you before you delete critical files and has a temporary deletion bin, both features to appeal to the less attentive user. Of course, there are many others.

The **scrubbers**, erase an entire hard drive, overwriting everything including the operating system. These work from floppies or CDs and function independently of the operating systems of Windows or Macintosh. They do a very complete job. DataEraser, by Ontrack

Software, and Declasfy, by Mares & Company are popular and usable by us amateurs. Most of the dozen programs cost $30-60 and will erase all kinds of media.

Laptop or portable computers and removable media (everything but the hard drive inside your personal computer) also require controls on where they can be taken and maintain confidentiality.

Laptops or portable computers including palmtops require that deletions be done regularly as well but arranging regular cleaning is more difficult. Small "syncing" programs coordinate files on different machines when they are connected and can remove files to the trash for later erasure.

E-mail presents additional complexities as it is often stored in several locations. There is no convenient protection method at present so don't use email for PHI.

One last problem to be addressed occurs when you have a computer problem - a file or set of files is corrupted and you make copies or print them out. What happens to the partial files, the copies, and the print out after the restoration?

Using a records destruction company

Hiring a professional records destruction company to destroy your larger records is easier and more reliable than trying to shred your larger files yourself. The contract with the company should include the following points:

❑ The specific methods used for each kind of medium on which the PHI is recorded.
❑ Describe the safeguards the company will use to prevent breaches of confidentiality.
❑ Indemnify you against any losses due to unauthorized disclosure of the PHI when it is in the possession of the destruction company. This is provided for by your Business Agreement with them. All of these companies now have sample BA forms ready for you.
❑ The destruction company will furnish to the privacy officer the following information on the destruction of records:
    - The date of destruction.
    - The method(s) of destruction used. E. g. burning, shredding, pulping, demagnetizing, overwriting, pulverizing, etc.
    - Description(s) of the records destroyed.
    - Description of the inclusive dates of the records destroyed.
    - The name and signature of the their staff person(s) supervising and witnessing the destruction.

For more on procedures see section 878

760   A security To Do list

The list below addresses most of the practical aspects of maintaining control over your clinical records. It is designed to function as both an assessment device and a implementation checklist. Since the Security and Privacy Rules are logically and technologically linked this list addresses both. The list can also be used as a source of wording for your HIPAA Policies and Procedures Manual (see section 800)

A checklist of threats and responses to possible breaches of confidentiality

Circle True, False, or ? for "I don't know "to each statement and take immediate actions to block potential threats to privacy.

1. Personnel

T F ? a. Privacy and Security Officer. One person has been made responsible for data security. He or she keeps informed about legal developments such as HIPAA and technical issues such as hardware and software, does training of all staff and new hires, temporary workers, makes necessary changes when an employee leaves the practice, etc.

T F ? b. We conduct background checks on all new hires and comply with all laws about employees.

T F ? c. Staff have been trained in all our office privacy rules and the consequences of breaking them.

T F ? d. All staff and employees receive initial training in privacy and security, periodic security reminders, in-service training, and monitoring from the Privacy officer.

T F ? e. These training efforts and their outcomes are documented and evaluated.

2. Physical controls over information

T F ? a. The staff area is locked at the end of the day and whenever no staff member is present. The waiting area may be left unlocked during regular office hours.

T F ? b. Former employees do not have keys or access to the office, files, or computers.

T F ? c. Passwords and IDs are not written in any easily accessible locations on paper or on the computers.

T F ? d. All of our office's computers are in areas which patients never have access to, or have hoods or are arranged so that no client can see the screen.

T F ? e. We do not call out patients' names in the waiting room and do not have patients sign in on a sheet other patients might see.[52]

T F ? f. All papers with PHI are either placed in locked files or shredded on the premises by the time the office is closed for the day.

T F ? g. Only bonded records destruction companies are employed.

T F ? h. The privacy officer keeps records of all equipment containing PHI which we own, lease, or operate. The officer monitors these at regular intervals and before sent for maintenance, repair, or replacement.

---

[52] The thinking seems to be that violations like these are "incidental" disclosures (see section 540) are not prosecutable violations of HIPAA. My view is to consider both the legal pressures for privacy, the impression even a minor violation would make on all patients' confidence in your ability to maintain *their* privacy, and the likely small costs in time and effort required to be more protective before deciding what is your best solution.

T F ? i. We do not use social security numbers for record keeping or identification purposes. When these need to be recorded, access to them is limited or they are encrypted.

3. Security of electronic data

T F ? a. Each staff member needing records access has a different, unguessable, sufficiently long, regularly changed, password.

T F ? b. Every computer on our network has virus protection programs and the virus files are updated every 48 hours.

T F ? c. All computers with internet access have a software firewall as well as hardware firewall or similar protections which are updated and tested regularly by the Privacy officer.

T F ? d. We use sleep programs, password-activated automatic screen-savers, timed log-off programs, or other means as appropriate to make access to PHI unavailable when a computer is not being used.

T F ? e. Portable computers are locked up in the office or only used in secure locations. They have full encryption programs and password access.

T F ? f. Encryption is used for all messages transmitted from outside the office to the office's computers or between our offices.

T F ? g. Passwords are used on portable digital assistants, personal organizers, and similar devices.

T F ? h. Automatic encryption programs are used to prevent the storage or transmission of all patient information including EPHI in any readable format.

T F ? i. If we use e-mail for any kind of PHI we encrypt it.

T F ? j. Backups of all patient data are frequent, automatic, checked for accuracy, stored off-site, and destroyed at regular intervals.

T F ? k. There is a written plan to handle emergencies and recover our computers' PHI and other records from disasters such as fire, flood, vandalism, burglary and other thefts, virus attacks, natural disaster, etc.

T F ? l. The contingency plan is reviewed and tests of its components are regularly conducted and documented by the Privacy Officer.

T F ? m. The computer system will not allow any new software to be added by anyone except under supervision of the Privacy officer.

T F ? n. All computer drives, magnetic tapes, diskettes, CD-ROMs, or other data storage devices which hold PHI or other confidential data are either physically destroyed or wiped with a proven utility program before they are junked, sold, donated, or sent for service.

4. Telephones, answering machines, and facsimile machines

T F ? a. Staff keep their voices down so that their phone and all conversations cannot be overheard by patients or uninvolved staff.

T F ? b All staff have been trained in how to respond to callers asking for any information about our clients.

T F ? c. The privacy officer regularly arranges calls which ask for patient information to test our telephone security measures.[53]

T F ? d. Staff know to leave only non-specific messages on client's answering machines unless the client had previously agreed to the leaving of confidential messages at that location. Messages being left are done so out of the hearing of clients or any untrained persons.

---

[53] Although it may seem clever and a really good test, do not call pretending to be a law enforcement officer. Impersonating an officer is a felony. (Advice from a lawyer friend.)

T F ? e. The office's answering machine's volume is set when messages
            are picked up so that no one else can hear.
T F ? f. All fax machines have been programmed for confidential fax transmissions
            with a cover sheet with the phone numbers, number of pages, a note about
            content's confidentiality and what do to in case of mistaken transmissions.
T F ? g. Users of the fax check the intended recipient's phone number against the
            one stored in the fax and do not use numbers not stored in the fax (so as
            to prevent dialing errors).
T F ? h. When there is any concern, the recipient is called to confirm reception of
            the fax.
T F ? i. No confidential information is ever discussed on portable, cordless,
            wireless, or cellular telephones.

5. Releasing records

T F ? a. Records are reviewed by a single designated person before being released.
T F ? b. The Authorization/Request for Records Form is examined for compliance
            and completeness, etc.
T F ? c. No records are released until all uncertainties are resolved.
T F ? d. Non-essential information is deleted, obliterated, or masked.
T F ? e. Only the HIPAA-compliant minimum necessary information is sent out
            unless an Authorization has been created.
T F ? f. The recipient is verified if there is any concern.

6. Administration

T F ? a. We have HIPAA-compliant Business Associate contracts with all
            appropriate entities.
T F ? b. The privacy officer tests or arranges for testing of all of these safeguards at
            irregular, unannounced intervals, documents the results,
            and forwards them to senior management.
T F ? c. Changes and improvements to these safeguards are budgeted and
            implemented in a timely fashion.

800   A HIPAA Policies and Procedures Manual

This is not labeled: "The" manual because this must be tailored to your practice and must evolve over the changes that will occur over time.

Because the manual should have its own table of contents, rather than duplicate it here, as I have done in previous chapters, see section 803.

801   Developing a HIPAA compliance policy and procedures manual

I. Policies and Procedures and Documentation Requirements (§ 164.316)

We proposed **requiring documented policies and procedures** for the routine and nonroutine receipt, manipulation, storage, dissemination, transmission, and/or disposal of health information. We proposed that the documentation be reviewed and updated periodically.

We have emphasized throughout this final rule the **scalability** allowed by the security standards. This final rule requires covered entities to implement policies and procedures that are **reasonably designed, taking into account the size and type of activities** of the covered entity that relate to electronic protected health information, and requires that the **policies and procedures must be documented in written form,** which may be in electronic form. This final rule also provides that a covered entity **may change its policies and procedures at any time,** provided that it documents and implements the changes in accordance with the applicable requirements. Covered entities must also document designations, for example, of affiliation between covered entities (see § 164.105(b)), and other actions, as required by other provisions of the subpart. (Boldface added)

Clinicians and especially those in independent practice are often both unfamiliar with or even intolerant of the paperwork exemplified in a **Policies and Procedures Manual** (P&PM). One of their main motivations for choosing the difficult path of private practice may have been the opportunity to avoid such petty rules and micromanagement. And, in truth, when you have only yourself and a part-time secretary to manage, you don't really need such a collection of rules.

The regulations offer little guidance but do require the development of a set of policies and procedures [§ 164.530(I)] to comply with HIPAA. I will call this the **HIPAA Policy and Procedures Manual (HP&PM).** The good news is that your set need not be complex or large. HHS has repeatedly stated that the Privacy Rule is *scalable* and gives flexibility for providers to tailor the rule's requirements to fit their size and need.

> • The policies and procedures of small providers may be more limited under the Rule than those of a large hospital or health plan, based on the volume of health information maintained and the number of interactions with those within and outside of the health care system. *OCR Guidance Explaining Significant Aspects of the Privacy Rule -* December 4, 2002

However, just because it can be smaller does not mean it can be irrelevant. "... a compliance plan is not just the paper document but also the **action plan** for adhering to the principles underlying the plan." And, "A compliance plan doesn't have to be complicated. It needs to be **workable**. It needs to be something that providers and staff alike can understand and can put into practice on an everyday basis." Both quotations are from 2001, *Healthcare Management Alternatives.*

In the next sections you will find a set of office procedures and understandings regarding the privacy and security of client information and cross references to the sections of the book where more information can be found. It is my best guess at the issues and contents such a HIPAA Policy and Procedures Manual **(HP&PM)** would address. As indicated above, they are likely to need to be edited or reorganized to be more consistent with your style, practice, or other office manuals. In areas especially important to your practice, you might want to borrow more material to include in your HP&PM.

- Please note that *this is not a complete mental health office P&PM* which would address issues such as personnel (job descriptions, hiring, promotion, firing, etc), financial (billing, accounting, collections, etc) administrative procedures (purchasing, maintenance, leases, etc.), a professional will, and others.
- In the manual in this section page numbers as well as section numbers were assigned, for learning and access. As you develop your own version you should probable eliminate the   page number so that you can include larger amounts of text than appears here.
- Because of your practice's methods and larger size you may need to develop polices to address issues such as the Transition Period rules, employer policies about compliance with OSHA and Workers' Compensation as well as HIPAA, employee health benefits plans and HIPAA, or any of these organizational structures for your practice: Single Affiliated Entity, Hybrid Entity, or Organized Health Care Arrangement.

Next steps?

In creating your HP&PM Manual, you should include and integrate it with your other office procedures which concern privacy and security. The practice brochure you give clients to describe how your office functions, their rights and responsibilities and mutual expectations should be consistent with the contents of the HP&PM manual as should any other handouts and your NPP. **The draft Manual that follows does not separately address the Security Rule** because 1. Much of it is beyond my ability to formulate for a small office and 2. I expect more guidance from above (Washington). See the APAPO offering in section 701 for some of this.

If your practice is larger or grows larger you are likely to need an office P&P manual because you cannot be everywhere to make decisions and implement policies. I know of none specifically designed for mental health office and would appreciate you informing me of what is available. Write to me at <mail@hipaahelp.info>

Resources for writing your own HP&PM

There are hundreds of manuals available for sale. For example:
--- *Policy and Procedure Manual* Texas Medical Association, 401 West 15th Street, Austin TX 78701 Ph: 800/880-1300, 512/370-1300
<http://store.texmed.org/store/product.asp?dept%5Fid=2&pf%5Fid=300> Sept. 20, 2005.

These sites offer samples of many forms, policies, and client education materials needed for HIPAA compliance. Note that all are copyrighted and none tailored to MH.
- HIPAA Collaborative of Wisconsin
  <http://www.hipaacow.org/hipaacow/index.html> Accessed Sept 24, 2005.
- Strategic National Implementation Process (SNIP) *Small Practice Implementation,*

Version 2.0 10/15/2002, Discussion Draft. Workgroup for Electronic Data Interchange <http://www.wedi.org/snip/public/articles/200211012.0final.pdf> Appendix VII is a 16 page Policy Manual. Accessed Sept 24, 2005.
- HIPAA Awareness and Readiness for Kansas (HARK) <http://www.hark.info/forms_templates.pdf>. Accessed Sept 24, 2005.

The regulations

§ 164.530 Administrative requirements.
(i)

(1) Standard: policies and procedures. A covered entity must implement **policies and procedures** with respect to protected health information that are designed to comply with the standards, implementation specifications, or other requirements of this subpart. The policies and procedures must be reasonably designed, taking into account the size of and the type of activities that relate to protected health information undertaken by the covered entity, to ensure such compliance. This standard is not to be construed to permit or excuse an action that violates any other standard, implementation specification, or other requirement of this subpart.

(2) Standard: **changes to policies or procedures.**

(i) A covered entity must change its policies and procedures as necessary and appropriate to comply with changes in the law, including the standards, requirements, and implementation specifications of this subpart;

(ii) When a covered entity changes a privacy practice that is stated in the notice described in § 164.520, and makes corresponding changes to its policies and procedures, it may make the changes effective for protected health information that it created or received prior to the effective date of the notice revision, if the covered entity has, in accordance with § 164.520(b)(1)(v)(C), included in the notice a statement reserving its right to make such a change in its privacy practices; or

(iii) A covered entity may make any other changes to policies and procedures at any time, provided that the changes are documented and implemented in accordance with paragraph (i)(5) of this section.

(3) Implementation specification: changes in law. Whenever there is a **change in law** that necessitates a change to the covered entity's policies or procedures, the covered entity must promptly document and implement the revised policy or procedure. If the change in law materially affects the content of the notice required by § 164.520, the covered entity must promptly make the appropriate revisions to the notice in accordance with § 164.520(b)(3). Nothing in this paragraph may be used by a covered entity to excuse a failure to comply with the law.

(4) ---

(5) Implementation specification: **changes to other policies or procedures.** A covered entity may change, at any time, a policy or procedure that does not materially affect the content of the notice required by § 164.520, provided that:

(i) The policy or procedure, as revised, complies with the standards, requirements, and implementation specifications of this subpart; and

(ii) Prior to the effective date of the change, the policy or procedure, as revised, is documented as required by paragraph (j) of this section.

(j) (1) Standard: **documentation**. A covered entity must:

(i) Maintain the policies and procedures provided for in paragraph (i) of this section in written or electronic form;

(ii) If a communication is required by this subpart to be in writing, maintain such writing, or an electronic copy, as documentation; and

(iii) If an action, activity, or designation is required by this subpart to be documented, maintain a written or electronic record of such action, activity, or designation.

(2) Implementation specification: retention period. A covered entity must retain the documentation required by paragraph (j)(1) of this section **for six years from the date of its creation or the date when it last was in effect, whichever is later.**

802   Our HIPAA Policy and Procedures Manual

(On your letterhead)

This is the Policies and Procedures Manual for Complying with HIPAA for our Practice

- As you use this manual you may need to refer to the forms indicated. They are included at the end of this manual.
- Please ask your supervisor or our privacy officer any questions you have as you read and use the manual. Our privacy officer is _____ and can be reached at _____.

This is version _____ and is to be in effect from _____ until it is replaced by a later version. Its contents will be reviewed at least yearly and modified as necessary by the privacy officer of this practice.

Conventions used in this manual

1. This manual is referred to below as HP&PM.

2. In this HP&PM the words "we" and "our" means the clinical mental health practice of this letterhead.

3. The words client, patient, consumers, all are interchangeable terms for the children, adults, their personal representatives, and organizations to whom we provide services.

4. Protected Healthcare Information (PHI) and Electronic Protected Healthcare Information (EPHI) may also be referred to as health information, client's information, or just information. It refers to most of the contents of our clinical records or medical charts. The terms PHI and EPHI should be considered as interchangeable in most uses.

5. Medical record, records, file, and chart are interchangeable terms for the same data collections.

6. TPO means Treatment, Payment, or Healthcare Operations.

7. Regulations, laws, and rules are interchangeable terms as used here.

8. Releasing, disclosing, and sharing of records are interchangeable terms for the same processes when used here.

9. For the definitions of other terms in this Manual see section 1040 which is the glossary of the book *HIPAAHelp* by Ed Zuckerman, available in the office

10. When no person or title is specified, the privacy officer will perform the procedure or will delegate and supervise the procedure.

11. An initial capital is used to designate a form or product; when not capitalized, the same word designates a procedure or process. For example, one gets consent and records in on a Consent form.

803 Table of contents

810   The privacy officer

Policy

The privacy officer is responsible for our privacy and security program, its policies and associated procedures.

Procedures

1. We will always have a staff member who is our privacy officer.

2. This person may be referred to as the privacy or security officer or official.

3. Starting on _____ _____, _____ our privacy officer is:

    Name _____

    Position or title _____

    Mailing address _____

    Telephone number(s) _____   _____

    E-mail address(es) _____

    Physical location _____

    Times available to staff and clients _____

4. The privacy officer is responsible for many tasks including:

    a. Receiving all privacy and security related materials and communications about HIPAA from the Office of Civil Rights and the Centers for Medicare and Medicaid Services.

    b. Planning and developing materials to implement HIPAA for our practice.

    c. Ensuring that our policies and procedures conform to local and federal laws and regulations and our codes of professional ethics.

    d. Training all staff.

    e. Evaluating our information handling policies and methods both in the office and with other entities.

    f. Receiving and responding to all complaints, inquiries, and investigations of our privacy and security policies and procedures.

    g. Other duties as assigned.

    h. For more information on the duties of the privacy officer see other areas of this HP&PM.

820   Obtaining Consents and Authorizations

821   Obtaining Consent

Policy

As a direct health care providers we will make a good faith effort to obtain a written acknowledgment of receipt of our Notice of Privacy Practices from all of our clients. We are required to obtain consent in order to provide treatment.

We will use procedures and practices consistent with local laws and regulations to obtain informed and voluntary consent from all competent clients.

Procedures

1. Our privacy officer will develop, modify in light of changes in the laws and regulations, and update as necessary:
    a. Our Notice of Privacy Policies.
    b. Our Consent form.
    c. Procedures for implementing the above.

2. We will provide all new clients of the practice with a copy of our NPP either by mail before their first appointment or at the time of intake/first appointment before beginning treatment.

3. Except in an emergency, we will make a good faith effort to obtain a written acknowledgment of receipt of the Notice of Privacy Practices. If the written acknowledgment is not obtained, the clinician will document his or her good faith efforts to obtain such acknowledgment and the reason why the acknowledgment was not obtained.

4. We will retain the written acknowledgment as part of the client's medical record and it will be kept by us for the period required by local laws or for a minimum period of six years after the last date of service.

822   When an Authorization is and is not needed

Policy

Many uses and disclosures do not require an authorization under HIPAA but do under our more stringent state and local laws. It is our policy to discuss the these situations with each client and then to seek a signed Authorization. The clinician involved with the client most recently, or in the absence of a clear clinical contact, the privacy officer, will discuss the nature of the PHI involved, those seeking the EPHI/PHI, and other aspects of the disclosure with the client and obtain informed consent.

Procedures

An Authorization is NOT required under HIPAA for these uses and disclosures (but we may choose to have one considered anyway):

We may choose to not discuss the following uses and releases with a client:

1. For our own treatment, payment, or health care operations.

2. To a CE for their treatment, payment, or health care operations.

3. To our business associates.

4. To appropriate individuals or organizations for evaluating health care fraud or detecting abuse or legal non-compliance.

5. To family members or close personal friends if the information is directly relevant to the person's involvement in the individual's care or payment of health care costs.

6. To certain public health authorities for public health purposes.

7. To a government authority if we come to believe that the client is a victim of abuse, neglect or domestic violence, or as otherwise required or permitted by law.

8. When a valid court order for our records has been issued.

9. To law enforcement personnel for suspect, witness and victims of crimes identification and location purposes.

10. To coroners and medical examiners to identify the decedent or determine the cause of death or to funeral directors to carry out their duties.

11. To appropriate individuals or organization to comply with laws relating to Workers' Compensation or similar programs. To Social Security, Medicaid, and other benefit programs. However we will rely on the authorization form we receive from them and disclose what they ask for.

12. To an a client's employer.

An Authorization is required for these uses and disclosures:

1. Disclosing PHI to an non-health care insurer for, for example, life insurance underwriting.

2. To release psychotherapy notes (which should be extremely rare).

3. For any other disclosure not covered by a Consent.

There may be other circumstances of which we are presently unaware and others which may arise. The Privacy officer will evaluate these circumstances as they come to his or her attention and develop and adopt policies to fit these circumstances.

830 Uses and disclosures of EPHI/PHI

Policy

Because we receive requests for records of many kinds our records clerk (with the assistance of the privacy officer when needed) will evaluate each request and determine what is sought, by whom, for what purposes, and other relevant aspects.

831 Non-routine uses and disclosures of PHI

Policy

If a request does not seem reasonable because it ask for more or different information than seems needed by the requester to meet the stated needs, or if the identity of the requester is unfamiliar, or the requester is asking for information in our records which was created by a person or entity outside our office, or anything else which raises any kind of suspicion, it become a non-routine disclosure.

Procedures

1. When an request to disclose records is received by any staff member it is to be forwarded to the Records Clerk.

2. The clerk will review the request and decide if it is a routine or non-routine disclosure of PHI and will follow the appropriate procedures for each, as described below.

3. If the request is for a disclosure of the kinds listed below the records clerk will consult with the privacy officer before proceeding.
    a. Providing information to family, friends, or others involved in a client's care.
    b. Providing PHI to personal representatives.
    c. Disclosures of PHI as required by law, for law enforcement, judicial and administrative proceedings, public health, health oversight, and cooperating with a federal complaint investigation
    d. Disclosures of PHI about victims of child abuse, other abuse, neglect, or domestic violence.
    e. Allowable disclosures to avert a serious threat.
    f. Requests for uses and disclosures of PHI in emergency situations.
    g. Uses and disclosures related to deceased individuals
    h. When the client has been granted restrictions on the use and disclosure of his or her PHI.
    i When the request is for psychotherapy notes.
    j. Requests for uses and disclosures of PHI in research
    k. Requests to use or disclose PHI for marketing and fundraising activities.
    l. Requests for other disclosures and determining the appropriate amount of information to release.
    m. Requests for the entire record or chart.
    n. Requests from any kind of school system.
    o. Requests from or for a lawyer.

4. We will, where allowed to by law and regulation, make an effort to disclose only the minimum PHI necessary to allow the recipient of the PHI to perform the task or achieve the purpose stated on the request for records.

832   Routine uses and disclosures of EPHI/PHI

Routine uses of PHI

Since the office manager and secretarial staff arrange billing, review case records to disclose parts of them to other CEs, and perform other functions as needed it is entirely reasonable for her or him to have access to the entire medical record of each client.

Procedures for releasing records under a Consent or Authorization

1. When a request to disclose records is received by any staff member it is to be forwarded to the Records Clerk.

2. The records clerk will verify the identity of the person, organization, or CE requesting the PHI.

3. The PHI sought is for TPO and from a CE, the records clerk will collect the requested information.

4. For Authorizations seeking disclosure of psychotherapy notes, the clerk will consult with the privacy officer.

5. If the request for records is an Authorization, the records clerk will examine the Authorization to see if it has any of these qualities which would make it invalid.
   a. The current date is beyond its expiration date or the expiration event has passed.
   b. The authorization has not been filled in completely.
   c. The authorization contains information the CE knows to be false.
   d. The authorization is known by the CE to have been revoked.
   e. The authorization is a prohibited type.
      - It conditions treatment, payment, enrollment or eligibility upon the signing of the authorization by the client.
      - It improperly compounds authorization types. Each Authorization for the use of disclosure of PHI must be separate except:
      - A research Authorization can be combined with another Authorization or a Consent when they are all concern PHI from the research study.
      - An Authorization for use or disclosure of psychotherapy notes may only be combined with another Authorization for psychotherapy notes.

6. If the Authorization is valid, the records clerk will collect the PHI that is sought.

7. The records clerk will follow the procedure below for releasing only the minimum necessary information before proceeding.

8. The clerk may notify the person or organization requesting records of any copying costs. The requester may then modify the request.

9. When appropriate, the records clerk will make a entry in the Medical Access Log.

10. The clerk will send the information to the requester consistent with the request. If a request asks for specific information (i.e., results of testing performed on a specified date), only the information requested should be released.

11. If the records clerk or others have any questions about the request, the PHI sought, the client, or any other aspect of the use or disclosure, contact the privacy officer.

Minimum necessary information

We will, where allowed to by law and regulation, make an effort to disclose only the minimum PHI necessary to allow the recipient of the PHI to perform the task or achieve the purpose stated on the request for records.

1. Disclosures to a CE for treatment purposes, to the client, to the Secretary of DHHS, or pursuant to law are exempt from the Minimum Necessary Protected Healthcare Information (MNPHI) rule.

2. Disclosures for payment or health care operations must be evaluated for the MNPHI.

3. If the client has signed an Authorization, those releases are exempt for the MNPHI requirements.

4 We are allowed to trust the requester of our records to ask for the minimum necessary information when the requester is a CE or a business associate of ours.

5. Releases authorized by a client for PHI to be used internally by the CE need to be evaluated for MNPHI.

6 Other Authorizations received should be directed to the privacy officer for an opinion.

833 Procedures for requesting records

When a clinician, clerk or other staff member wants to obtain PHI about a client from a covered entity or other source the staff member should consult the records clerk, and if necessary, the privacy officer about the correct procedure and form needed.

1. Use the appropriate request form and comply with the instructions on it.

2. Place a copy of any Authorization in the client's file.

840   Clients' rights to control their EPHI/PHI

Clients will not ever be required to waive or limit their rights as described here or under other laws as a condition of TPO or in regard to filing a complaint.

841   Clients' access to their records

Policy

We will honor a client's rights to inspect his or her PHI in our records and obtain a copy of this PHI for as long as we have those records and the request conforms to the federal and state laws and regulations.

Procedures

1. Whenever a client or his or her personal representative requests access to or a copy of his or her records they shall be referred to our privacy officer.

2. The privacy officer will explain our privacy policy and assist the client in submitting the request in writing.

3. We will act within 30 days of receiving the request.

4. The officer will examine the records as to their size, contents, legibility, costs of copying, options for creating a summary, and other related access considerations.

5. The privacy officer will contact the client to evaluate the client's needs and questions. The client may be offered a summary, selected parts of the record, photocopies, or other appropriate options. For example, clients generally do not have access to their psychotherapy notes but we are allowed to grant access.

6. The privacy office will, if he or she deems it necessary, consult with other staff and arrive at a decision about access.

7. The privacy officer will send the request and our decision to our records clerk for action on disclosure.

If we grant access to or supply a copy of the records

1. The privacy officer will contact the client to agree upon a format for the records which meets the client's needs. The first copy in each twelve month period will be provided at no cost but subsequent copies will be charged copying costs (and mailing if the client wishes it mailed). If a summary of the information in the record is desired, the client must be told the cost an he or she may accept and pay for or refuse this option.

2. The privacy officer will contact the client to arrange a mutually convenient time and place for the inspection or arrange for the copy to be delivered.

3. We will provide the agreed upon form or forms of the records or a readable paper copy.

4. If, after inspection, the client believes the record is incomplete or inaccurate in any way, the client may request amendments. Seer our policy on amending records.

If we deny or refuse access or supplying a copy, in whole or in part

1. We will provide the client with our decision in plain language, stating why we have denied access, telling the client of his or her rights of review, and explaining how to make a complaint to our privacy officer and/or to the Secretary of Health and Human Services.

2. If we denied access because we don't have the requested PHI but do know where it is, we will inform the client how to seek access there.

3. If we deny access to part(s) of the record we will remove it or them and allow full access to the remaining parts.

4. If we have denied access as permitted in HIPAA §164.524 the client will be informed that he or she has the right to have our decision reviewed by a licensed health care professional (the second professional) we select but who did not participate in the original decision to deny access.

5. The client must request this review in writing to the privacy officer.

6. The second professional will make a timely decision, we will provide the client with a notice of the professional's decision, and we will comply with the second professional's decision.

842 Clients' right to request amendment of their EPHI/PHI

Policy

We will honor clients' requests to amend their records as long as we maintain their records if they believe the information is incomplete or incorrect and unless there is a compelling reason, as indicated below, to not do so.

Procedures

1. Requests for amendment should be directed to the privacy officer who will provide a form indicating the needed information to identify what records the client wants to have amended and the reasons for such amendment. The privacy officer will assist the client or his or her personal representative in completing this form.

2. We may deny amendment if:
   a. We did not create the information and we believe the originator is still available to act on a request for amendment.
   b. The indicated information is not part of the client's records in our office.
   c. The information is not accessible to the client because of state or federal laws.
   d. We believe the information is accurate and complete.

3. We will act on the request within 30 days. The privacy office will consult with the individual(s) responsible for the entry or entries in the record and they will jointly decide to grant or deny the request or, in the absence of such a person, the privacy officer will make the decision.

If we grant the request for amendment we will do the following

1. Inform the client that the request was granted.

2. Provide a link or references from the site in the record of the information which is the subject of the request for amendment to the information to be added as an amendment. No information is to be deleted or obliterated. The original entry and the added information will be annotated with the date of the addition.

3. Ask the client with whom, if anyone he or she wishes to have the amended information shared.

4. On a timely basis, make reasonable efforts to send the amended information to those entities named by the client and to others whom we know to have the PHI which was amended and whom we believe may have relied or might rely on the original information to the detriment of the client.

If we deny the request for amendment we will do the following:

1. We will inform the client, on a timely basis, in writing and in plain language of the following;
   a. What parts, if any, of the request we have denied.
   b Why we have denied the request based on the criteria in #2 above.
   c. Of his or her right to and the procedures for making a written Statement of

Disagreement with our decision.

    d. That if he or she does not submit such a Statement of Disagreement he or she may ask, in writing, that we include the Request for amendment and our Denial statement with all our disclosures of the PHI which he or she wanted to have amended.

    e. How the client may complain to our privacy officer by mail or phone.

    f. How the client may complain to the Secretary of Health and Human Services.

2. We will include the client's written Statement of Disagreement with our decision but may limit the size of this statement.

3. We may make a written Rebuttal to this statement of disagreement. If we do so, we will provide a copy to the client.

4. We will, in our records, include and identify the information which the client sought to amend and append or otherwise link to it the following:

    a. The client's Request for amendment

    b. Our Denial of the request

    c. The client's Statement of Disagreement, if any, and

    d. Our Rebuttal, if any

5. If the client made a written Statement of Disagreement we will include the materials appended (see #4, above) or an accurate summary of that information whenever we disclose the PHI of which amendment was requested.

6. If the client did not submit a written Statement of Disagreement, we will include the client's Request for amendment and our Denial, or an accurate summary of this information whenever we disclose the PHI to which amendment was requested but only if the client has asked, in writing (see #1, d, above) that we do so.

7. When we later disclose the PHI whose amendment was requested using a standard transaction which does not allow the inclusion of any additional material, we will transmit the required information separately.

8. We will keep records of the persons and titles who were responsible for processing requests for amendments for at least six years after the resolution of the request for amendment.

9. If we are told by another CE of an amendment to PHI in our possession we will make the amendment to our PHI and will also inform our business associates who might use or rely upon the PHI of the amendment.

843   Requests for an Accounting of disclosures

Policy

We will honor client's requests for an Accounting of the disclosures we made of his or her during the last six years but no earlier than April 14, 2003.

Procedures

1. We will keep an Account of disclosures of each client's PHI for at least six years after the last request or last time they received treatment here. We will keep copies of this Accounting on paper or electronically in each client's medical record or file.

    We will keep a copy of the request and of the subsequent written accounting and the names of the persons who completed the accounting for at least six years after the last treatment or disclosure whichever is later.

2. Each Account will include the following information:
    a. The date of each disclosure.
    b. The name of the individual or entity to whom we sent the information and their address.
    c. A brief description of the disclosed PHI.
    d. A copy of the client's written authorization.

3. The accounting need not contain a record of disclosures made:
    a. Prior to April 14, 2003.
    b. To law enforcement or correctional institutions as provided in state law.
    d. To the individual client.
    e. For national security or intelligence purposes.
    f. To people significantly involved in the client's care.
    g. For notification purposes including identifying and locating a family member.
    h. For TPO.
    i. When the client signed an Authorization for this disclosure.

    All other disclosures of PHI must be indicated on the account.

4. Disclosures made in any manner that coveys PHI are to be included, not just photocopies of paper records or electronic PHI.

5. A client may request an accounting on a form available from our privacy officer.

6. Clients can request an account for up to six years before the request but no further back than April 14, 2003.

7. We will provide this accounting within 30 days after receiving the request.
    a. We will release the Account to the client or to someone the client designates in writing.
    b. There will be no charge for the first Account in any twelve month period. A reasonable fee will be charged for any subsequent Accounts. We will tell the client of this fee and allow him or her to withdraw or modify the request.

844   Requests for restrictions on disclosures

Policy

As indicated in the HIPAA regulations and as part of our commitment to respecting the privacy of our clients we will endeavor to comply with all requests made by clients or their representatives to restrict the disclosure of their EPHI/PHI.

Procedures

1. Our policy and the option to restrict disclosure will be explained in our Notice of Privacy Procedures which is furnished to all new clients at the first meeting or before.

2. Clients may make such requests at any time during their treatment here.

3. All requests for any restriction on the disclosures of an individual's PHI received by any staff member are to be forwarded promptly to the privacy officer.

4. The privacy officer will assist the client, if necessary, to make this request in writing to the privacy officer.

5. The privacy officer, in consultation with other staff when necessary, will decide whether a request is reasonable based solely on the administrative difficulty of accommodating the request.

6. The privacy officer will notify the client of our decision and its implementation.

7. We may deny a client's requests if the request is contrary to laws, regulations, or other legally required procedures.

8. If we grant a client's request, the privacy officer will maintain a written record of the request, our decision, and the actions taken for a minimum of six years after the end of treatment.

9. The privacy officer will communicate the accommodations to all relevant staff. Staff are required to comply with the accommodations.

845   ## Requests for confidential communications

Policy

Clients have the right to request some restrictions on how and where their EPHI/PHI is communicated and we will support all reasonable requests.

Procedures

1. Requests to receive communications of PHI by alternative means or at alternative locations may be directed to any staff member who will note this request in the client's progress notes and direct the client to the privacy officer.

2. The privacy officer will assist the client if necessary to make such a request in writing to the privacy officer.

3. We will not require that clients provide a reason for their requests. If a client does offer a reason, this reason will not be used to determine whether the accommodation is reasonable.

4. We will decide whether a request is reasonable based solely on the administrative difficulty of accommodating the request.

5. Clients may make such requests at any time during their treatment here.

6. We may deny a client's requests if:
    a. The client does not offer an alternative address or other method to contact him or her.
    b. The client does not offer information about how payment for services, when applicable, will be arranged.

8. If we grant a client's request, the privacy officer will maintain a written record of the request, our decision, and the actions taken.

9. The privacy officer will communicate the accommodations to all relevant staff. Staff are required to comply with the accommodation.

846   Requests to revoke an Authorization

Policy

Clients have the right to revoke any Authorization they have completed at any time.

Procedures

1. All staff will refer a client seeking to limit disclosure of his, her, or their child's PHI by revoking or canceling an Authorization for disclosure to the privacy officer.

2. The privacy officer will explore the concerns of the client and help the client submit a written request for revocation or other appropriate efforts.

3. The privacy officer will explain that disclosures already made cannot be recalled but will be limited by the revocation as soon as it is completed.

4. Copies of the original Authorization, notes by the privacy officer evaluating the situation, and any request for revocation will be kept for at least six years after the revocation takes effect.

850 Complaints about privacy violations or privacy policy

Policy

We will provide ways for clients to file a complaint if they come to believe that their privacy rights have been violated or want to comment or complain about our privacy policies and procedures even if they do not allege a violation.

851 Handling complaints

Procedures

1. Our Notice of Privacy Practices includes an explanation of our complaint processes.

2. When any staff member receives a complaint, he or she will direct the client to our privacy officer and/or to the procedure described in number 3, below.

3. A client may telephone, write, or come in person to the Privacy Officer to make the allegation of a privacy violation or complaint.

4. The Privacy Officer will assist the client to complete the problem/complaint form.

5. Clients can have a representative of their choice represent their interests during this process.

6. We recognize the client's right to file a complaint with the federal Department of Health and Human Services. We will fully cooperate with a federal investigation of a client's complaint to the authorities.

852 Anonymous reporting mechanism

Procedures

1. We will maintain, in the common client waiting area, a box prominently labeled "Is there a problem?" along with a form for making a complaint of any kind. This will be located in an area easily accessible to staff and clients but not too close to the office so that those using it cannot be easily observed by staff (to allow anonymity).

2. The form will explain that completing a form will lead to an investigation by the privacy officer of the complaint or report about our privacy procedures.

3. If the problem or complaint is not suitable for investigation by the privacy officer, the officer will forward it to a more appropriate staff member or members or explain this situation to the client and, where appropriate, explain how to deal with the problem.

4. The form explains that we promise to take appropriate actions to ameliorate the problem and mitigate its effects.

5. It also explains that the form need not be signed and that there will be no retaliation against the person filing the complaint if that person is identified.

853 Investigating complaints

Procedures

1. The Privacy Officer will investigate the complaint and write up a report of the complaint, findings, and actions taken.

2. A written response will be made to the complainer within 30 days from the date the complaint was filed, if the complaint form was signed.

3. All complaints received, reports of the investigation, and their dispositions will be retained for six years.

854 Non-retaliation for the exercise of privacy rights (including Whistleblowers)

1. We will not tolerate any form of intimidation, coercion, threat, discrimination, or retaliation against the client, client's family, friends, or other persons who exercise their legal rights to file a complaint. The same applies to any staff member or Business Associate or other members of the workforce of this practice.

2. The privacy officer will explain this policy to everyone making a complaint.

3. Employees who violate this policy will receive disciplinary action, up to and including firing. See Corrective Actions.

860   ## Corrective actions in response to a complaint

861   ## Sanctions

Policy

Employees who violate our privacy policies will receive disciplinary action, up to and including being fired.

Procedures

1. The disciplinary protocol will be consistent with relevant state and federal laws.

2. All sanctions will be documented and records will be retained for not less than six years after the last date of the sanction.

862   ## Mitigation

Policy

We will make all appropriate and reasonable efforts to mitigate any harmful consequences of any violations of our client's privacy because of our or our own or our business associates action or failure to act.

Procedures

1. If, as a result of the investigation of a complaint or reporting of a problems, the privacy officer finds that there have been deleterious effects of one or more unauthorized or erroneous disclosures, the officer will propose a plan to mitigate these effects.

2. This plan will be shared with the person lodging the complaint, if known, and all relevant staff members or business associates.

3. The privacy officer will, with any other appropriate staff members or business associates, carry out the mitigation   plan.

4. The privacy officer will keep all relevant records for a period of not less than six years after the last date of the mitigation plan.

870   Safeguards

871   Staff training in privacy rights

Policy

We intend to train all staff to comply with the patient privacy regulations of the Health Insurance Portability and Accountability Act of 1996 (HIPAA).

Procedures

1. Most of our policy about privacy and the use and disclosure of PHI is described in our Notice of Privacy Practices. Additional procedures have been or will be included in our Office's Policy and Procedures Manual.

2. During training all staff will be made aware for the following clients' rights:

    a. The right to receive our privacy notice in a timely manner when first becoming a client of this practice and when the policy has changed substantially.

    b. The right to ask for some restrictions on how his or her PHI is used or to whom the information is disclosed

    c. The right to ask that we communicate with them in different ways or places.

    d. Clients have the right to inspect and obtain a copy of their PHI unless we use the HIPAA procedures to limit this access.

    e. Clients have the right to ask us to amend their records.

    f. Clients may have the right to ask for a list of the disclosures of their PHI.

    g. Clients have the right to file a complaint with us and with the federal Department of Health and Human Services's Office of Civil Rights if they believe their privacy rights have been violated.

3. The privacy officer will maintain awareness of changes to privacy policy, laws, and procedures and will provide appropriate means of training staff when changes occur. Additional contents for training will be developed by the privacy office

4. The privacy officer will evaluate each employee's needs for training and choose the best methods to conduct the training. Methods can range from providing reading materials to many hours of classroom and on the job training.

5. The privacy officer will decide on who will conduct staff training and document it.

6. All new staff will receive training on a timely basis on current policy and procedures.

7. Records of the dates, contents, and staff receiving training will be kept by the privacy officer for at least six years after the training was done.

8. Staff will be regularly reminded of both clients' rights and our policies and procedures on a regular basis during staff meetings, with posters in the office, and other ways devised and documented by our privacy officer.

872   Monitoring of compliance with HIPAA regulations

Policy

As part of our commitment to protect the privacy of the PHI entrusted to us, we will monitor our compliance with HIPAA and other privacy regulations over time.

Procedures

1. We will hire a privacy officer from an equivalent practice to conduct an audit of current practices, record keeping, and polices to monitor adherence to all laws and office policies.

2. These audits will be on a random basis but at least once each two calendar years.

3. The privacy officer will document both compliant practices and all non-compliance found.

4   Our privacy officer will devise and implement appropriate corrective actions and document these.

5. Our privacy officer will keep these records for at least six years from the date of the last audit.

873   Passwords

Policy

To gain access to our information systems users must supply individual user passwords.

Procedures

1. Passwords will be required to access all of our computers and records.

2. Each employee will be assigned a unique user ID and password by the privacy officer.

3. As soon as employees are terminated or their job changes so that they should no longer have access or have different records access, their access privileges will be deleted by the privacy officer.

4. Standard and widely acceptable security practices will be applied to passwords and accounts.

5. All employees will be trained in the proper use of the password system.

6. System users who deliberately violate this policy will be subject to disciplinary action.

874 Faxes

Policy

Sending and receiving facsimile transmissions involve risks of unauthorized disclosures of PHI and so we will take all appropriate steps to assure their privacy.

Procedures

1. All staff will be trained in secure uses of our fax machines by the privacy officer.

2. Those sending faxes are not to enter numbers by hand for each transmission but to depend on the numbers stored on the machine.

3. All sent faxes are to have a current version of our cover page attached.

4. Staff picking up received faxes are to count the number of pages and match them to the number in the cover page so that each set of faxed pages is complete and not mixed up with another fax.

5. The records clerk is to check the logs on the fax machine on a weekly basis and investigate any suspicious calls. The clerk and the privacy officer will design changes to further reduce risks of disclosures.

875 Messages and answering machines

Policy

Both in receiving and in leaving messages which might contain or reveal PHI we will be careful and discreet.

Procedures

1. Employees will not place messages which contain PHI or can easily be associated with a client's care in this office on any answering machine or at any number with any person which the client has not designated as acceptable for this purpose. See section 845.

876 Encryption and digital signatures

Policy

As soon as practicable all electronic patient data will be encrypted to keep it from being read, used, shared, or exploited by the unauthorized. Digital or electronic signatures will be adopted as soon as practicable to assure the authenticity of the creator and integrity of our electronic documents.

Procedures

1. The privacy officer will determine which methods for encryption and electronic signatures we will use and when they will be implemented.

877　Disaster recovery plan

Policy

The privacy officer is responsible for developing, maintaining, and revising contingency, emergency, and disaster plans.

Continuity priority: The most important functions to be protected or restored are those addressing PHI. Financial records and systems are secondary. Other business functions and systems such as personnel are tertiary. All other system come after these.

Procedures

1. The privacy officer is responsible for carrying out and documenting the operation of the disaster recovery plan.

2. All computers (servers, monitors, external drives, Internet connections) have Uninterruptible Power Supplies (UPS). This will assure sufficient running time to save current files and recent changes before shut down. Unattended shutdown will be incorporated by the Privacy officer as soon as practicable.

3. All client data of any kind is backed up daily, weekly, monthly, and yearly. Backups are stored offsite. Backups are tested weekly for full restorability.

4. All program files (operating systems, applications, etc.) are backed up monthly. Backups are stored offsite. These backups are tested semi-annually for restorability.

5. Documentation of the backup and restoration procedures is the responsibility of the privacy officer.

6. Documentation of all backups and restoration checks are maintained by the privacy officer.

7. In the event of a disaster the privacy officer will obtain the backups and restore operations in the most effective and quickest ways consistent with maintaining privacy of the PHI.

878   The disposal and destruction of PHI and EPHI

Policy

As part of our policy to ensure the privacy and security of PHI we have developed a policy for the eventual destruction and/or disposal of records in any media. This policy will be consistent with federal and state laws.

Procedures

1. The records of PHI/EPHI may be in any medium which includes but is not limited to:
   a. Paper documents such as client chart notes, letters, etc.
   b. Photographs, microfilm, etc.
   c. Audio and/or video recordings and other magnetic media such as tape, floppy disks, etc.
   d. Optical media such as CDs and DVDs.
   e. Other recording methods yet to be adopted in our practice.

2. Monitoring the adherence to our records destruction policy will be the responsibility of our privacy officer. The officer will document all destruction as indicated below.

3. We will not destroy records which are necessary for any currently open investigation, audit or litigation.
   a. All staff who become aware of the need for preservation of any records in thee or similar circumstances are to notify the privacy officer who will make suitable arrangements for their preservation.
   b. When such needs are resolved these records will be destroyed.
   c. If copies of the records were requested and forwarded to any party for a judicial or administrative hearing or similar actions, the privacy officer will ensure that the records are returned and destroyed when the matters are resolved.

4. Any records provided to a business associate will require as part of the contract with the business associate, that the records involved will be returned to us when the business purpose has been accomplished.

5. Records that have exceeded the our retention period will be destroyed/disposed of in an appropriate manner.

6. Destruction of records will be in accord with federal and state laws and our office policy. This policy will be reviewed annually so as to be current with technology, accepted practices, the availability of cost-effective services, etc.

7. Records will be maintained in ways to prevent unauthorized access until their destruction is complete.

8. Records' destruction will be performed in appropriate and effective methods under the monitoring and direction of the privacy officer.

9. The privacy officer will maintain a record of destruction permanently. The officer will add a statement that the records were destroyed in the normal course of business and in accord with our records maintenance and destruction policy.

880   Other Policies

[These Policies and Procedures are not necessarily a complete collection for your particular practice and so you should add any which you design, modify, or require.]

890   Forms

[You should include here a list and reference or master copies of all the forms from elsewhere in this book which you have decide to used. I have not done so for several reasons: to avoid the added costs of repetition, because they should not appear without your own letterhead replacing my titles and page numbers and, because you are likely to need to modify some of them and should include only the customized version. Also, include here copies of forms and materials you develop.

900   Minor (at least for therapists) topics

910   Personal representatives and minors under HIPAA

"The Department recognizes that there may be times when individuals are legally or otherwise incapable of exercising their rights, or simply choose to designate another to **act on their behalf with respect to these rights**. Under the Rule, a person authorized (under State or other applicable law, e.g., tribal or military law) to act on behalf of the individual in making health care related decisions is the individual's **personal representative**."

"... the Privacy Rule requires covered entities to **treat an individual's personal representative as the individual** with respect to uses and disclosures of the individual's protected health information, as well as the individual's rights under the Rule."(Boldface added) *OCR HIPAA Privacy Guidance*, December 3, 2002.

Basically, HIPAA does not change local law or practice in this area and so you don't have to do a preemption analysis. You don't have to change your practices (assuming that you have been conforming to your local laws).

Access and decisions are linked

The common understanding is that healthcare *information* should be under the control of the person who has the legal right to control the *healthcare* itself. In the case of minors, this is usually the parent, legal guardian, or other personal representative. The personal representative's authority derives from state laws. Therefore, in most cases a parent would be the personal representative of the minor just as a legal guardian or similarly named person would the personal representative of a mentally incompetent person and would exercise the person's rights and, under HIPAA, authorize disclosures.

Where the authority is limited, the personal representative's actions are limited. A person with a health care power of attorney could decide about, for example, artificial life support, or the disclosure of information about medical conditions but is not legally able to make decisions about other uses or disclosures.

Carve outs

The Privacy Rule specifies three circumstances in which the parent is not the personal representative because of common state laws.

> 1. "• **When State or other law does not require the consent of a parent** or other person before a minor can obtain a particular health care service, and the minor consents to the health care service; "(Boldface added) *OCR HIPAA Privacy Guidance,* December 3, 2002.

Many states allow an older minor to obtain some health care services without parental consent. Services for pregnancy, substance abuse, sexually transmitted diseases (STDs), and mental health treatment, are typical exceptions to parental control and usually after age 14. If you are treating a minor for these and the minor has not asked that anyone else be his or her personal representative, HIPAA allows you to deal with just the minor around consent but know your local laws.

> 2. "• **When a court determines** or other law authorizes someone other than the parent to make treatment decisions for a minor;
>
> Example: A court may grant authority to make health care decisions for the minor to an adult other than the parent, to the minor, or the court may make the decision(s) itself." Ibid.

> 3. "• **When a parent agrees**[54] **to a confidential relationship** between the minor and the physician.
>
> Example: A physician asks the parent of a 16-year-old if the physician can talk with the child confidentially about a medical condition and the parent agrees." Ibid.

HIPAA recognizes that even in these cases (where the parent is not the personal representative) other laws may require, permit, or prohibit the CE from disclosing PHI to the parent and HIPAA defers to state law. **Where state laws are silent**, and many are, HIPAA permits the CE to use professional judgment and discretion to decide what to do.

Problems can arise for many reasons with these carve outs. The most common occurs when parents seek PHI because they pay the child's medical bills and want to know for what they are paying. In some cases, the child may be on the parent's health insurance up to age 25 and so fully an adult. When billed, the parents will know what services their child had even if the child has the legal right to not share this information. Ultimately, this problem will require the health plan to modify their agreements. But for you, HIPAA does allow a minor who has legal rights to the control of his or her PHI to ask for **alternative means of communication** and so to have bills sent elsewhere than the parental home (see section 540).

When the personal representative is a danger to the client

> "**Abuse, Neglect, and Endangerment Situations.** When a physician or other covered entity reasonably believes that an individual, including an unemancipated minor, has been or may be **subjected to domestic violence, abuse or neglect by the personal representative**, or that **treating a person as an individual's personal representative could endanger the individual**, the covered entity may choose not to treat that

---

[54] This would be more correctly called "assents."

person as the individual's personal representative, if in the exercise of professional judgment, doing so would not be in the best interests of the individual." (Boldface added) Ibid.

This will uses reasonable belief which is higher threshold than the suspicion standard of many states' laws. You must know your state laws.

Divorce and custody

You should follow your state's (likely complex) rules. Physical custody, legal custody, joint or shared custody, non-custodial parents, and other categories make decisions complex. Feel free to ask why a parent wants the records. And, feel free to ask for proof of identity, parentage, custody, etc. Do these in a context of asserting that you will never deny access to information to which the parent has legal rights.

Other complexities

Q: If a girl (say, an unemancipated minor of 15) were treated and later as a adult (say, at 19) asks for her records, present **and past**, would she have control over access to all the records because she is now an adult?
A: Yes. Minors can become emancipated for reasons that differ across states, and can then make their own decisions about treatment and releases of their PHI.

> "•**Q:** **How can family members of a deceased individual obtain the deceased individual's protected health information that is relevant to their own health care?**
> **A:** ... The Rule provides two ways for a surviving family member to obtain the protected health information of a deceased relative. First, **disclosures of protected health information for treatment purposes even the treatment of another individual do not require an authorization;** thus, a covered entity may disclose a decedent's protected health information, without authorization, to the health care provider who is treating the surviving relative. Second, a covered entity must treat a deceased individual's legally authorized **executor** ... as a personal representative .... Therefore, if it is within the scope of such personal representative's authority under other law, the Rule permits the personal representative to obtain the information or provide the appropriate authorization for its disclosure." (Boldface added) Ibid.

Note that **confidentiality survives death** in state laws and that many states do not allow an executor to authorize the release of medical records.

> "• **Q:** May adults with **mental retardation** control their protected health information if they are able to authorize uses and disclosures of their protected health information?
> **A:** Individuals may control their protected health information under the HIPAA privacy rule to the extent State or other law permits them to act on their own behalf. Further, even if an individual is deemed incompetent under State or other law to act on his or her own behalf, covered entities may decline a request by a personal representative for protected health information if the individual objects to the disclosure (or for any other reason), and the disclosure is merely permitted, but not required, under the Rule." Ibid

§ 164.502 Uses and disclosures of protected health information: general rules.
(g)

(1) Standard: personal representatives. As specified in this paragraph, a covered entity must, except as provided in paragraphs (g)(3) and (g)(5) of this section, treat a personal representative as the individual for purposes of this subchapter.

(2) Implementation specification: adults and emancipated minors. If under applicable law a person has authority to act on behalf of an individual who is an adult or an emancipated minor in making decisions related to health care, a covered entity must treat such person as a personal representative under this subchapter, with respect to protected health information relevant to such personal representation.

(3) Implementation specification: unemancipated minors. If under applicable law a parent, guardian, or other person acting in loco parentis has authority to act on behalf of an individual who is an unemancipated minor in making decisions related to health care, a covered entity must treat such person as a personal representative under this subchapter, with respect to protected health information relevant to such personal representation, except that such person may not be a personal representative of an unemancipated minor, and the minor has the authority to act as an individual, with respect to protected health information pertaining to a health care service, if:

(i) The minor consents to such health care service; no other consent to such health care service is required by law, regardless of whether the consent of another person has also been obtained; and the minor has not requested that such person be treated as the personal representative;

(ii) The minor may lawfully obtain such health care service without the consent of a parent, guardian, or other person acting in loco parentis, and the minor, a court, or another person authorized by law consents to such health care service; or

(iii) A parent, guardian, or other person acting in loco parentis assents to an agreement of confidentiality between a covered health care provider and the minor with respect to such health care service.

(4) (omitted)

(5) Implementation specification: abuse, neglect, endangerment situations. Notwithstanding a State law or any requirement of this paragraph to the contrary, a covered entity may elect not to treat a person as the personal representative of an individual if:

(i) The covered entity has a reasonable belief that:

(A) The individual has been or may be subjected to domestic violence, abuse, or neglect by such person; or

(B) Treating such person as the personal representative could endanger the individual; and

(ii) The covered entity, in the exercise of professional judgment, decides that it is not in the best interest of the individual to treat the person as the individual's personal representative.

920   Using client information for fundraising

Therapists working in a service setting dependent, even in part, on charitable contributions need to know what client information can be shared for these purposes. Fundraising activities include appeals for money, sponsorship of events, etc. They do not include royalties or remittances for the sale of products of third parties (except auctions, rummage sales, etc.).

Organizations' comments to the Secretary of DHHS suggested that having to obtain client authorization to share information for purposes clearly not TPO would raise costs and reduce contributions. And yet there are privacy concerns when PHI is released to anyone.

> "Covered entities, their business associates, or institutionally related non-profit foundations may use or disclose client's demographic data and the dates of treatment only if : they tell the person they may be contacted for fundraising purposes in the NPP; all fundraising materials tell how to opt-out of future messages and; the CE makes reasonable efforts to honor these requests."

> "We agree that such communications raise privacy concerns. In the final rule, we limit the information that can be used or disclosed for fundraising, and exclude information about diagnosis, nature of services, or treatment." From the comments and responses about section 164.510(f).

The final regulations steer a middle ground but may still lead to disconcerting violations.

The regulations

§ 164.514 Other requirements relating to uses and disclosures of protected health information.

(f) (1) Standard: uses and disclosures for fundraising. A covered entity may use, or disclose to a business associate or to an institutionally related foundation, the following protected health information for the purpose of raising funds for its own benefit, without an authorization meeting the requirements of § 164.508:
    (i) Demographic information relating to an individual; and
    (ii) Dates of health care provided to an individual.
  (2) Implementation specifications: fundraising requirements.
    (i) The covered entity may not use or disclose protected health information for fundraising purposes as otherwise permitted by paragraph (f)(1) of this section unless a statement required by § 164.520(b)(1)(iii)(B) is included in the covered entity's notice;
    (ii) The covered entity must include in any fundraising materials it sends to an individual under this paragraph a description of how the individual may opt out of receiving any further fundraising communications.
    (iii) The covered entity must make reasonable efforts to ensure that individuals who decide to opt out of receiving future fundraising communications are not sent such communications.

930   HIPAA's rules about marketing

HIPAA allows CEs to use the PHI they acquire for some marketing and fundraising without obtaining a written Authorization because these have been included into the definition of "health care operations." The logic is that CE's are businesses and so need to do marketing as part of their routine operations and "such a significant intrusion into the business practices of the covered entity is [not] warranted." However, HIPAA is certainly breaking new ethical ground in both privacy and conflicts of interest.

Some of the worst possibilities have been ruled out. Sorry, but you can't increase your income by selling the names and addresses of your depressed and anxious clients so that a drug company can mail or call them encouraging them to use their drugs (instead of your psychotherapy?) but you *can* sell their names to a cruise line for advertising "get away from it all vacations" as an alternative treatment. (Don't forget to get an Authorization.)

Marketing situations

The Privacy Rule defines marketing as "a communication about a product or service a purpose of which is to encourage recipients of the communication to purchase or use the product or service."

The general rule is that being *paid* for recommending a product or service *not* related to health is marketing and so an authorization is required. Therefore, being paid or not to recommend a health-related service is not marketing (see the section just below). And presumably you would not be recommending a non-health-related service because it is not part of the therapeutic relationship although HIPAA thinks you might do this, even when unpaid. If you did, it would not be marketing.

Marketing under a Consent

There are three situations in which PHI can be used or disclosed for marketing *without* the client's written Authorization (but based on just the initial Consent form). See § 164.506.

❑   In face-to-face communications with the client discussing services or products from the CE or from a third party. This allows you to discuss treatment options you or others can provide.

❑   When the communication involves services or products of nominal value such as calendars, pens, and similar promotional materials. If the item is given as a part of treatment, such as a book about a disorder or treatment it would not be covered here but would be exempt from marketing as a part of treatment.

❑   If the communication about health-related products or services meets all of these criteria it can be done under just the Consent:
  ❑   It is from the CE or a third party working as a business associate of the CE .
  ❑   It discloses that the CE will receive some direct or indirect payment for making the communication.
  ❑   It contains instructions on how to opt-out of future communications.
  ❑   It explains how the person had been selected for the communication when his or her PHI was used (e. g. the diagnosis led to this discussion or mailing).

All other marketing activities require an Authorization.

Marketing which requires an Authorization

The Secretary recounts some history to explain the rationale for the rules. Before HIPAA these were legal:

- Selling PHI to third parties for their use and re-use. Under the [HIPAA] rule, a hospital or other provider may not sell names of pregnant women to baby formula manufacturers or magazines.

- Disclosing PHI to outsiders for the outsiders' independent marketing use. Under the rule, doctors may not provide client lists to pharmaceutical companies for those companies' drug promotions.

These activities can occur today [before HIPAA] with no authorization from the individual. In addition, for the marketing activities that are allowed by the rule without authorization from the individual, the Privacy Rule requires covered entities to offer individuals the ability to opt-out of further marketing communications.

Similarly, under the business associate provisions of the rule, a covered entity may not give PHI to a door-to-door salesperson, or other marketer it has hired unless that marketer has agreed by contract to use the information only for marketing on behalf of the covered entity. Today, there may be no restrictions on how marketers re-use information they obtain from health plans and providers. (Excerpted from Standards for Privacy of Individually Identifiable Health Information. From the Office of Civil Rights, January 14, 2002..)

What is not marketing

Situations that are not considered to be marketing under HIPAA, (and so do not require an Authorization), are very broad:

1. When you are *not* paid for recommending a product or service.
   - No authorization is required.

Example: A pharmacy on its own initiative recommends a different medicine to avoid adverse drug reaction.

2. When you are being *paid* for recommending a health-related product or service *as part of managing treatment.*
   - No Authorization or Consent is required.
   - No opting-out of future communications need be offered.
   - No notification is needed that covered entity is paid to encourage purchase or use product or service.
   - No identification of source of the PHI used to select the target of the communication needs to be offered.

A covered entity is not marketing when it:

- Describes the participating providers or plans in a network. For example, a health plan is not marketing when it tells its enrollees about which doctors and hospitals are preferred providers, which are included in its network, or which providers offer a particular service. Similarly, a health insurer notifying enrollees of a new pharmacy that has begun to accept its drug coverage is not engaging in marketing.

• Describes the services offered by a provider or the benefits covered by a health plan. For example, informing a plan enrollee about drug formulary coverage is not marketing.

Furthermore, it is not marketing for a covered entity to use an individual's PHI to tailor a health-related communication to that individual, when the communication is:

• Part of a provider's treatment of the client and for the purpose of furthering that treatment. For example, recommendations of specific brand-name or over-the-counter pharmaceuticals or referrals of clients to other providers are not marketing.

• Made in the course of managing the individual's treatment or recommending alternative treatment. For example, reminder notices for appointments, annual exams, or prescription refills are not marketing. Similarly, informing an individual who is a smoker about an effective smoking-cessation program is not marketing, even if that program is offered by someone other than the provider or plan making the recommendation. Excerpted from Standards for Privacy of Individually Identifiable Health Information. From the Office of Civil Rights, January 14, 2002.

Examples of when a communication related to health is or is not marketing

1. A drug company pays a pharmacy to identify and send prescription refill reminders to clients taking the drug company's brand of medicine. *My opinion:* Seems relatively harmless if the mailing itself does not reveal the medication or condition treated. Note, however that the pharmacy does not have to tell the client that they can be removed from future mailings nor that the drug company is paying the pharmacy to send the letters.

2. A drug company pays a pharmacy to identify clients taking certain drugs and to send letters encouraging them to switch to the drug company's brand. This is allowed as not marketing and so does not need an authorization. *My opinion:* The problem here is that the letter is not based on anyone's determination of what would be best for the client but only on a way to make money for the drug company and their payments to the pharmacy. Seems very harmful.

3. A clinician doing a private evaluation recommends a treatment such as a specific partial hospital program or residential facility or even seeing a particular psychiatric practice for medication evaluation and prescriptions. These are seen under HIPAA as part of the treatment you are providing and not marketing.

But what if the clinician is employed by any of these and will receive a income when he or she provides services in the program to the adolescent, or receives a referral fee when the client enters the program? These practices are acceptable under HIPAA and do not require telling the client of the arrangement or the client's authorization, but are unlikely always to put the client's best interests ahead of the clinician's and so will lead to conflicts of interest. *My opinion:* Seems an abuse of power. At best, they lower the confidence of the client and the public in all clinicians' integrity and professionalism.

4. A non-profit organization which serves, say HIV+ clients, abortion seekers, or sexual minorities sells demographic information and dates of treatment (these are not PHI), without authorization, for the marketing of health related products or services.

Legally, it can do this without an authorization as long as it told clients, in its NPP, that they might be contacted for fundraising/marketing, and, in the marketing effort it tells clients why they were selected (Because they are HIV+? Had an abortion? Are engaging in unusual sexual practices?) and how to opt out and it then makes reasonable efforts to honor those requests it receives. *My opinion:* This is not privacy protection. Even the envelope may reveal private information and it sounds like a great opportunity to use 6 point type - 1/12th of an inch high, like this - for telling them how to opt out.

Can I send out a practice newsletter without Authorizations?

Yes. Appointment reminders, newsletters, program bulletins, information about new services or initiatives from your practice or organization, and similar efforts are acceptable under HIPAA. These services don't even have to be yours but can be those of a business associate or other third-parties such as weight reduction or smoking cessation programs tailored to the client's diagnosis. You need only to have told clients in your NPP that you would be using their information for marketing. You don't even have offer a way for them to opt out of receiving these missives. Really!

Disease management

Therapists will be doing more disease management activities such as health promotion, preventive care, client education, and wellness programs. If these fall under marketing the rules will have to be followed. The Office of Civil Rights says that CE's must examine their plans and methods, compare them with the examples in the regulations and decide.

The regulations

§ 164.514 Other requirements relating to uses and disclosures of protected health information.

(e) (1) Standard: uses and disclosures of protected health information for marketing. A covered entity may not use or disclose protected health information for marketing without an authorization that meets the applicable requirements of § 164.508, except as provided for by paragraph (e)(2) of this section.
　　(2) Implementation specifications: requirements relating to marketing.
　　　　(i) A covered entity is not required to obtain an authorization under § 164.508 when it uses or discloses protected health information to make a marketing communication to an individual that:
　　　　　　(A) Occurs in a face-to-face encounter with the individual;
　　　　　　(B) Concerns products or services of nominal value; or
　　　　　　(C) Concerns the health-related products and services of the covered entity or of a third party and the communication meets the applicable conditions in paragraph (e)(3) of this section.
　　　　(ii) A covered entity may disclose protected health information for purposes of such communications only to a business associate that assists the covered entity with such communications.
　　(3) Implementation specifications: requirements for certain marketing communications. For a marketing communication to qualify under paragraph (e)(2)(i) of this section, the following conditions must be met:
　　　　(i) The communication must:
　　　　　　(A) Identify the covered entity as the party making the communication;
　　　　　　(B) If the covered entity has received or will receive direct or indirect remuneration for making the communication, prominently state that fact; and
　　　　　　(C) Except when the communication is contained in a newsletter or similar type

of general communication device that the covered entity distributes to a broad cross-section of clients, enrollees, or other broad groups of individuals, contain instructions describing how the individual may opt out of receiving future such communications.

(ii) If the covered entity uses or discloses protected health information to target the communication to individuals based on their health status or condition:

(A) The covered entity must make a determination prior to making the communication that the product or service being marketed may be beneficial to the health of the type or class of individual targeted; and

(B) The communication must explain why the individual has been targeted and how the product or service relates to the health of the individual.

(iii) The covered entity must make reasonable efforts to ensure that individuals who decide to opt out of receiving future marketing communications, under paragraph (e)(3)(i)(C) of this section, are not sent such communications.

940 Portability and pre-existing conditions

While not central to therapists implementing HIPAA privacy regulations, I will discuss it because it is likely to apply to your clients and was the original impetus of HIPAA.

One of HIPAA's main motivations was to address the seemingly arbitrary exclusion from coverage of those who changed jobs and thus, in the American employment-based health insurance model, health insurance plans. They were routinely denied coverage for what were called "pre-existing"[55] conditions. This denial could be for an extended period or permanently. The HIPAA regulations were designed to prevent this pejorative cost reduction strategy but the rules are rather complex.

1. First, you have to be *HIPAA-eligible* (see <http://www.cms.hhs.gov/hipaa/online/tellmemore/620001.asp> for more information). You have to meet *all* of these seven criteria when you apply for individual coverage:
    a. You have at least 18 months of continuous creditable coverage without any significant breaks.
    b. Your most recent coverage was under a group health plan.
    c. You are not eligible for coverage under another group health plan.
    d. Your most recent health coverage was not cancelled because you did not pay your premiums or because you committed fraud.
    e. You are not eligible for Medicare or Medicaid.
    f. If you were offered COBRA, Temporary Continuation of Coverage (TCC), or State continuation coverage, you purchased and exhausted the coverage.
    g. You did not accept a conversion policy or a short-term limited duration policy.

2. Second, the rules for individual and group coverage differ and have to be addressed (see <http://cms.hhs.gov/hipaa/online/default.asp>).

3. Only then comes the central issue of the regulations.
    a. **A pre-existing condition is** a condition for which you received medical advice, diagnosis, care or treatment in the six months prior to enrolling in your current health plan. This is called a six month "look back" period and is much shorter than was customary.
    b. The maximum pre-existing condition exclusion period is generally 12 months from the date on which you enrolled in the plan. If there is a waiting period as well they both must start from the same date and cannot be added together.
    c. **HIPAA applies only to those who switch from one group plan to another.** If you had no coverage and then obtained group coverage through a new job your condition may not be covered or you may have to wait for a substantial period of time before it gets covered. Similarly, if you had individual coverage and then switched to either group coverage or to another individual plan your condition may not be covered at all or for a specified period of time.
    d. When you change jobs and switch from one group plan to another group plan and enroll within 63 days of leaving your old plan you will not have to meet the exclusions of pre-existing conditions.

Obviously, there is more to this insurance issue that I can address here and clients should be encouraged to examine carefully their health insurance policies and benefits.

---

[55] As an example of bureaucratic illiteracy this has few peers. What is meant, of course, are existing conditions. If they no longer exist at the time of enrollment they are not conditions. If no longer active they are simply inactive and not in need of treatment (or insurance coverage).

950   De-identifying information in the record

One more way of insuring the privacy of individuals and yet allowing some health information to be collected for research purposes, public health policy decisions, or evaluations of health care operations is to remove from the record all information that would identify that particular person. Doing so creates a "safe harbor" and such "de-identified" information can be shared without client authorization. The recipients only have to agree to not re-identify the persons involved and to limit their use of this data set and who can receive and use it.

Q: **How can you show you have altered the PHI of an individual so that it is no longer individually identifiable?**
A: There are two ways offered in the regulations:

A1.   A trained professional determines that there is a very small risk of anyone's using it to identify an individual.

§ 164.514

(1) A person with appropriate knowledge of and experience with generally accepted statistical and scientific principles and methods for rendering information not individually identifiable:

(i) Applying such principles and methods, determines that the risk is very small that the information could be used, alone or in combination with other reasonably available information, by an anticipated recipient to identify an individual who is a subject of the information; and

(ii) Documents the methods and results of the analysis that justify such determination;

or

A2.   Certain specified information is removed from the record.

§ 164.514

(2)(i) The following identifiers of the individual or of relatives, employers, or household members of the individual, are removed:

(A) Names;

(B) All geographic subdivisions smaller than a State, including street address, city, county, precinct, zip code, and their equivalent geocodes, except for the initial three digits of a zip code if, according to the current publicly available data from the Bureau of the Census:

(1) The geographic unit formed by combining all zip codes with the same three initial digits contains more than 20,000 people; and

(2) The initial three digits of a zip code for all such geographic units containing 20,000 or fewer people is changed to 000.

(C) All elements of dates (except year) for dates directly related to an individual, including birth date, admission date, discharge date, date of death; and all ages over 89 and all elements of dates (including year) indicative of such age, except that such ages and elements may be aggregated into a single category of age 90 or older;

(D) Telephone numbers;

(E) Fax numbers;

(F) Electronic mail addresses;

(G) Social security numbers;

(H) Medical record numbers;

(I) Health plan beneficiary numbers;

(J) Account numbers;

(K) Certificate/license numbers;

(L) Vehicle identifiers and serial numbers, including license plate numbers;

(M) Device identifiers and serial numbers;

(N) Web Universal Resource Locators (URLs);

(O) Internet Protocol (IP) address numbers;

(P) Biometric identifiers, including finger and voice prints;

(Q) Full face photographic images and any comparable images; and

(R) Any other unique identifying number, characteristic, or code; and

(ii) The covered entity does not have actual knowledge that the information could be used alone or in combination with other information to identify an individual who is a subject of the information.

The limited data set

There is also the concept of a limited data set to create a collection of data which included some information which would be essential for some research purposes but excluded all of the above. The rules are not needed by therapists, are quite detailed, and so are not reprinted here but can be found in § 164.514.

960   E-Mail Confidentiality Notices

Since e-mail is not secure (unless encrypted) you shouldn't send PHI or other sensitive or personal information. Even for other uses, you might place a personalized version of these "disclaimers" in an automatic "sig file" at the end of each of your emails.

1. Please be aware that it is impossible to assure privacy of any communication by electronic means. If you are uncomfortable with this possible threat to your privacy, please communicate by other means. Also, e-mail may sometimes be delayed, so never rely upon email for any urgent matter.

E-mail transmission cannot be guaranteed to be secure or error-free as information could be intercepted, corrupted, lost, destroyed, arrive late or incomplete, or contain viruses. The sender therefore does not accept liability for any errors or omissions in the contents of this message, which arise as a result of e-mail transmission. If verification is required please request a hardcopy version.

2. This electronic message and its attachments may contain information that may be confidential, legally privileged, or otherwise protected from unauthorized disclosure by federal and/or state laws.

3. The information contained in this electronic e-mail transmission and any attachments are intended only for the use of the individual or entity to whom or to which it is addressed or the employee or other agent responsible for delivering this communication to the intended recipient.

If the reader of this communication is not the intended recipient, or the employee or agent responsible for delivering this communication to the intended recipient, you are hereby notified that any dissemination, distribution, disclosure, copying, or storage or other use of this communication and any attachment is illegal and prohibited.

4. Any interception, retransmission, dissemination, or other use of, or taking of any action upon this information by persons other than the intended recipient is prohibited by law and may subject them to criminal or civil liability.

5. If you have received this communication in error we ask that you immediately contact the sender, by name at [landline telephone number or secured e-mail address] so that we may jointly decide on how to destroy or return this communication, at no cost to you. Delete the original communication and any attachment from any computer, server or other electronic recording or storage device or medium.

We will be very grateful for your cooperation in correcting any error in our transmission of this message and assure you we will follow the above rules if we ever receive any mistaken communication from you.

6. This e-mail does not constitute a consent to the use of sender's contact information for direct marketing purposes or for transfers of data to third parties.

Your receiving this message in error does not waive any attorney-client, physician-patient or other privilege.

7. Although this e-mail and any attachments are believed to be free of any virus or other defect that might negatively affect any computer system into which it is received and opened, it is the responsibility of the recipient to ensure that it is virus free and no responsibility is accepted by the sender for any loss or damage arising in any way in the event that such a virus or defect exists.

1000   Resources and references

1010   References

___ (2002). *Standards for Privacy of Individually Identifiable Health Information.* From the Office of Civil Rights. Last revised: January 14, 2002. Accessed Sept. 28, 2005.
<http://www.hhs.gov/ocr/hipaa/finalmaster.html>

Amatayakul, M., Brandt, M. D., & Dennis, J. C. (2002). Implementing the Minimum Necessary Standard. *Journal of American Health Information Management Association, 73,* (9), 96A-F.

Diecidue, A. S. (2002). Power up the shredder: A switch to electronic medical records may be easier than you thought.
<http://www.revoptom.com/index.asp?page=2_359.htm> Accessed Sept 28, 2005.

Gue, D. G. (2002). The HIPAA Security Rule (NPRM): Overview. *HIPAAdvisory.* Phoenix Health Systems. <http://www.hipaadvisory.com/regs/securityoverview.htm> Accessed Sept 28, 2005.

Guilfoy, H. (2002). The new transactions standards: A wakeup call for providers. *HIPAAdvisory.* Phoenix Health Systems.
<http://www.hipaadvisory.com/action/transwake.htm> Accessed Sept. 28, 2005.

Health Insurance Portability and Accountability Act of 1996. Public Law 104-191. *Federal Register* / Vol. 65 No. 250 / Thursday, December 28, 2000 / Rules and Regulations.
<http://www.hhs.gov/ocr/hipaa/finalreg.html> This is the Privacy Rule. Accessed Sept. 28, 2005.

Electronic Protected Health Information Sections 164.302 -318 and 261-Appendix A.
<http://www.cms.hhs.gov/regulations/hipaa/cms0003-5/0049fecon-ofr-2-12-03.pdf> Accessed Sept. 28, 2005.

Joint Healthcare Information Technology Alliance. Accessed Sept. 21, 2002. Not available Sept. 28, 2005. <http://www.jhita.org/hipaarule.htm>

Lazarus, S. S. (2001). *HIPAA Tips for the Physician Office.* Accessed Sept 28, 2005..
<http://www.hipaainfo.net/ahima040601.htm>

National Institute of Standards and Technology (NIST) 800 Series of Special Publications (SP). *SP 800-30 - Risk Management Guide for Information Technology Systems.*

Newman, R. (2002). *APA Comments: Proposed Rule Providing Modifications to Standards for Privacy of Individually Identifiable Health Information.* April 24, 2002. Accessed Sept. 28, 2005. <http://www.apa.org/practice/privacy_302.html>

Zuckerman, E. (2005). *Clinicians' Thesaurus: The guidebook for writing psychological reports.* Sixth edition. New York: Guilford Press. <http://www.guilford.com/cgi-bin/cartscript.cgi?page=ct/zuckerman.htm&cart__id=473881.8238>

Zuckerman, E. (2003). *The Paper Office: Forms, guidelines, and resources. The tools to make your psychotherapy practice work ethically, legally, and profitably.* Third edition. New York: Guilford Press. <http://www.guilford.com/cgi-bin/cartscript.cgi?page=ct/zuckerman2.htm&cart__id=204941.21059>

Guilford can be reached at 1-800-365-7006 or at www.Guilford.com.

1020   HIPAA documents and resources available online

These are free and public resources. If you don't want to type the URLs, go to <www.hipaahelp.info/URLs> to download this list with live links.

___ (2002). *Standards for Privacy of Individually Identifiable Health Information*. From the Office of Civil Rights. Last revised: January 14, 2002. <http://www.hhs.gov/ocr/hipaa/finalmaster.html> Accessed Oct. 3, 2005. 11, 2002

Health Insurance Portability and Accountability Act of 1996. Public Law 104-191. *Federal Register* / Vol. 65 No. 250 / Thursday, December 28, 2000 / Rules and Regulations. <http://www.hhs.gov/ocr/hipaa/finalreg.html> This is the Privacy Rule. Accessed Sept. 28, 2005.
A searchable version of this same document is available at <http://www.hipaadvisory.com/regs/finalprivacymod/index.htm> Accessed Dec. 1, 2002.

III. Section-by-section Discussion of Comments. <http://www.hhs.gov/ocr/part3.html> Accessed Sept. 21, 2005. This is part of the Preamble to HIPAA. It consists of the Secretary's responses to the comments received on the first draft proposal of the HIPAA regulations and follows the structure of the Final Rule. When printed out it is almost 400 pages.

Guidance Explaining Significant Aspects of the Privacy Rule - December 4, 2002. From the Office of Civil Rights. <http://www.hhs.gov/ocr/hipaa/privacy.html> Accessed Sept. 28, 2005.
This is a regularly revised and official clarification of the major issues with responses to questions raised. It is quite readable and now 123 pages.

HIPAA Ohio - *Guide to the HIPAA Privacy Rule*. <http://www.state.oh.us/hipaa/privacyrule/index.htm> Accessed Oct. 3, 2005. The HIPAA regulations do not come with a table of contents of easy links to the topics. However, the Statewide Project Privacy Workgroup has reorganized it into a searchable and logical table. Thank you very much.

HIPAA Sample Documents. <http://www.nchica.org/HIPAA/Samples/Portal.asp> Accessed Oct. 4, 2005.
The North Carolina Healthcare Information and Communications Alliance, Inc. (NCHICA) has developed a number of forms and checklists and, while they are copyrighted and so require you to seek permission to use or reproduce them, are very valuable resources for your becoming informed about HIPAA.

Phoenix Health Systems <http://www.phoenixhealth.com/> offers a number of products and very generously offers these to which you might want to subscribe:
    An e-mail news bulletin at <http://www.hipaadvisory.com/alert/index.htm>
    An interactive mailing list at <http://www.hipaadvisory.com/live/index.htm>

If you need the transaction codes, claim forms, and related materials, the site of the official publishing organization, Washington Publishing Company, has them both for sale as printed and free when downloaded. <http://www.wpc-edi.com/hipaa> Accessed Oct. 5, 2005.

The sites below are free and public resources. At <www.hipaahelp.info/URLs> you will find this list with live links and which is current and downloadable.

American Mental Health Association
<http://americanmentalhealth.com>
This group of private practitioners is doing a splendid job in raising awareness of the continuing erosion of our health privacy. Michaele P. Dunlap, Psy.D. has generously organized the regulations for those without a legal turn of mind and collected many excellent resources. If you find their materials valuable, please join them. Accessed Sept. 29, 2005.

Centers for Medicare and Medicaid Services
<http://cms.hhs.gov/hipaa/>
This is the official website of the CMS part of the DHHS which is assigned to address HIPAA. You can find the official word, offer feedback, read FAQs, and even ask questions. Look under Professional in the top bar. Accessed Sept. 29, 2005.

Health Hippo
<http://hippo.findlaw.com/hippohome.html>
Everything HIPAA and some fun. A commercial site. Accessed Sept. 29, 2005.

HIPAAdirect
<http://www.HIPAAdirect.com/>
If you need something unusual this is a directory with over 1,200 categorized links to HIPAA information on the internet. Accessed Sept. 29, 2005.

HIPAAdvisory
<http://www.hipaadvisory.com/>
The HIPAA hub of the Internet Modern Healthcare. A rich set of sites (18, I think) with current and lively coverage of events, FAQs, Q&As, and other stuff. Accessed Sept. 29, 2005.

Medicare Program; Scope of Medicare Benefits and Application of the Outpatient Mental Health Treatment Limitation to Clinical Psychologist and Clinical Social Worker Services
<http://frwebgate3.access.gpo.gov/cgi-bin/waisgate.cgi?WAISdocID=965429453+17+0+0&WAISaction=retrieve>
(Federal Register: April 23, 1998 (Volume 63, Number 78)). Accessed Sept. 29, 2005.

There are at least several thousand consultants and several hundred software firms offering HIPAA advice and products and all on the web. If you need more than this book offers a Google search (<www.google.com>) will keep you entertained for hours.

Because I cannot know all your needs here are some other sites:
- American Health Information Management Association (AHIMA), <www.ahima.org>
- American Health Lawyers Association, <www.healthlawyers.org> has listserves on many topics including Health Information and Technology
- Workgroup for Electronic Data Interchange (WEDI), <www.wedi.org>

All were accessed Sept. 29, 2005.

1030   Glossary - Definitions for the terms used in HIPAA

Below is a list of terms and acronyms commonly used in HIPAA and in this book. If you don't find it here, see the list of sites with definitions at the end of the list. (If you know the source for this glossary, I would greatly appreciate your directing me to it. I have not been able to relocate it.-Ed)

Accounting   Patients have the right to receive an listing of disclosures of protected health information made by providers in the six years prior to the date on which the accounting is requested.

Administrative Simplification In the HIPAA legislation, Congress ordered Administrative Simplification of specific health data transactions. The goals were to 1) reduce costs associated with the processing of medical claims, 2) increase the efficiency of claims handling, and 3) increase the privacy and security of health data.

Authorization   Patient "authorization" is needed for all disclosures of protected health information, except disclosures for treatment, payment, or health care operations (for which "consent" is optional).

Breach. See Security incident.

Centers for Medicare and Medicaid Services - CMS. (*nee* HCFA- the Health Care Financing Agency). The DHHS agency responsible for Medicare and parts of Medicaid.

Clearinghouse   Any organization, including billing services and claims processing companies, that electronically processes health information in any kind of transaction.

CMS   The Centers for Medicare and Medicaid Services. [Only one "m"]

Confidentiality   The property of data or information such that it is not made available or disclosed to unauthorized persons or processes.

Consent   A patient's consent (as documented on a Consent form) is optional only for the release of information for *treatment, payment, and health care operations*. All other disclosures require a patient's Authorization.

Covered Entity (CE)   Health plans, healthcare clearinghouses, healthcare providers and providers of discount drug cards who transmit health information electronically in connection with a standard transaction (e.g., claims, coordination of benefits, payment and remittance advice, claims status, etc.) are covered entities, according to HIPAA regulations. Providers whose information is electronically transmitted on their behalf, for example by a billing service or hospital are also CEs.

Current Procedural Terminology (CPT)   A medical code set, maintained and copyrighted by the American Medical Association, and revised each year, that has been selected for use under HIPAA for non-institutional and non-dental professional transactions.

Department of Health and Human Services (DHHS): The federal government department that has overall responsibility for implementing HIPAA.

Designated Record Set   (What patients can have access to.) A group of records maintained by or for a covered entity that is:

(i) The medical records and billing records about individuals maintained by or for a covered health care provider;

(ii) The enrollment, payment, claims adjudication, and case or medical management record systems maintained by or for a health plan; or

(iii) Used, in whole or in part, by or for the covered entity to make decisions about individuals.

Disclosure   The release, transfer, provision of access to, or divulging in any other manner of information outside the entity holding the information.

EDI Transaction   Any sending or receiving electronic information using Electronic Data Interchange procedures or formats.

Encryption   The use of an formula or process to transform data into a form in which there is a low probability of assigning meaning without use of a confidential process or key.

EPHI   Electronic PHI. PHI on computers or any electronic storage or transmission media.

Health care means care, services, or supplies related to the health of an individual. Health care includes, but is not limited to, the following:
(1) Preventive, diagnostic, therapeutic, rehabilitative, maintenance, or palliative care, and counseling, service, assessment, or procedure with respect to the physical or mental condition, or functional status, of an individual or that affects the structure or function of the body; and
(2) Sale or dispensing of a drug, device, equipment, or other item in accordance with a prescription.

Health care operations

Any of the following activities of the covered entity to the extent that the activities are related to covered functions, and any of the following activities of an organized health care arrangement in which the covered entity participates:
1) Conducting quality assessment and improvement activities, including outcomes evaluation and development of clinical guidelines, provided that the obtaining of generalizable knowledge is not the primary purpose of any studies resulting from such activities; population-based activities relating to improving health or reducing health care costs, protocol development, case management and care coordination, contacting of health care providers and patients with information about treatment alternatives; and related functions that do not include treatment;
2) Reviewing the competence or qualifications of health care professionals, evaluating practitioner and provider performance, conducting training programs in which students, trainees, or practitioners in areas of health care learn under supervision to practice or improve their skills as health care providers, training of non-health care professionals, accreditation, certification, licensing, or credentialing activities;
3) Underwriting, premium rating, and other activities relating to the creation renewal or replacement of a contract of health insurance or health benefits, and ceding, securing, or placing a contract for reinsurance of risk relating to claims for health care (including stop-loss insurance and excess of loss insurance), provided that the requirements of §164.514(g) are met, if applicable;
(4) Conducting or arranging for medical review, legal services, and auditing function, including fraud and abuse detection and compliance programs;
(5) Business planning and development, such as conducting cost-management and planning-related analyses related to managing and operating the entity, including formulary development and administration, development or

improvement of methods of payment or coverage policies; and
(6) Business management and general administrative activities of the entity, including, but not limited to:

(i) Management activities relating to implementation of and compliance with the requirements of this subchapter;

(ii) Customer service, including the provision of data analyses for policy holders, plan sponsors, or other customers, provided that protected health information is not disclosed to such policy holder, plan sponsor, or customer.

(iii) Resolution of internal grievances;

(iv) Due diligence in connection with the sale or transfer of assets to a potential successor in interest, if the potential successor in interest is a covered entity or, following completion of the sale or transfer, will become a covered entity; and

(v) Consistent with the applicable requirements of §164.514, creating deidentified health information, fundraising for the benefit of the covered entity, and marketing for which an individual authorization is not required as described in §164.514(e)(2).

Health Care Provider   A provider of services (as defined in the Social Security Act), and any other person or organization who furnishes, bills, or is paid for health care in the normal course of business.

The following quotations from the legislation have been edited (by ELZ) to focus on the definitions of mental health providers.

"a provider of services (as defined in section 1861(u) of the [Social Security] Act, 42 U.S.C. 1395x(u)), a provider of medical or health services (as defined in section 1861(s) of the Act, 42 U.S.C. 1395x(s)), and any other person or organization who furnishes, bills, or is paid for health care in the normal course of business."
42 U.S.C. 1395x(u) [section 1861(u)]:
(u) Provider of services
The term provider of services means a hospital, critical access hospital, skilled nursing facility, comprehensive outpatient rehabilitation facility, home health agency, hospice program, or, for purposes of section 1395f(g) and section 1395n(e) of this title, a fund.
42 U.S.C. 1395x(u) [section 1861(s)]:
(s) Medical and other health services
The term "medical and other health services" means any of the following items or services:
1) physicians' services;
2) (E) rural health clinic services and Federally qualified health center services;

(H) (ii) services furnished pursuant to a risk-sharing contract under section 1395mm(g) of this title to a member of an eligible organization by a **clinical psychologist** (as defined in subsection (hh)(2) of this section), and such services and supplies furnished as an incident to such clinical psychologist's services or clinical social worker's services to such a member as would otherwise be covered under this part if furnished by a physician or as an incident to a physician's service;

(M) qualified psychologist services;

(N) clinical social worker services (as defined in subsection (hh)(2) of this section)

HIPAA   The Health Insurance Portability and Accountability Act of 1996

ICD-9-CM   *International Classification of Diseases, Revision 9, Clinical Modification*

Individually Identifiable Health Information Information that is a subset of health information, including demographic information collected form an individual, and
(1) Is created or received by a health care provider, health plan, employer, or health care clearinghouse; and
(2) Relates to the past, present, or future physical or mental health or condition of an individual; the provision of health care to an individual, and
 (i) That identifies the individual; or
 (ii) With respect to which there is a reasonable basis to believe the information can be used to identify the individual.
Data elements that make information individually identifiable include:
  • Name
  •Address
  • Employer
  • Relatives' names
  • DOB Date of Birth
  • Telephone and fax numbers
  • E-mail addresses
  • SSN Social Security Number
  • Medical record numbers
  • Member or account number
  • Certificate/license number
  • Voice/fingerprints
  • Photos
  • Other number, code or characteristics such as occupation
Note: The standards apply to information, not to specific records.

Integrity The property that data or information have not been altered or destroyed in an unauthorized manner.

Malicious software (or malware) means programs, for example, a virus, designed to damage or disrupt a system.

MNPHI   Minimum Necessary Protected Health Information (my acronym)

Notice of Privacy Practices NPP   Covered providers must give written notice of the uses and disclosures of protected health information that may be made by the provider, as well as notice about individuals' rights and the provider's legal duties with respect to protected health information. Covered providers must make a good faith effort to obtain the patient's written acknowledgment of receipt of the Notice.

NPRM   Notice of Proposed Rule Making

Password Confidential authentication information composed of a string of characters.

Payment   Very broadly defined in HIPAA to include:
 (1) The activities undertaken by:
 (i) A health plan to obtain premiums or to determine or fulfill its responsibility for coverage and provision of benefits under the health plan; or
 (ii) A covered health care provider or health plan to obtain or provide reimbursement for the provision of health care; and
 (2) The activities in paragraph (1) of this definition relate to the individual to whom health care is provided and include, but are not limited to:
 (i) Determination of eligibility or coverage (including coordination of benefits or the determination of cost sharing amounts), and adjudication or subrogation of health benefit claims;
 (ii) Risk adjusting amounts due based on enrollee health status and

demographic characteristics;

(iii) Billing, claims management, collection activities, obtaining payment under a contract for reinsurance (including stop-loss insurance and excess of loss insurance), and related health care data processing;

(iv) Review of health care services with respect to medical necessity, coverage under a health plan, appropriateness of care, or justification of charges;

(v) Utilization review activities, including precertification and preauthorization of services, concurrent and retrospective review of services; and

(vi) Disclosure to consumer reporting agencies of any of the following protected health information relating to collection of premiums or reimbursement:

(A) Name and address;
(B) Date of birth
(C) Social Security Number
(D) Payment history
(E) Account number; and
(F) Name and address of the health care provider and/or health plan

Privacy Rule   Set of regulations relating to the privacy of patients' medical information, promulgated under the Administrative Simplification provisions of HIPAA.

PHI Protected health information Individually identifiable health information that is maintained or transmitted by a covered entity, including such information when it is in electronic form, paper form or discussed orally

Protected health information means individually identifiable health information:

(1) Except as provided in paragraph (2) of this definition, that is:

(i) Transmitted by electronic media;

(ii) Maintained in any medium described in the definition of electronic media at §164.103 of this subchapter; or

(iii) Transmitted or maintained in any other form or medium

(2) Protected health information *excludes* individually identifiable health information in:

(i) Education records covered by the Family Educational Right and Privacy Act, as mended, 20 U.S.C. 1232g; and

(ii) Records described at 20 U.S.C. 1232g(a)(4)(B)(iv)

All individually identifiable health information is covered when used or disclosed by an entity that is covered under HIPAA administrative simplification. Only health information that is not individually identifiable (de-identified) is not covered.

Psychotherapy notes   Information recorded (in any medium) by a health care provider who is a mental health professional documenting or analyzing the contents of conversation during a private counseling session or a group, joint, or family counseling session and that are separated from the rest of the individual's medical record.

Psychotherapy notes excludes medication prescription and monitoring, counseling session start and stop times, the modalities and frequencies of treatment furnished, results of clinical tests, and any summary of the following items: diagnosis, functional status, the treatment plan, symptoms, prognosis, and progress to date. Federal Register / Vol. 65, No. 250 / Thursday, December 28, 2000 / Rules and Regulations. p 82497 *Psychotherapy Notes* Section 164.508(a)(3)(iv)(A)

Research   Systematic investigation, including research development, testing, and evaluation, designed to develop or contribute to generalizable knowledge

Security incident   The attempted or successful unauthorized access, use, disclosure, modification, or destruction of information or interference with system operations in an information system. See § 164.304

TPO   Treatment, payment, and health care operations which are very broadly defined to cover many management functions. See each of their definitions.

Treatment   The provision, coordination, or management of health care and related services by one or more health care providers, including the coordination or management of health care by a health care provider with a third party; consultation between health care providers relating to a patient; or the referral of a patient for health care from one health care provider to another.

Use   With respect to individually identifiable health information, use means the sharing, employment, application, utilization, examination, or analysis of such information within an entity that maintains such information.

User   A person or entity with authorized access.

Workstation   An electronic computing device, for example, a laptop or desktop computer, or any other device that performs similar functions, and electronic media stored in its immediate environment.

Other Glossaries

A Glossary of HIPAA Terms
<http://www.calhipaa.com/main/hipaa_glossary1.shtml>
Accessed Oct. 13, 2005.
Here you will find a glossary of about 6 pages.

A HIPAA Glossary
<http://www.wedi.org/snip/public/articles/HIPAA_GLOSSARY.PDF> Accessed Oct. 2, 2005.
This 24 page Glossary and Acronymary (Hey!) is complete and kept current by the organization most responsible for designing the EDI parts of HIPAA.

When you are stumped for the meaning of a healthcare regulations term try <http://www.cms.hhs.gov/glossary/> which explains terms found on the CMS web site. If the term is an acronym, try the parallel site: <http://www.cms.hhs.gov/acronyms/> Accessed Oct. 3, 2005.

The Massachusetts Health Data Consortium has an *Acronym Glossary* at <http://www.mahealthdata.org/data/library/acronym.html> and links to other glossaries. Accessed Sept. 29, 2005.

If none of these helps, try a Google search at <www.google.com>

1040   What do you think? - Feedback Form

I would greatly appreciate receiving your comments (positive and negative), suggestions, or shared experiences so that I might improve this book to better meet your needs. Also, updates and similar information will be available at
    <www.hipaahelp.info/updates
I you are unhappy, don't do nothing, complain! To me. Email to mail@hipaahelp.info or by postal mail to PO Box 222, Armbrust, PA 15616-0222

My overall evaluation of HIPAAHelp is that it is   ❏ Superb ❏ Great ❏ Good ❏ OK
    ❏ Poor ❏ Other: _____ .

I suggest that you

Add: _____

Remove: _____

Modify: _____

Correct: _____

I also want to ask you this question:_____

Other comments and ideas: _____

_____

Thanks, Ed

1050   Other clinical tools you might find helpful

The Reference List of Psychiatric Diagnoses from ICD-9-CM

Because of HIPAA the *International Classification of Disorders, Ninth edition, Clinical Modification* is replacing the *Diagnostic and Statistical Manual* for diagnoses.
If you need
   to know the name of the disorder when all you received was the code number
   the exact wording or precise 5-digit codes for a report
   the changes and additions made each year to ICD
   the speediest lookup – only four sides, bound and laminated in heavy plastic
   just an inexpensive reference - $10.95 including mailing
then have a look at Ed's **Reference List of Psychiatric Diagnoses from ICD-9-CM**
Strangely there is no comparable list available anywhere else!

<www.ICD9Codes.info> or <www.ThreeWishesPress.com>

These three are available from Guilford Press in New York
at www.guilford.com or 1-800-365-7006

The Paper Office 3

Now in a revised and expanded third edition, this popular manual and CD-ROM provide the clinical, financial, and legal record-keeping tools that every psychotherapy practice needs. It is ideal both for new practitioners who want to hit the ground running, and seasoned pros who want to overhaul their paperwork and risk-reduction procedures.

Learn to organize your practice from the best publications and the most experienced clinicians

Clinician's Thesaurus 6

This VERY popular guidebook provides easy and organized access to the entire language of the mental health professions. More than a giant collection of synonyms, the *Thesaurus* offers practical guidelines for how to shape raw data into a cogent report. Tens of thousands of useful words, phrases, and interview questions are provided to help practitioners collect the client information they need and accurately describe almost any clinical situation.

Hard to believe until you see it. Check out the website.

Clinician's Electronic Thesaurus 6

This timesaving companion software puts the entire language of mental health no more than three clicks away. Here are thousands of words to describe almost any clinical situation; interview questions to aid in gathering data; opening and closing statements to structure reports; and tools to build custom formats for intakes, diagnostic work-ups, psychological evaluations, treatment plans, managed care and court reports, and more.

Both a report writing companion and a endless text library for your career.

1060   Index